BAYESIAN DECISION PROBLEMS AND MARKOV CHAINS

PUBLICATIONS IN OPERATIONS RESEARCH

Operations Research Society of America

Editor for Publications in Operations Research

DAVID B. HERTZ

No. 1. QUEUES, INVENTORIES AND MAINTENANCE
Philip M. Morse

No. 2. FINITE QUEUING TABLES
L. G. Peck and R. N. Hazelwood

No. 3. EFFICIENCY IN GOVERNMENT THROUGH SYSTEMS ANALYSIS
Roland N. McKean

No. 4. A COMPREHENSIVE BIBLIOGRAPHY ON OPERATIONS RESEARCH
Operations Research Group, Case Institute

No. 5. PROGRESS IN OPERATIONS RESEARCH, VOLUME I
Edited by Russell L. Ackoff

No. 6. STATISTICAL MANAGEMENT OF INVENTORY SYSTEMS
Harvey M. Wagner

No. 7. PRICE, OUTPUT, AND INVENTORY POLICY
Edwin S. Mills

No. 8. A COMPREHENSIVE BIBLIOGRAPHY ON OPERATIONS RESEARCH, 1957–1958
Operations Research Group, Case Institute

No. 9. PROGRESS IN OPERATIONS RESEARCH, VOLUME II
David B. Hertz and Roger T. Eddison

No. 10. DECISION AND VALUE THEORY
Peter C. Fishburn

No. 11. HANDBOOK OF THE POISSON DISTRIBUTION
Frank A. Haight

No. 12. OPERATIONS RESEARCH IN SELLER'S COMPETITION: A STOCHASTIC MICROTHEORY
S. Sankar Sengupta

No. 13. BAYESIAN DECISION PROBLEMS & MARKOV CHAINS
J. J. Martin

BAYESIAN DECISION PROBLEMS AND MARKOV CHAINS

J. J. MARTIN

Operations Research Specialist, U.S. Navy

John Wiley & Sons, Inc., New York · London · Sydney

Library of Congress Catalog Card Number: 67-19941
Printed in the United States of America

To Betty

PREFACE

There is evident in the history of science an alternation between theoretical activity and engineering applications. The awareness of problem areas stimulates theoretical developments which, in turn, unveil new problem areas, and so on. The field of operations research is not exempt from this cyclic phenomenon. The easy problems in operations research have, for the most part, been solved. New advances in methodology must be made if the field is to continue to unfold and broaden its applicability.

Two areas in which current research is seeking methodological advances are those of Markov processes and Bayesian decision theory. During the last few years a number of the faculty and students at the Massachusetts Institute of Technology have attempted to combine these two lines of development in the study of Markovian decision processes. This book, which evolved from much of the work of the M.I.T. group, deals with a theoretical foundation for the solution of decision problems in a Markov chain with uncertain transition probabilities and considers both sequential sampling and fixed-sample-size problems. After a brief summary of the relevant concepts from Markov chain theory and Bayesian decision theory the notion of a family of distributions closed under sampling is introduced, then applied to the study of adaptive control problems. The expectations of certain quantities such as the steady-state probability vector are examined and used in the discussion of terminal control problems. The latter part of the book is devoted to prior-posterior and preposterior analysis of a Markov chain with uncertain transition probabilities when the sample size is fixed. This theoretical structure, although substantial, is in no sense complete, and in the concluding chapter areas for further research are discussed. The principal emphasis throughout is on problems of existence and convergence, but questions of efficient methods of numerical computation are considered as they arise.

Although the necessary ideas from the theory of Markov chains and Bayesian decision theory are summarized in the first chapter, it is assumed that the reader has some familiarity with these subjects. An elementary knowledge of mathematical analysis is also required. Liberal use has been made of matrix notation, but little more in the way of matrix theory is required of the reader.

I am indebted to Ronald A. Howard, George R. Murray, Ralph L. Miller, and particularly to Gordon M. Kaufman for reading portions of the manuscript and to all my colleagues at the M.I.T. Operations Research Center for their stimulating comments and criticism. The members of the M.I.T. Library Staff, especially the Information and Reference Section, were most helpful. I am grateful to the Massachusetts Institute of Technology for permission to publish this manuscript, which was originally submitted as a Ph.D. Thesis. All machine computations were performed at the M.I.T. Computation Center. I am particularly grateful to the U.S. Navy for supporting in full the research documented here. Finally, I must acknowledge the valuable contribution of my wife Betty, who carefully typed several drafts of a manuscript, the notation of which can only be described as tortuous.

J. J. Martin

Limekiln Lake, N.Y.
July, 1966

CONTENTS

BAYESIAN DECISION PROBLEMS AND MARKOV CHAINS

Chapter 1

INTRODUCTION

1.1. HISTORICAL PERSPECTIVE

The basic concept of a Markov chain was introduced by A. A. Markov in 1907, and since that time the literature on the subject has grown remarkably. Fundamental investigations by Kolmogorov in the 1930's extended the mathematical theory to chains with an infinite number of states; Doeblin and Doob made important contributions during the period of 1935 to 1945. The present state of the theory of Markov chains is summarized by Chung [12].†

By 1950 it was well recognized that the Markov chain is a useful model for a multitude of physical processes, and an increasing number of applications of the mathematical theory have been made to problems in such fields as physics, chemistry, biology, and operations research. In these applications it is generally assumed that the matrix of transition probabilities is known, although, since 1954, questions of hypothesis testing and maximum-likelihood estimation have been investigated. These latter results are summarized by Billingsley [10], who gives extensive references.

During the past two decades Savage's interpretation of the work of de Finetti on subjective probability has renewed interest in Bayesian decision theory. Contributions in this area have been made by many researchers, including Von Neumann, Wald, Blackwell, and Girshick, leading to the current work of Raiffa and Schlaifer [33], which, to a large degree, presents a unified theory of statistical decisions suitable for applications.

Recent research at the Massachusetts Institute of Technology [13, 14, 38] has been directed toward the application of Bayesian decision theory to various models based on Markov chains with uncertain transition probabilities. These efforts have demonstrated both the feasibility of

† Numbers in brackets refer to the bibliography at the end of the book.

such decision models and the need for a more thorough investigation of the underlying mathematical theory. This book attempts to establish a theoretical basis for some decision models which involve a finite Markov chain with uncertain transition probabilities; particular attention is given to sequential decision models. Although we have dealt, for the most part, with matters of existence and convergence, the question of numerical computation has not been neglected. There are, however, many problems of numerical computation in this area which are yet to be solved.

Decision problems involving Markov chains have received increasing attention during the last decade. In 1953, L. S. Shapley [36], using a game-theoretic formulation, studied one of the earliest sequential decision models in a Markov chain with alternative transition probabilities, which were assumed to be known. Similar game formulations have been examined more recently by Zachrisson [42] and Shor [37]. A more general class of Markovian decision models with known transition probabilities have been investigated by Blackwell [11], Derman [16], Howard [22], and others, using the techniques of linear and dynamic programming. These models have been extended to semi-Markov processes by Howard [23] and Jewell [24, 25]. Further references are given by Jewell [25].

Silver [38] has investigated various questions in a Markov chain with uncertain transition probabilities and rewards. In particular, he has treated the problem of a natural conjugate distribution for the data-generating process of a Markov chain and he has attempted to find the expected value of certain functions of the transition probabilities, such as the steady-state probability vector. These results assumed a specific prior distribution for the transition probabilities, a generalization of the beta distribution, which we shall call the matrix beta distribution.† Many of Silver's results are generalized in this book.

Cozzolino [13] has examined a sequential decision model involving a two-state chain with uncertain transition probabilities. In a related study, Cozzolino *et al.* [14] have developed heuristic methods for treating sequential decisions in a Markov chain with uncertain transition probabilities. Their findings are based on Monte Carlo studies.

The results of the present study are obtained under the assumption that the prior distribution function of the matrix of transition probabilities belongs to a family of distributions which is closed under consecutive sampling. This concept is formally defined in Chap. 2, where some properties of such families of distributions are derived. In particular, it is shown that there is an arbitrarily large number of such families, thus providing considerable generality to the entire study. Additional generality

† See Sec. 6.3.

is obtained by stating all theorems in terms of distribution functions and Riemann-Stieltjes integrals, making them applicable to both discrete and continuous prior distributions.

In Chap. 3 we consider a discounted adaptive control model in which alternative transition probabilities in a Markov chain are sampled over an infinite time period. The problem of choosing a sequence of policies which maximizes the expected discounted reward over an infinite period is formulated in terms of a set of functional equations. It is shown that these equations have a unique solution, and a method of successive approximations which converges monotonically to this solution is considered.

Certain functions of the transition probabilities, such as the n-step transition probabilities, the steady-state probabilities, the discounted total reward, and the process gain, are treated in Chap. 4, where we obtain recursive equations for the means, variances, and covariances of these quantities. An important result of this chapter is a proof that, under quite general conditions, the mean n-step transition-probability matrix approaches the matrix of mean steady-state probabilities as $n \to \infty$.

These results are applied in Chap. 5, where discounted and undiscounted terminal control models are studied. In these models of a Markov chain with alternative transition probabilities the decision maker can sample various alternatives by paying a sampling cost. After a certain amount of information about the process is gained in this manner, it becomes profitable for him to cease sampling and to choose a policy under which the system operates indefinitely. These models are formulated as functional equations and it is shown that, with probability one, a terminal decision point is reached under an optimal sampling strategy. We then show that there exists a unique solution to the functional equations and we investigate a method of successive approximations.

The results of the first six chapters are obtained for any prior distribution function which belongs to a family closed under consecutive sampling. In Chaps. 6 through 8 we consider a specific distribution for the transition probabilities which we call the matrix beta distribution. This distribution is defined in Chap. 6 and its main properties are derived. We also introduce, in this chapter, the Whittle distribution and the beta-Whittle distribution. These probability distributions are utilized in Chap. 7, where we do prior-posterior and preposterior analysis for a Markov chain when the sample size is fixed. The transition count is identified as a sufficient statistic and is shown to have the Whittle distribution, conditional on a fixed value of the transition probability matrix. The natural conjugate distribution for this data-generating process is the matrix beta, and the unconditional distribution of the transition count is the beta-Whittle distribution.

In Chap. 8 we consider the results of Chaps. 2 through 6 in the case of a two-state Markov chain when the prior distribution of the transition probabilities is matrix beta. Explicit formulas for the expected values of various functions of the transition probabilities are given in terms of the parameters of the matrix beta distribution.

Areas for future research are discussed in Chap. 9.

1.2. NOTATION

The matrix with generic element p_{ij} is denoted by an upper case letter, $\mathbf{P} = [p_{ij}]$; the row vector with generic element p_i is written with a lower case letter, $\boldsymbol{p} = (p_1, \ldots, p_N)$. The matrix $\mathbf{P}^t$ is the transpose of $\mathbf{P}$. Upper case script letters will occasionally be used to denote matrices.

A vector $\boldsymbol{x} = (x_1, \ldots, x_N)$ is a point in the N-dimensional Euclidean space E_N, and we shall use the customary norm, or distance function $\|\boldsymbol{x}\|$, defined by

$$\|\boldsymbol{x}\| = \left[\sum_{i=1}^{N} x_i^2\right]^{1/2}. \tag{1.2.1}$$

Similarly, the $M \times N$ matrix $\mathbf{P}$ is a point in E_{MN} and has the norm

$$\|\mathbf{P}\| = \left[\sum_{i=1}^{M}\sum_{j=1}^{N} p_{ij}^2\right]^{1/2}. \tag{1.2.2}$$

Random quantities are denoted by the tilde; thus, $\tilde{\mathbf{P}}$, $\tilde{\boldsymbol{p}}$, $\tilde{p}_{ij}$ are, respectively, a random matrix, a random vector, and a random variable. The probability of the event A is denoted $P[A]$, and the conditional probability of A given B is $P[A \mid B]$. The expectation operator with respect to the distribution of the random variable $\tilde{x}$ is devoted $E_x[\cdot]$, and the conditional expectation operator taken with respect to the distribution of $\tilde{x}$, given that $\tilde{y} = y$, is $E_{x|y}[\cdot]$. When no confusion will result, the subscript may be dropped.

Let $h(\mathbf{P})$ be a scalar function of the $M \times N$ matrix $\mathbf{P}$. Assume that each row of $\mathbf{P}$ is subject to the constraint

$$\sum_{j=1}^{N} p_{ij} = 1, \qquad i = 1, \ldots, M. \tag{1.2.3}$$

If $F(\mathbf{P})$ is a distribution function, the Riemann-Stieltjes integral of h is to be interpreted as an $M(N-1)$-fold iterated integral over the functionally independent elements of $\mathbf{P}$:

$$\int h(\mathbf{P})\, dF(\mathbf{P}) = \int \cdots \int h(p_{11}, \ldots, p_{1,N-1}, p_{21}, \ldots, p_{M,N-1})\, dF(p_{11}, \ldots, p_{M,N-1}). \tag{1.2.4}$$

If $\mathbf{h}(\mathbf{P}) = [h_{ij}(\mathbf{P})]$ is a matrix-valued function of $\mathbf{P}$, the Riemann-Stieltjes integral of $\mathbf{h}$ is to be interpreted as the matrix of the integrals of each element:

$$\int \mathbf{h}(\mathbf{P})\, dF(\mathbf{P}) = \left[\int h_{ij}(\mathbf{P})\, dF(\mathbf{P})\right]. \tag{1.2.5}$$

1.3. MARKOV CHAINS AND BAYESIAN DECISION THEORY

In this section some of the theory of Markov chains and Bayesian decision processes are summarized. It must be emphasized that these summaries are in no sense a complete review of the theory; only those concepts are defined that are required as background for subsequent chapters.

Markov Chains

Consider a system or process which can exist in one of an at most denumerable number of states, labeled 1, 2, ... At discrete times the system can make a transition from one state to another. Let $x_0, x_1, \ldots$ denote the sequence of states occupied by the system, where x_0 is the initial state and x_n is the state occupied immediately following the nth transition. If, for all finite sequences of states $x_0, x_1, \ldots, x_n$,

$$P[\tilde{x}_{n+1} \mid x_0, x_1, \ldots, x_n] = P[\tilde{x}_{n+1} \mid x_n], \qquad n = 0, 1, 2, \ldots, \tag{1.3.1}$$

then the system is said to constitute a *Markov chain*. That is to say, in a Markov chain, the conditional probability of transitions to future states depends only on the state presently occupied by the system and not on the history of the system prior to entering that state. The conditional probabilities of Eq. 1.3.1 are called *transition probabilities* and will be assumed to be constant with regard to n. Moreover, we shall deal here with *finite Markov chains*, in which there are a finite number of states, labeled $1, 2, \ldots, N$. Then the probability of a transition from state i to state j may be denoted by

$$P[\tilde{x}_{n+1} = j \mid \tilde{x}_n = i] = p_{ij}, \qquad i, j = 1, \ldots, N, \quad n = 0, 1, 2, \ldots, \tag{1.3.2}$$

and arranged in an $N \times N$ matrix $\mathbf{P} = [p_{ij}]$, called the *transition probability matrix*. Since the elements of $\mathbf{P}$ are probabilities,

$$p_{ij} \geqslant 0, \qquad i, j = 1, \ldots, N, \tag{1.3.3}$$

and, since a transition must be made to some state,

$$\sum_{j=1}^{N} p_{ij} = 1, \qquad i = 1, \ldots, N. \tag{1.3.4}$$

A square matrix with the properties of Eqs. 1.3.3 and 1.3.4 is called a *stochastic matrix*. The probabilistic behavior of a Markov chain is completely determined by the transition probability matrix **P**, together with a probability distribution over the initial state $\tilde{x}_0$.

Let $p_{ij}^{(n)}$ denote the conditional probability that the system will occupy state j after n transitions, given that the system presently occupies state i. The probability $p_{ij}^{(n)}$ is termed the *n-step transition probability*. Clearly, $p_{ij}^{(1)} = p_{ij}$, and if

$$\begin{aligned} \delta_{ij} &= 0, \qquad i \neq j, \\ &= 1, \qquad i = j, \end{aligned} \tag{1.3.5}$$

is the Kronecker delta, $p_{ij}^{(0)} = \delta_{ij}$. More generally, $p_{ij}^{(n)}$ satisfies a special case of the Chapman-Kolmogorov equation,

$$p_{ij}^{(n)} = \sum_{k=1}^{N} p_{ik}^{(m)} p_{kj}^{(n-m)},$$

$$i, j = 1, \ldots, N, \quad m = 0, 1, \ldots, n, \quad n = 0, 1, 2, \ldots, \tag{1.3.6}$$

since, in order to pass from state i to state j in n transitions, the system must enter some state k on the mth transition. It follows inductively from Eq. 1.3.6 that the $N \times N$ matrix of n-step transition probabilities is the nth power of the transition probability matrix **P**,

$$[p_{ij}^{(n)}] = \mathbf{P}^n, \qquad n = 0, 1, 2, \ldots. \tag{1.3.7}$$

Let the system initially occupy state j and allow an infinite number of transitions to occur. From **P** can be computed the probability that the system ever returns to state j, denoted f_j. The states of a finite Markov chain are classified as *transient* or *persistent* according to $f_j < 1$ or $f_j = 1$. Additionally, the state j is *periodic* with period $\nu > 1$ if $p_{jj}^{(n)} = 0$ whenever n is not divisible by ν (i.e., a return to j is impossible except, perhaps, in ν, 2ν, 3ν, . . . steps). Persistent, nonperiodic states are called *ergodic*.†

A state j can be reached from a state i if there exists an integer n such that $p_{ij}^{(n)} > 0$. A Markov chain is called *irreducible* if every state can be reached from every other state. It can be shown that, in an irreducible chain, all states have the same classification and period. Thus, the states of a chain can be grouped into one or more sets, each of which constitutes an irreducible chain that can, therefore, be treated independently of the other sets. When dealing with an irreducible chain, since the states all have the same classification and period, the classification is also applied

† Unfortunately, there is not universal agreement on the terminology for classification of states. The one used here, however, is widely followed.

generically to the transition probability matrix. Thus, for example, in an irreducible chain consisting of ergodic states, the transition probability matrix is said to be ergodic.

Assume that $\mathbf{P}$ is ergodic. Let $p_j(n)$ be the unconditional probability that the chain occupies state j after n transitions and let $\boldsymbol{p}(n) = (p_1(n), \ldots, p_N(n))$ be the corresponding n-step probability vector. Then $\boldsymbol{p}(0)$ determines the distribution of the initial state and, in general,

$$p_j(n) = \sum_{k=1}^{N} p_k(m) p_{kj}^{(n-m)},$$

$$j = 1, \ldots, N, \quad m = 0, 1, \ldots, n, \quad n = 0, 1, 2, \ldots. \tag{1.3.8}$$

Clearly, $p_j(n) \geqslant 0$ and $\sum_{j=1}^{N} p_j(n) = 1$ for $n = 0, 1, 2, \ldots$; therefore, $\boldsymbol{p}(n)$ is a probability mass function. It can be shown that $\lim_{n\to\infty} p_j(n) = \pi_j$ exists and, with $m = n - 1$ in Eq. 1.3.8, letting $n \to \infty$, we have

$$\pi_j = \sum_{k=1}^{N} \pi_k p_{kj}, \qquad j = 1, \ldots, N. \tag{1.3.9}$$

The quantities π_j also have the properties

$$\pi_j \geqslant 0, \qquad j = 1, \ldots, N$$

$$\sum_{j=1}^{N} \pi_j = 1, \tag{1.3.10}$$

and are called *steady-state probabilities*. Let $\boldsymbol{\pi} = (\pi_1, \ldots, \pi_N)$ be the *steady-state probability vector*. Equation 1.3.9 can then be written in matrix notation,

$$\boldsymbol{\pi} = \boldsymbol{\pi}\mathbf{P}. \tag{1.3.11}$$

The vector $\boldsymbol{\pi}$ is the unique vector satisfying Eqs. 1.3.10 and 1.3.11. It can be shown that, in an ergodic chain,

$$\lim_{n\to\infty} p_{ij}^{(n)} = \pi_j, \qquad i, j = 1, \ldots, N, \tag{1.3.12}$$

and $\boldsymbol{\pi}$ can thus be interpreted as the distribution of the state occupied by the Markov chain if it is examined at some random time after a large number of transitions have occurred.

A more complete treatment of the theory of finite Markov chains together with a discussion of models based on such chains is given by Kemeny and Snell [26]. The more general theory of Markov chains with a denumerable number of states is summarized by Chung [12].

Bayesian Decision Theory

Bayesian decision theory is a formal mathematical structure which guides a decision maker in choosing a course of action in the face of uncertainty about the consequences of that choice. The course of action recommended by the theory is one which is consistent with the decision maker's preference for various consequences and his considered judgment about the uncertainties involved in the problem. More formally, the Bayesian decision problem is defined in terms of the following sets, which may be finite, denumerable, or nondenumerable:

1. A space of possible acts which are available to the decision maker, $A = \{a\}$.
2. A space of possible states of nature, $\Theta = \{\theta\}$. The states of nature summarize those aspects of the world that are relevant to the decision problem and about which the decision maker is uncertain. Nature exists in exactly one state $\theta \in \Theta$.
3. A family of possible experiments, $E = \{e\}$. The decision maker can use one of these experiments to obtain information about the state of nature. E includes the dummy experiment which consists of making an immediate decision with no experimentation.
4. A space of possible outcomes, $Z = \{z\}$, for the experiments in E.

Each combination $(a, \theta, e, z) \in A \times \Theta \times E \times Z$ determines a consequence for the decision maker.

The axioms and basic theorems of Bayesian decision theory have been stated in various forms, but essentially involve the following:

1. There exists a preference relation $\succ$ over the set of all consequences $C = \{c\}$ such that, if c_i and c_j belong to C, then either $c_i \succ c_j$, $c_j \succ c_i$, or both, and such that, if $c_i \succ c_j$ and $c_j \succ c_k$, then $c_i \succ c_k$.
2. The decision maker can express his preference for consequences by a real-valued function $u(\cdot)$, such that $c_i \succ c_j$ if and only if $u(c_i) > u(c_j)$. The function $u(\cdot)$ is called a *utility function*.
3. The decision maker can express his judgments about the relative likelihood of the states of nature and the experimental outcomes by means of a probability function $P_{\theta,z}$ on $\Theta \times Z$. From $P_{\theta,z}$ can be obtained the marginal probability function P'_θ on Θ, called the *prior probability distribution* of the states of nature (i.e., prior to experimentation). If an experiment e results in an outcome z, the decision maker's prior knowledge is modified by means of Bayes' theorem to yield the *posterior probability distribution* of the states of nature P''_θ, defined to be the conditional probability of $\tilde{\theta}$, given z,

$$P''_{\theta|z}[\tilde{\theta} \mid z] = \frac{P_{z|\theta}[\tilde{z} \mid \theta] P'_\theta[\tilde{\theta}]}{P_z[\tilde{z}]}. \tag{1.3.13}$$

A single prime signifies "prior to experimentation," whereas a double prime denotes "after experimentation."

From the foregoing it can be shown that, if the decision maker is to act consistently with his preference for consequences and his judgment about nature, he should choose the act that maximizes the expected utility of the consequence of that act, the expectation being taken with respect to $P_{\theta,z}$. In symbols, he should choose that experiment e^* and act a^* such that

$$E_{\theta,z}[u(a^*, \tilde{\theta}, e^*, \tilde{z})] = \max_{\substack{a \in A \\ e \in E}} E_{\theta,z}[u(a, \tilde{\theta}, e, \tilde{z})]. \tag{1.3.14}$$

For simplicity, we neglect here the distinction between the maximum and supremum.

Letting $\bar{u}(a, e) = E_{\theta,z}[u(a, \tilde{\theta}, e, \tilde{z})]$, Eq. 1.3.14 can be written as

$$\bar{u}(a^*, e^*) = \max_{e \in E} E_z\left[\max_{a \in A} E''_{\theta|z}[u(a, \tilde{\theta}, e, \tilde{z})]\right] \tag{1.3.15}$$

This formulation is one method of solving the decision problem and leads to the distinction between prior-posterior and preposterior analysis. Assuming a specific experiment e and a specific outcome z, the posterior expected utility $E''_{\theta|z}[u(a, \tilde{\theta}, e, z]$ is computed for each act $a \in A$ and the maximizing act $a^*(e, z)$ determined. This is *prior-posterior analysis* and uses the posterior distribution of $\tilde{\theta}$, $P''_{\theta|z}$. The unconditional sampling distribution of $\tilde{z}$, denoted P_z, is then used to find the unconditional expected utility $E_z\left[\max_{a \in A} E''_{\theta|z}[u(a, \tilde{\theta}, e, \tilde{z})]\right]$ for each $e \in E$, and the experiment which maximizes this expectation is determined. This latter phase is called *preposterior analysis* because it involves averaging prior-posterior analysis over all $z \in Z$ before an experiment is actually performed.

Often a decision problem is based upon a mathematical model such as independent repeated Bernoulli trials or independent, identically distributed observations from a normal population. Such a model will be called a *data-generating process* and specifies the conditional sampling distribution $P_{z|\theta}$. The state space Θ then is the space of parameters for the conditional sampling distribution. To include both the discrete and continuous cases in one notation, we define the *likelihood function* $\ell(z \mid \theta)$ to be either the conditional probability of the outcome z, given that $\tilde{\theta} = \theta$ (when $\tilde{z}$ is a discrete random variable), or the value of the conditional probability density function of $\tilde{z}$, given that $\tilde{\theta} = \theta$ (when $\tilde{z}$ is a continuous random variable). Assuming that $\tilde{\theta}$ has a prior probability density function $f'(\theta)$, the posterior density function of $\tilde{\theta}$, given the outcome z, is obtained from Bayes' theorem,

$$f''(\theta \mid z) = \frac{\ell(z \mid \theta) f'(\theta)}{\int_{\Theta} \ell(z \mid \theta) f'(\theta)\, d\theta}. \tag{1.3.16}$$

In general, the sample outcome is a point in a multidimensional space, and it may often be possible to express the essential information of the sample in terms of points in a space Y of fewer dimensions. Any function $y(z)$ which maps the space of outcomes Z onto another space Y is called a *statistic*. A statistic is said to be *sufficient* if use of y in place of z does not affect the decisions made by the decision maker; i.e., $y(z)$ is a sufficient statistic if, for all $y \in Y$ and all $z \in Z$, $P''_{\theta|y(z)} = P''_{\theta|z}$. It can be shown that this definition of sufficiency is equivalent to the definition of a sufficient statistic used in classical statistics and that y is a sufficient statistic if and only if

$$\ell(z \mid \theta) = k(y(z) \mid \theta) r(z), \tag{1.3.17}$$

where $k(\cdot \mid \cdot)$ is a function of y and θ only, while $r(\cdot)$ is a function of z only.

A *kernel* of the likelihood function is defined to be any function $k(z, \theta)$ such that

$$\frac{\ell(z \mid \theta)}{k(z, \theta)} = g(z), \tag{1.3.18}$$

where $g(\cdot)$ is a function of z only. Thus, in Eq. 1.3.17, $k(y(z) \mid \theta)$ is a kernel of the likelihood function. Similarly, if $f(\theta \mid \psi)$ is a probability density function for $\tilde{\theta}$ with the parameter ψ, a kernel of $f(\theta \mid \psi)$ is any function $\kappa(\theta)$ such that

$$\frac{f(\theta \mid \psi)}{\kappa(\theta)} = \rho(\psi), \tag{1.3.19}$$

where $\rho(\cdot)$ is a function of ψ only. Given $\kappa(\theta)$, the requirement

$$\int_{\Theta} f(\theta \mid \psi)\, d\theta = 1$$

implies that

$$\rho(\psi) = \frac{1}{\int_{\Theta} \kappa(\theta)\, d\theta}, \tag{1.3.20}$$

and, therefore, a kernel uniquely determines its corresponding density function. Thus, we may write the correspondence

$$f(\theta \mid \psi) \propto \kappa(\theta). \tag{1.3.21}$$

Let $y(z)$ be a sufficient statistic and let the likelihood function be factored as in Eq. 1.3.17. Then $k(y(z) \mid \theta)$ may be regarded as a function of θ and taken as the kernel of a prior density function on Θ,

$$f(\theta \mid \psi') \propto k(y \mid \theta). \tag{1.3.22}$$

A prior density function formed in this way is called a *natural conjugate prior density function*. It can be shown that, if $f(\theta \mid \psi')$ is a natural conjugate prior density function, the kernels of the prior density function and the likelihood function combine in such a fashion that the posterior density function $f(\theta \mid \psi'')$ has the same functional form as the prior density function. Thus, prior-posterior analysis can be done by operating solely on the prior parameter ψ'; often this operation is extremely simple. Natural conjugate density functions for the more common data-generating processes form a rich class of distributions, giving the decision maker considerable flexibility in choosing a prior distribution for $\tilde{\theta}$. Often the set of prior parameters can be easily enlarged to give additional flexibility, resulting in what is called an *extended natural conjugate distribution*.

In many cases, the elements of the family of experiments E will consist of the same type of observation and will differ only in the number of observations made, that is, in the sample size. The sample size may be regarded as determined by some stopping rule. If the size of the sample does not provide the decision maker with any information about the state of nature, then the stopping rule is said to be *noninformative*.

The foregoing review of Bayesian decision theory, particularly that related to natural conjugate priors, is considerably amplified and extended by Raiffa and Schlaifer [33].

Markov Chains With Alternatives

When we refer to a Markov chain with alternatives, we mean the following process. Let there be N states which the system can occupy. When the system is in state i, the decision maker can choose one of K_i alternative transition vectors, $\boldsymbol{p}_i^k = (p_{i1}^k, \ldots, p_{iN}^k)$, where p_{ij}^k is the probability that the system makes a transition to state j, given that it is currently in state i and the kth alternative is used. The vectors $\boldsymbol{p}_i^k$ are *stochastic vectors*; that is,

$$p_{ij}^k \geqslant 0, \qquad k = 1, \ldots, K_i, \quad i, j = 1, \ldots, N, \tag{1.3.23a}$$

$$\sum_{j=1}^{N} p_{ij}^k = 1, \qquad k = 1, \ldots, K_i, \quad i = 1, \ldots, N. \tag{1.3.23b}$$

With each transition vector $\boldsymbol{p}_i^k$ is associated a reward vector,

$$\boldsymbol{r}_i^k = (r_{i1}^k, \ldots, r_{iN}^k),$$

where r_{ij}^k is the reward (or, more generally, the utility) earned when the system makes a transition from state i to state j under the kth alternative ($-\infty < r_{ij}^k < \infty, k = 1, \ldots, K_i;\ i, j = 1, \ldots, N$).

The transition vectors can be arranged in a $K \times N$ matrix $\mathscr{P}$, where $K = \sum_{i=1}^{N} K_i$:

$$\mathscr{P} = \begin{bmatrix} p_1^1 \\ \cdot \\ \cdot \\ \cdot \\ p_1^{K_1} \\ \cdot \\ \cdot \\ \cdot \\ p_N^{K_N} \end{bmatrix}. \tag{1.3.24}$$

Let the corresponding reward matrix be denoted by $\mathfrak{R}$. Reserving the term *stochastic matrix* for square matrices of nonnegative elements whose rows sum to unity, we shall call a $K \times N$ matrix whose elements satisfy Eq. 1.3.23 a *generalized stochastic matrix.*

A *policy* consists of the selection of one alternative in each state and may be expressed as a row vector $\boldsymbol{\sigma} = (\sigma_1, \ldots, \sigma_N)$, where σ_i is the index of the alternative selected in state i ($\sigma_i = 1, \ldots, K_i$). The stochastic matrix which governs the transitions of the Markov chain under a specific policy $\boldsymbol{\sigma}$ will be denoted by $\mathbf{P}(\boldsymbol{\sigma})$ or, if no confusion will result, merely by $\mathbf{P}$. The corresponding reward matrix under policy $\boldsymbol{\sigma}$ is $\mathbf{R}(\boldsymbol{\sigma})$ or $\mathbf{R}$. The set of all possible policy vectors $\boldsymbol{\sigma}$ is denoted Σ and is a finite set.

The matrix $\mathscr{P}$ can be regarded as the parameter of a Markov chain with alternatives; uncertainty about $\mathscr{P}$ is expressed by regarding $\mathscr{P}$ as a random matrix with a prior probability distribution function $H(\mathscr{P} \mid \psi)$, which has the parameter ψ. In general, ψ is a point in a multidimensional Euclidean space. The range set of $\tilde{\mathscr{P}}$ is the set of all $K \times N$ generalized stochastic matrices, denoted $\mathcal{S}_{KN}$:

$$\mathcal{S}_{KN} = \left\{ \mathscr{P} \mid \mathscr{P} \text{ is } K \times N,\ p_{ij}^k \geqslant 0,\ \sum_{j=1}^{N} p_{ij}^k = 1 \right. \\ \left. (k = 1, \ldots, K_i;\ i, j = 1, \ldots, N) \right\}. \tag{1.3.25}$$

We remark that $\mathcal{S}_{KN}$ is a closed and bounded, hence, compact subset of the KN-dimensional Euclidean space E_{KN}. The distribution function $H(\mathscr{P} \mid \psi)$ is a function of the $K(N - 1)$ independent elements of $\mathscr{P}$,

$p_{i1}^k, \ldots, p_{i,N-1}^k$, for $k = 1, \ldots, K_i$ and $i = 1, \ldots, N$. $H(\mathscr{P} \mid \psi)$ has the usual properties of a multivariate distribution function; in particular,

$$\int_{\mathcal{S}_{KN}} dH(\mathscr{P} \mid \psi) = 1. \tag{1.3.26}$$

From $H(\mathscr{P} \mid \psi)$ can be obtained the marginal distributions of the $\prod_{i=1}^{N} K_i$ possible stochastic matrices, $\tilde{\mathbf{P}}(\boldsymbol{\sigma})$. The marginal distribution function of $\tilde{\mathbf{P}}(\boldsymbol{\sigma})$ is denoted $F_{\boldsymbol{\sigma}}(\mathbf{P} \mid \psi)$ or, when the dependence on $\boldsymbol{\sigma}$ is clear, simply by $F(\mathbf{P} \mid \psi)$. The range set of $\tilde{\mathbf{P}}$ is $\mathcal{S}_N$, the set of all $N \times N$ stochastic matrices:

$$\mathcal{S}_N = \left\{ \mathbf{P} \mid \mathbf{P} \text{ is } N \times N,\ p_{ij} \geqslant 0,\ \sum_{j=1}^{N} p_{ij} = 1 \quad (i, j = 1, \ldots, N) \right\}. \tag{1.3.27}$$

Chapter 2

FAMILIES OF DISTRIBUTIONS CLOSED UNDER SAMPLING

Much of the discussion presented in the following chapters is carried out under the assumption that the prior probability distribution of $\tilde{\mathscr{P}}$ is a member of a family of distributions closed under a given sampling rule. We formally define this concept in this chapter and derive some properties of such closed families of distributions which will be used in the sequel.

The notion of a family of distributions closed under sampling is not a new one. In Great Britain, Barnard [5] in 1954 and, more recently, Wetherill [40], have applied this concept to sampling inspection problems. In this country, Bellman [6] and Bellman and Kalaba [8] have used the idea in connection with adaptive control processes. A particular class of distributions closed under sampling, known as *natural conjugate distributions*, forms the basis of recent research by Raiffa and Schlaifer [33] in statistical decision theory. However, the properties of closed families of distributions which are derived in this chapter and their application to decision problems in a Markov chain with alternatives are original with the present work.

2.1. FAMILIES OF DISTRIBUTIONS CLOSED UNDER A SAMPLING RULE

Consider a sequence of transitions within a Markov chain with alternatives. A *sampling rule* is a set of specifications used to determine the following:

1. The distribution of the initial state of the chain and the initial policy under which the process is operated.
2. The transitions at which policy changes may occur. These transitions may be determined probabilistically.

3. The distribution of the new policy when a policy change occurs. This distribution is a probability mass function over the set of policies Σ and allows for randomized selection of policies.

4. The transitions after which the state of the process is made known to the decision maker, possibly including the zeroth transition which places the chain in its initial state. Those transitions may be determined probabilistically and, when they do occur, an *observation* of the process is said to have taken place, or the process is said to have been *sampled.* An observation of the process is a random variable the range of which is the set of state indices, $\{1, \ldots, N\}$.

5. A rule for termination of sampling.

We adopt the convention that, if a policy change or an observation occurs at the nth transition, it takes place immediately after the nth transition has occurred.

There are two sampling rules that are of particular importance in succeeding chapters: consecutive sampling and ν-step sampling.

A *consecutive sampling rule of size n* is characterized as follows: A specific initial state and initial policy are selected with probability one. A total of n transitions are to occur, with n selected in advance. Each transition is observed. Policy changes, if they occur, take place at predetermined transitions and, at each change, a predetermined policy is chosen with probability one. Thus, a consecutive sampling rule of size n consists of n consecutive observations of the states of a Markov chain with alternatives under a sequence of policies which is selected in advance of sampling. In succeeding chapters it will be useful to interpret sequential, adaptive sampling as a step-by-step application of the consecutive sampling rule with $n = 1$.

A *ν-step sampling rule of size n* may be described as follows: A positive integer n, a sequence of n positive integers called transition intervals $\{\nu_1, \ldots, \nu_n\}$, and a sequence of n policies $\{\boldsymbol{\sigma}_1, \ldots, \boldsymbol{\sigma}_n\}$, are selected in advance of sampling. We allow the possibility that some or all of the $\boldsymbol{\sigma}_i$ are equal. A specific initial state is chosen with probability one and a sequence of ν_1 transitions are allowed to occur under the policy $\boldsymbol{\sigma}_1$. The state of the Markov chain is observed after the ν_1th transition. Then ν_2 transitions occur under policy $\boldsymbol{\sigma}_2$, the state being observed after the ν_2th transition, and so on. A total of n observations are taken in this manner. The ν-step sampling rule will be used in one of the terminal control models of Chap. 5.

We now proceed with the definition of a family of distributions closed under a sampling rule. A collection $\mathcal{H}$ of probability distribution functions is said to be a *family of distributions indexed by* ψ if all members of the collection have the same functional form and differ only in the values assigned to the parameter ψ. The set of values which ψ can assume is denoted Ψ, termed the *admissible parameter set.* The admissible parameter set is assumed to be a connected subset of a (possibly multidimensional) Euclidean space.

Let a sampling rule be specified and assume that a sample of n observations, $\boldsymbol{x}_n = (x_1, \ldots, x_n)$, has resulted under that sampling rule. Denote by $\ell(\boldsymbol{x}_n \mid \mathscr{P})$ the likelihood of the sample $\boldsymbol{x}_n$ under the given sampling rule, given that $\tilde{\mathscr{P}} = \mathscr{P}$. Let the prior distribution function of $\tilde{\mathscr{P}}$ be $H(\mathscr{P} \mid \psi')$, a member of $\mathcal{H}$, a family of distributions indexed by ψ. Then, if $dH(\mathscr{P} \mid \psi')$ is the prior probability that $\tilde{\mathscr{P}}$ lies in an infinitesimal neighborhood of $\mathscr{P}$, the posterior distribution function of $\tilde{\mathscr{P}}$ is $H(\mathscr{P} \mid \psi', \boldsymbol{x}_n)$, defined by means of Bayes' theorem:

$$dH(\mathscr{P} \mid \psi', \boldsymbol{x}_n) = \frac{\ell(\boldsymbol{x}_n \mid \mathscr{P})\, dH(\mathscr{P} \mid \psi')}{\int_{S_{KN}} \ell(\boldsymbol{x}_n \mid \mathscr{P})\, dH(\mathscr{P} \mid \psi')}. \tag{2.1.1}$$

If $H(\mathscr{P} \mid \psi', \boldsymbol{x}_n) \in \mathcal{H}$ for all $\psi' \in \Psi$ and all samples $\boldsymbol{x}_n$ of nonzero probability, then $\mathcal{H}$ is said to be closed with respect to the sampling rule which determines $\ell(\boldsymbol{x}_n \mid \mathscr{P})$. In this case the posterior distribution is denoted $H(\mathscr{P} \mid \psi'')$, where

$$\psi'' = T(\psi'). \tag{2.1.2}$$

Here T is the mapping of Ψ into Ψ induced by the transformation (2.1.1) when $\mathcal{H}$ is closed under the given sampling rule.

In the special case where the sample consists of a single transition from state i to state j under the kth alternative in state i, ψ'' will be written

$$\psi'' = T_{ij}^{k}(\psi'). \tag{2.1.3}$$

If a fixed policy $\boldsymbol{\sigma}$ is in force, the superscript $k = \sigma_i$ may be suppressed in Eq. 2.1.3.

In Sec. 2.3, families of distributions which are closed relative to the consecutive sampling and ν-step sampling rules are discussed in detail. To carry out this discussion, some properties of the matrix beta distribution are required. Those properties are summarized in the next section.

2.2. THE MATRIX BETA DISTRIBUTION

The matrix beta density function, defined by Eq. 2.2.1, will be shown to be the natural conjugate distribution for the likelihood function of the consecutive sampling rule and, hence, is of intrinsic importance. Moreover, as will be seen in Sec. 2.3, many of the properties of arbitrary families of distributions which are closed relative to the consecutive sampling rule or the ν-step sampling rule are related to characteristics of the matrix beta distribution. For these reasons, the principal facts about this distribution are summarized in this section without proof. Complete derivations are given in Chap. 6.

The $K \times N$ random generalized stochastic matrix, $\tilde{\mathscr{P}} = [\tilde{p}_{ij}^k]$, is said to have the matrix beta distribution with parameter $\mathcal{M} = [m_{ij}^k]$ if $\tilde{\mathscr{P}}$ has the joint density function

$$\begin{aligned} f_{M\beta}^{(K,N)}(\mathscr{P} \mid \mathcal{M}) &= k(\mathcal{M}) \prod_{\substack{i=1\\j=1}}^{N} \prod_{k=1}^{K_i} (p_{ij}^k)^{m_{ij}^k - 1}, \qquad && \mathscr{P} \in \mathcal{S}_{KN} \\ &= 0 && \text{elsewhere.} \end{aligned} \tag{2.2.1}$$

The normalizing constant $k(\mathcal{M})$ is given by

$$k(\mathcal{M}) = \prod_{i=1}^{N} \prod_{k=1}^{K_i} \frac{\Gamma(M_i^k)}{\prod_{j=1}^{N} \Gamma(m_{ij}^k)}, \tag{2.2.2}$$

where

$$M_i^k = \sum_{j=1}^{N} m_{ij}^k, \qquad k = 1, \ldots, K_i, \quad i = 1, \ldots, N. \tag{2.2.3}$$

The parameter $\mathcal{M}$ is a $K \times N$ matrix such that

$$m_{ij}^k > 0, \qquad k = 1, \ldots, K_i, \quad i, j = 1, \ldots, N. \tag{2.2.4}$$

It is shown in Chap. 6 that

$$\int_{\mathcal{S}_{KN}} f_{M\beta}^{(K,N)}(\mathscr{P} \mid \mathcal{M}) \, d\mathscr{P} = 1. \tag{2.2.5}$$

For $k = 1, \ldots, K_i$ and $i, j = 1, \ldots, N$, the means and variances of the elements of $\tilde{\mathscr{P}}$ are given by the formulas

$$E[\tilde{p}_{ij}^k] = \frac{m_{ij}^k}{M_i^k} = \bar{p}_{ij}^k \tag{2.2.6}$$

and

$$\begin{aligned} \operatorname{var}[\tilde{p}_{ij}^k] &= \frac{m_{ij}^k(M_i^k - m_{ij}^k)}{(M_i^k)^2(M_i^k + 1)} \\ &= \frac{\bar{p}_{ij}^k(1 - \bar{p}_{ij}^k)}{M_i^k + 1}. \end{aligned} \tag{2.2.7}$$

The covariances of the elements of $\tilde{\mathscr{P}}$ are

$$\begin{aligned}\operatorname{cov}[\tilde{p}^k_{\alpha\beta}, \tilde{p}^j_{\gamma\delta}] &= \frac{-m^k_{\alpha\beta}m^k_{\alpha\delta}}{(M^k_\alpha)^2(M^k_\alpha + 1)}, & j = k &= 1, \ldots, K_\alpha, \\ & & \alpha = \gamma &= 1, \ldots, N, \\ & & \beta, \delta &= 1, \ldots, N, \\ & & \beta &\neq \delta, \\ &= 0, \qquad j \neq k \quad \text{or} \quad \alpha \neq \gamma. & & \end{aligned} \tag{2.2.8}$$

Let $\boldsymbol{x}_n = (x_0, x_1, \ldots, x_n)$ be a sample of n transitions observed under the consecutive sampling rule, where x_0 is the initial state, known in advance of sampling. Let f^k_{ij} denote the number of transitions in $\boldsymbol{x}_n$ from state i to state j under the kth alternative in state i ($k = 1, \ldots, K_i$; $i, j = 1, \ldots, N$) and define the *transition count* of the sample as the $K \times N$ matrix $\mathbf{F} = [f^k_{ij}]$. Then the conditional probability, given that $\tilde{\mathscr{P}} = \mathscr{P}$, of observing the sample $\boldsymbol{x}_n$ is

$$\prod_{\substack{i=1 \\ j=1}}^{N} \prod_{k=1}^{Ki} (p^k_{ij})^{f^k_{ij}}. \tag{2.2.9}$$

If the rule by which the sample size n was selected is noninformative in the sense of Raiffa and Schlaifer [33], then Eq. 2.2.9 is the likelihood of the sample $\boldsymbol{x}_n$. It is clear that $\mathbf{F}$ is a sufficient statistic for this data-generating process and that the natural conjugate distribution is the matrix beta distribution.

Theorem 2.2.1. Let $\tilde{\mathscr{P}}$ have the marix beta distribution with parameter $\mathscr{M}'$ and suppose that a sample with transition count $\mathbf{F}$ is observed under the consecutive sampling rule with noninformative stopping. Then the posterior distribution of $\tilde{\mathscr{P}}$ is matrix beta with parameter

$$\mathscr{M}'' = \mathscr{M}' + \mathbf{F}. \tag{2.2.10}$$

Proof. By Bayes' theorem the posterior density function, $d(\mathscr{P} \mid \mathscr{M}', \mathbf{F})$, is proportional to the product of the kernel of the likelihood function and the kernel of the prior density function,

$$d(\mathscr{P} \mid \mathscr{M}', \mathbf{F}) \propto \prod_{\substack{i=1 \\ j=1}}^{N} \prod_{k=1}^{K_i} (p^k_{ij})^{m'^k_{ij} + f^k_{ij} - 1}. \tag{2.2.11}$$

The right side of Eq. 2.2.11 is the kernel of a matrix beta density function with parameter $\mathscr{M}' + \mathbf{F}$. Q.E.D.

Corollary 2.2.2. The family of matrix beta distributions is closed with respect to the consecutive sampling rule.

Proof. The corollary follows directly from Theorem 2.2.1. Q.E.D.

2.3. FAMILIES OF DISTRIBUTIONS CLOSED UNDER THE CONSECUTIVE SAMPLING RULE OR THE ν-STEP SAMPLING RULE

In the following chapters we shall confine our attention to models based on either the consecutive sampling rule or the ν-step sampling rule. Some properties of families of distributions which are closed under either of these rules are established in this section. Specifically, it is shown that there are an unlimited number of distinct families of distributions which are closed under the consecutive sampling rule, thus allowing the decision maker considerable latitude in selecting a prior distribution for $\tilde{\mathscr{P}}$. A lemma of fundamental importance for the development of consecutive sampling models is next established. We then turn to families of distributions closed under the ν-step sampling rule, and it is shown that such families may be formed from probability mixtures of distributions from a family closed under consecutive sampling. It is further demonstrated that any family of distributions closed under ν-step sampling is also closed under consecutive sampling. Finally, it is proved that, for an arbitrary prior distribution on $\tilde{\mathscr{P}}$, if n observations of the Markov chain are obtained under either sampling rule, then, with probability one, the probability mass of the posterior distribution tends to concentrate at $\mathfrak{Q}$, the true state of nature, as $n \to \infty$.

Families Closed Under Consecutive Sampling

In Sec. 2.2 it was shown that the natural conjugate distribution for the consecutive sampling rule is the matrix beta distribution. Extended natural conjugate distributions for this sampling rule can be constructed as follows. Let $g(\mathscr{P} \mid \omega)$ be a nonnegative Borel function† defined on $\mathcal{S}_{KN}$ which is positive over some subset of $\mathcal{S}_{KN}$. The parameter ω is a point belonging to Ω, a subset of a Euclidean space. Let $\mathcal{M} = [m_{ij}^k]$ be a $K \times N$ matrix with

$$m_{ij}^k > 0, \qquad k = 1, \ldots, K_i, \quad i, j = 1, \ldots, N. \tag{2.3.1}$$

We assume that $g(\mathscr{P} \mid \omega)$ is sufficiently well behaved that the integral

$$\int_{\mathcal{S}_{KN}} \prod_{\substack{i=1\\j=1}}^{N} \prod_{k=1}^{K_i} (p_{ij}^k)^{m_{ij}^k - 1} g(\mathscr{P} \mid \omega)\, d\mathscr{P} = \frac{1}{C(\mathcal{M}, \omega)} \tag{2.3.2}$$

exists for all $\omega \in \Omega$ and all $\mathcal{M}$ which satisfy Eq. 2.3.1. Let

$$\begin{aligned} h(\mathscr{P} \mid \mathcal{M}, \omega) &= C(\mathcal{M}, \omega) \prod_{\substack{i=1\\j=1}}^{N} \prod_{k=1}^{K_i} (p_{ij}^k)^{m_{ij}^k - 1} g(\mathscr{P} \mid \omega), \qquad \mathscr{P} \in \mathcal{S}_{KN} \\ &= 0 \text{ elsewhere.} \end{aligned} \qquad (2.3.3$$

† See Loève [28], pp. 106ff., for a discussion of Borel functions. A function which is continuous at all but a finite number of points can be shown to be a Borel function.

The function $h(\mathscr{P} \mid \mathcal{M}, \omega)$ is a nonnegative Borel function such that

$$\int_{S_{KN}} h(\mathscr{P} \mid \mathcal{M}, \omega)\, d\mathscr{P} = 1, \tag{2.3.4}$$

and is, therefore, a probability density function.

Corresponding to any function $g(\mathscr{P} \mid \omega)$ which satisfies the preceding requirements, we define the extended natural conjugate family $\mathcal{H}_g$, indexed by the ordered pair $(\mathcal{M}, \omega)$, as the collection of probability density functions $h(\mathscr{P} \mid \mathcal{M}, \omega)$, defined by Eq. 2.3.3. The following theorem shows that $\mathcal{H}_g$ is closed under the consecutive sampling rule.

Theorem 2.3.1. Let $\mathcal{H}_g$ be a family of probability density functions $h(\mathscr{P} \mid \mathcal{M}, \omega)$, as defined by Eq. 2.3.3. If the prior probability distribution on $\tilde{\mathscr{P}}$ is $h(\mathscr{P} \mid \mathcal{M}', \omega') \in \mathcal{H}_g$ and if a sample $\boldsymbol{x}_n = (x_0, \ldots, x_n)$ with transition count $\mathbf{F} = [f_{ij}^k]$ is observed by consecutive sampling, then the posterior distribution of $\tilde{\mathscr{P}}$ is $h(\mathscr{P} \mid \mathcal{M}' + \mathbf{F}, \omega') \in \mathcal{H}_g$. Thus, $\mathcal{H}_g$ is closed under the consecutive sampling rule.

Proof. The posterior distribution of $\tilde{\mathscr{P}}$, $d(\mathscr{P} \mid \mathcal{M}', \omega', \boldsymbol{x}_n)$, is proportional to the product of the kernel of the likelihood function and the kernel of the prior density function,

$$d(\mathscr{P} \mid \mathcal{M}', \omega', \boldsymbol{x}_n) \propto \prod_{\substack{i=1 \\ j=1}}^{N} \prod_{k=1}^{K_i} (p_{ij}^k)^{m'^k_{ij} + f^k_{ij} - 1} g(\mathscr{P} \mid \omega'), \tag{2.3.5}$$

from which the theorem follows. Q.E.D.

The parameter ω provides the decision maker with additional flexibility in expressing his prior knowledge about $\tilde{\mathscr{P}}$. It is to be noted, however, that ω remains unchanged in the posterior distribution and is, in that sense, a nuisance parameter. An example of an extended natural conjugate distribution is presented in Sec. 6.4.

The next result is of fundamental importance for the development of the succeeding chapters. Some additional notation is required. Let $y = (y_1, \ldots, y_{KN})$ be a point in the Euclidean space E_{KN} and let I denote an interval in E_{KN},

$$I = \{y \mid \alpha_i \leqslant y_i \leqslant \beta_i, (i = 1, \ldots, KN)\}, \tag{2.3.6}$$

where $\alpha_i < \beta_i\ (i = 1, \ldots, KN)$. Let Q be a partition of I into a finite number of mutually exclusive and exhaustive intervals, $I_1, \ldots, I_n$. For each I_ν, we define the volume

$$v(I_\nu) = \prod_{i=1}^{KN} (\beta_i - \alpha_i), \qquad \nu = 1, \ldots, n, \tag{2.3.7}$$

and let $v = \max_{\nu} \{v(I_\nu)\}$. Finally, let X_{ij}^k denote the event that a transition occurs from state i to state j under the kth alternative in state i.

Lemma 2.3.2. Let $H(\mathscr{P} \mid \psi) \in \mathcal{H}$, a family of distributions closed under the consecutive sampling rule, and let $g(\mathscr{P})$ be any integrable function of $\mathscr{P}$ defined on $\mathcal{S}_{KN}$. Then the following identity is valid:

$$\int_{\mathcal{S}_{KN}} p_{ij}^k\, g(\mathscr{P})\, dH(\mathscr{P} \mid \psi) = \bar{p}_{ij}^k(\psi) \int_{\mathcal{S}_{KN}} g(\mathscr{P})\, dH(\mathscr{P} \mid T_{ij}^k(\psi)),$$

$$\psi \in \Psi, \quad k = 1, \ldots, K_i, \quad i, j = 1, \ldots, N, \qquad (2.3.8)$$

where $\bar{p}_{ij}^k(\psi)$ is the marginal expectation of $\tilde{p}_{ij}^k$ relative to the prior distribution $H(\mathscr{P} \mid \psi)$.

Proof. Let I be an interval in E_{KN} which contains $\mathcal{S}_{KN}$. For any partition Q of I, let $\mathscr{P}_\nu = [(p_{ij}^k)_\nu]$ denote an arbitrary point of $I_\nu \cap \mathcal{S}_{KN}$ and let $\Delta_\nu(\psi) = P[\tilde{\mathscr{P}} \in I_\nu \cap \mathcal{S}_{KN} \mid \psi]$ when $\tilde{\mathscr{P}}$ has the distribution function $H(\mathscr{P} \mid \psi)$. Then

$$\int_{\mathcal{S}_{KN}} p_{ij}^k g(\mathscr{P})\, dH(\mathscr{P} \mid \psi) = \lim_{\substack{n \to \infty \\ v \to 0}} \sum_{\nu=1}^{n} (p_{ij}^k)_\nu g(\mathscr{P}_\nu)\, \Delta_\nu(\psi). \qquad (2.3.9)$$

Using Bayes' theorem, we have

$$\begin{aligned}\Delta_\nu(T_{ij}^k(\psi)) &= P[\tilde{\mathscr{P}} \in I_\nu \cap \mathcal{S}_{KN} \mid X_{ij}^k, \psi] \\ &= \frac{P[X_{ij}^k \mid \tilde{\mathscr{P}} \in I_\nu \cap \mathcal{S}_{KN}, \psi]\Delta_\nu(\psi)}{P[X_{ij}^k \mid \psi]}. \end{aligned} \qquad (2.3.10)$$

But

$$P[X_{ij}^k \mid \tilde{\mathscr{P}} \in I_\nu \cap \mathcal{S}_{KN}, \psi] = \int_{I_\nu \cap \mathcal{S}_{KN}} p_{ij}^k \frac{dH(\mathscr{P} \mid \psi)}{\Delta_\nu(\psi)}, \qquad (2.3.11)$$

and, by the mean-value theorem, there is a point $\mathscr{P}_\nu^* = [(p_{ij}^k)_\nu^*]$ of $I_\nu \cap \mathcal{S}_{KN}$ such that

$$P[X_{ij}^k \mid \tilde{\mathscr{P}} \in I_\nu \cap \mathcal{S}_{KN}, \psi] = (p_{ij}^k)_\nu^*. \qquad (2.3.12)$$

Since $\mathscr{P}_\nu$ is an arbitrary point of $I_\nu \cap \mathcal{S}_{KN}$, we may set $(p_{ij}^k)_\nu = (p_{ij}^k)_\nu^*$ in Eq. 2.3.9. Then, noting that

$$P[X_{ij}^k \mid \psi] = \int_{\mathcal{S}_{KN}} p_{ij}^k\, dH(\mathscr{P} \mid \psi) = \bar{p}_{ij}^k(\psi),$$

Eq. 2.3.10 yields

$$(p_{ij}^k)_\nu^* \Delta_\nu(\psi) = \bar{p}_{ij}^k(\psi)\Delta_\nu(T_{ij}^k(\psi)), \qquad (2.3.13)$$

and Eq. 2.3.9 becomes

$$\int_{S_{KN}} p_{ij}^k g(\mathscr{P})\, dH(\mathscr{P} \mid \psi) = \bar{p}_{ij}^k(\psi) \lim_{\substack{n\to\infty \\ v\to 0}} \sum_{\nu=1}^{n} g(\mathscr{P}_\nu^*)\Delta_\nu(T_{ij}^k(\psi))$$

$$= \bar{p}_{ij}^k(\psi) \int_{S_{KN}} g(\mathscr{P})\, dH(\mathscr{P} \mid T_{ij}^k(\psi)). \quad (2.3.14)$$

Q.E.D.

Families Closed Under ν-Step Sampling

Let us now consider the likelihood function associated with a ν-step sampling rule of size n. This sampling rule is described by the sequence of transition intervals $\{\nu_1, \ldots, \nu_n\}$ and by the sequence of policies $\{\boldsymbol{\sigma}_1, \ldots, \boldsymbol{\sigma}_n\}$. Let $\boldsymbol{x}_n = (x_0, \ldots, x_n)$ denote the resulting observations, where x_0 is the known initial state. Letting $p_{ij}^{(\nu)}(\boldsymbol{\sigma})$ denote the (i, j)th element of the matrix $\mathbf{P}(\boldsymbol{\sigma})$ raised to the νth power, the conditional probability, given that $\tilde{\mathscr{P}} = \mathscr{P}$, of observing the sample $\boldsymbol{x}_n$, is

$$p_{x_0x_1}^{(\nu_1)}(\boldsymbol{\sigma}_1)p_{x_1x_2}^{(\nu_2)}(\boldsymbol{\sigma}_2) \cdots p_{x_{n-1}x_n}^{(\nu_n)}(\boldsymbol{\sigma}_n) = \prod_{j=1}^{n} p_{x_{j-1},x_j}^{(\nu_j)}(\boldsymbol{\sigma}_j). \quad (2.3.15)$$

If the rule by which the sample size n was chosen is noninformative, then Eq. 2.3.15 is the likelihood of the sample $\boldsymbol{x}_n$.

Let $\mathcal{H}$ be a family of probability distributions indexed by $\psi \in \Psi$. For any fixed positive integer m let $\boldsymbol{\alpha} = (\alpha_1, \ldots, \alpha_m)$ be a stochastic vector. A *probability mixture* of distributions from $\mathcal{H}$ is defined to be the weighted sum

$$H^*(\mathscr{P} \mid \psi_1, \ldots, \psi_m, \boldsymbol{\alpha}) = \sum_{i=1}^{m} \alpha_i H(\mathscr{P} \mid \psi_i), \quad (2.3.16)$$

where $\mathcal{H}(\mathscr{P} \mid \psi_i) \in \mathcal{H}$ $(i = 1, \ldots, m)$. It is clear from the definition that $H^*(\mathscr{P} \mid \psi_1, \ldots, \psi_m, \boldsymbol{\alpha})$ is also a probability distribution function for $\tilde{\mathscr{P}}$. The *mixed extension* of $\mathcal{H}$ is defined to be $\mathcal{H}^*$, the family of all probability mixtures of distributions from $\mathcal{H}$ as $\boldsymbol{\alpha}$ ranges over S_{1m}—the set of m-dimensional stochastic vectors (for fixed m)—and as m ranges over the positive integers. Since $H(\mathscr{P} \mid \psi)$ is trivially a probability mixture, $\mathcal{H} \subset \mathcal{H}^*$. In general, however, $\mathcal{H} \neq \mathcal{H}^*$.

The following theorems establish that a family of distributions is closed under ν-step sampling if it is the mixed extension of a family closed under consecutive sampling and that such a mixed extension is also closed under the consecutive sampling rule.

Theorem 2.3.3. Let $\mathcal{H}$ be a family of distributions closed under consecutive sampling and let $\mathcal{H}^*$ be its mixed extension. Then $\mathcal{H}^*$ is also closed under consecutive sampling.

Proof. Let $\boldsymbol{x}_n$ denote a sample of size n obtained by consecutive sampling. If the prior distribution of $\tilde{\mathscr{P}}$ is $H^*(\mathscr{P} \mid \psi_1', \ldots, \psi_m', \boldsymbol{\alpha}') \in \mathcal{H}^*$, where $\boldsymbol{\alpha}' = (\alpha_1', \ldots, \alpha_m')$, and if $\ell(\boldsymbol{x}_n \mid \mathscr{P})$ is the likelihood function, then the posterior distribution is, using Bayes' theorem and Eq. 2.3.16,

$$dH^*(\mathscr{P} \mid \psi_1', \ldots, \psi_m', \boldsymbol{\alpha}', \boldsymbol{x}_n) = \frac{\ell(\boldsymbol{x}_n \mid \mathscr{P})\, dH^*(\mathscr{P} \mid \psi_1', \ldots, \psi_m', \boldsymbol{\alpha}')}{\int_{S_{KN}} \ell(\boldsymbol{x}_n \mid \mathscr{P})\, dH^*(\mathscr{P} \mid \psi_1', \ldots, \psi_m', \boldsymbol{\alpha}')}$$

$$= \frac{\sum_{i=1}^{N} \alpha_i' \ell(\boldsymbol{x}_n \mid \mathscr{P})\, dH(\mathscr{P} \mid \psi_i')}{\sum_{j=1}^{N} \alpha_j' \int_{S_{KN}} \ell(\boldsymbol{x}_n \mid \mathscr{P})\, dH(\mathscr{P} \mid \psi_j')}$$

$$= \sum_{i=1}^{N} \alpha_i'' \, dH(\mathscr{P} \mid \psi_i''), \tag{2.3.17}$$

where

$$\alpha_i'' = \frac{\alpha_i' \int_{S_{KN}} \ell(\boldsymbol{x}_n \mid \mathscr{P})\, dH(\mathscr{P} \mid \psi_i')}{\sum_{j=1}^{N} \alpha_j' \int_{S_{KN}} \ell(\boldsymbol{x}_n \mid \mathscr{P})\, dH(\mathscr{P} \mid \psi_j')} \qquad i = 1, \ldots, m, \tag{2.3.18}$$

and ψ_i'' is defined by Eq. 2.1.2. Since $\boldsymbol{\alpha}'' = (\alpha_1'', \ldots, \alpha_m'')$ is a stochastic vector, the posterior distribution of $\tilde{\mathscr{P}}$ is $H^*(\mathscr{P} \mid \psi_1'', \ldots, \psi_m'', \boldsymbol{\alpha}'') \in \mathcal{H}^*$. Q.E.D.

Theorem 2.3.4. Let $\mathcal{H}^*$ be a family of probability distributions indexed by $\psi^* \in \Psi^*$. A sufficient condition that $\mathcal{H}^*$ be closed under the ν-step sampling rule is that $\mathcal{H}^*$ be the mixed extension of $\mathcal{H}$, a family of distributions closed under consecutive sampling.

Proof. Assume first that $n = 1$. Let $X_{ij}(\nu, \boldsymbol{\sigma})$ denote the observation of a transition from i to j over a transition interval of length ν under the policy $\boldsymbol{\sigma} = (\sigma_1, \ldots, \sigma_N)$. The likelihood function is

$$p_{ij}^{(\nu)}(\boldsymbol{\sigma}) = \sum_{i_1=1 \cdots i_{\nu-1}=1}^{N} p_{ii_1}^{\sigma_i} p_{i_1 i_2}^{\sigma_{i_1}} \cdots p_{i_{\nu-1} j}^{\sigma_{i_{\nu-1}}}, \tag{2.3.19}$$

which is the sum of $N^{(\nu-1)}$ terms, each of which is the likelihood function for a sample sequence of ν transitions observed under the consecutive sampling rule. Let $H^*(\mathscr{P} \mid \psi^*) \in \mathcal{H}^*$ be the prior distribution of $\tilde{\mathscr{P}}$. The differential form of the posterior distribution has the kernel

$$dH^*(\mathscr{P} \mid \psi^*, X_{ij}(\nu, \boldsymbol{\sigma})) \propto \sum_{i_1=1 \cdots i_{\nu-1}=1}^{N} p_{ii_1}^{\sigma_i} \cdots p_{i_{\nu-1} j}^{\sigma_{i_{\nu-1}}} \, dH^*(\mathscr{P} \mid \psi^*). \tag{2.3.20}$$

If $\mathcal{H}^*$ is the mixed extension of a family $\mathcal{H}$ closed under consecutive sampling, then Eq. 2.3.20 implies that $H^*(\mathcal{P} \mid \psi^*, X_{ij}(\nu, \boldsymbol{\sigma}))$ is a probability mixture of distributions from $\mathcal{H}$ and, therefore, belongs to $\mathcal{H}^*$.

For $n > 1$, the differential form of the posterior distribution of $\tilde{\mathcal{P}}$ has the kernel

$$dH^*(\mathcal{P} \mid \psi^*, \boldsymbol{x}_n) \propto \prod_{j=1}^{n} p_{x_{j-1},x_j}^{(\nu_j)}(\boldsymbol{\sigma}_j)\, dH^*(\mathcal{P} \mid \psi^*)$$

$$\propto \prod_{j=2}^{n} p_{x_{j-1},x_j}^{(\nu_j)}(\boldsymbol{\sigma}_j)\, dH^*(\mathcal{P} \mid \psi^*, X_{x_0x_1}(\nu_1, \boldsymbol{\sigma}_1)), \quad (2.3.21)$$

and the theorem follows by induction. Q.E.D.

Corollary 2.3.5. If $\mathcal{H}^*$ is a family of distributions closed under the ν-step sampling rule, then $\mathcal{H}^*$ is also closed under the consecutive sampling rule.

Proof. The corollary follows immediately since consecutive sampling is a special case of ν-step sampling with all $\nu_i = 1$. Q.E.D.

Large Sample Theory

Let $H(\mathcal{P} \mid \psi)$ be an arbitrary prior distribution function of the $K \times N$ generalized stochastic matrix $\tilde{\mathcal{P}}$. We now show that, if a sample of size n is observed under either the consecutive or the ν-step sampling rule, the probability mass of the posterior distribution tends, as $n \to \infty$, to concentrate at the $K \times N$ generalized stochastic matrix $\mathfrak{Q}$, the true state of nature, with probability one. This statement is made more precisely in Theorems 2.3.8 and 2.3.9. Not only are these results of interest on their own merits but also an important application of Theorems 2.3.8 and 2.3.9 will be made in Chap. 5, where the question of termination of sampling is considered for terminal control models.

Consider a sample of size n obtained under the ν-step sampling rule. For a fixed state i, a fixed policy $\boldsymbol{\sigma}$, and a fixed transition interval ν, we shall say a trial occurs whenever the system makes a transition from state i to any other state over a transition interval of length ν under the policy $\boldsymbol{\sigma}$. For a fixed state j, let there be associated with the mth trial the random variable $X_m(j)$ which takes the value 1 if the system is next observed in state j, and the value zero otherwise. A sample of size n thus generates a sequence $\{X_1(j), \ldots, X_m(j)\}$ of independent, identically distributed random variables which, if $\mathfrak{Q}$ is the true state of nature, have the probability function

$$P[\tilde{X}_\alpha(j) = 1] = q_{ij}^{(\nu)}(\boldsymbol{\sigma}) \qquad \alpha = 1, 2, \ldots, j = 1, \ldots, N, \quad (2.3.22a)$$

$$P[\tilde{X}_\alpha(j) = 0] = 1 - q_{ij}^{(\nu)}(\boldsymbol{\sigma}) \qquad \alpha = 1, 2, \ldots, j = 1, \ldots, N, \quad (2.3.22b)$$

and expected value

$$E[\tilde{X}_\alpha(j)] = q_{ij}^{(\nu)}(\boldsymbol{\sigma}), \qquad \alpha = 1, 2, \ldots, j = 1, \ldots, N. \qquad (2.3.23)$$

The following lemma is an immediate consequence of the strong law of large numbers.

Lemma 2.3.6. Let $(X_1(j), \ldots, X_m(j))$ be an observation of size m of the sequence of trials defined above, for fixed states i and j, a fixed policy $\boldsymbol{\sigma}$, and a fixed transition interval ν. If, as $m \to \infty$, state i is entered an infinite number of times and the policy $\boldsymbol{\sigma}$ and transition interval ν are used infinitely often when in state i, we have, with probability one,

$$\lim_{m \to \infty} \frac{1}{m} \sum_{\alpha=1}^{m} X_\alpha(j) = q_{ij}^{(\nu)}(\boldsymbol{\sigma}), \qquad j = 1, \ldots, N, \qquad (2.3.24)$$

where $\mathfrak{Q}$ is the true state of nature.

We remark that, if $\nu = 1$ and $\sigma_i = k$, Lemma 2.3.6 applies to the consecutive sampling rule and Eq. 2.3.24 becomes

$$\lim_{m \to \infty} \frac{1}{m} \sum_{\alpha=1}^{m} X_\alpha(j) = q_{ij}^{k}, \qquad j = 1, \ldots, N, \qquad (2.3.25)$$

the limit holding with probability one.

A generalized stochastic matrix, $\mathscr{P} = [p_{ij}^k]$, is said to be *positive* if all of its elements are positive, which implies that

$$0 < p_{ij}^k < 1, \qquad k = 1, \ldots, K_i, \quad i, j = 1, \ldots, N. \qquad (2.3.26)$$

Lemma 2.3.7. Let $\boldsymbol{x}_n$ be a sample of size n obtained under the ν-step sampling rule. Assume that, as $n \to \infty$, a fixed state i is observed infinitely often and that, when in state i, the policy $\boldsymbol{\sigma}$ and transition interval ν are used infinitely often. Then, if the true state of nature $\mathfrak{Q}$ is a positive matrix, every state j $(j = 1, \ldots, N)$ is, with probability one, observed infinitely often.

Proof. For fixed states i and j, the policy $\boldsymbol{\sigma}$, and the transition interval ν, let $\{X_m(j)\}$ be the sequence of trials generated by the sample $\boldsymbol{x}_n$, as defined above. The hypotheses of the lemma imply that $m \to \infty$ as $n \to \infty$ and we have, by Lemma 2.3.6,

$$\lim_{m \to \infty} \frac{1}{m} \sum_{\alpha=1}^{m} X_\alpha(j) = q_{ij}^{(\nu)}(\boldsymbol{\sigma}), \qquad j = 1, \ldots, N, \qquad (2.3.27)$$

with probability one. Since $\mathfrak{Q}$ is positive, $q_{ij}^{(\nu)}(\boldsymbol{\sigma}) > 0$ for $j = 1, \ldots, N$ and, therefore, Eq. 2.3.27 implies that, with probability one, $X_\alpha(j) = 1$ infinitely often for each state j. Q.E.D.

This lemma can probably be proved under the weaker assumption that $\mathbf{Q}(\boldsymbol{\sigma})$ is ergodic, but it is sufficient for our purposes to assume that the true state of nature is a positive matrix. It will be shown in Chap. 4 that, for all prior distributions of $\tilde{\mathscr{P}}$ which satisfy a mild continuity condition, the set of nonpositive matrices is a set of measure zero.

We again remark that, by taking $\nu = 1$, Lemma 2.3.7 applies to samples obtained under the consecutive sampling rule as well as under the ν-step sampling rule.

Let ϵ be an arbitrary positive number and define $\boldsymbol{\epsilon}$ to be the $K \times N$ matrix each element of which is ϵ. For any $K \times N$ matrices $\mathscr{P}$ and $\mathfrak{Q}$, we say that

$$|\mathscr{P} - \mathfrak{Q}| < \boldsymbol{\epsilon} \tag{2.3.28}$$

if

$$|p_{ij}^k - q_{ij}^k| < \epsilon, \qquad k = 1, \ldots, K_i, \quad i, j = 1, \ldots, N. \tag{2.3.29}$$

Clearly, if Eq. 2.3.28 holds, then

$$\|\mathscr{P} - \mathfrak{Q}\| = \left(\sum_{\substack{i=1\\j=1}}^{N} \sum_{k=1}^{K_i} (p_{ij}^k - q_{ij}^k)^2\right)^{1/2} < \epsilon\sqrt{KN}, \tag{2.3.30}$$

and the norm, $\|\mathscr{P} - \mathfrak{Q}\|$, can be made arbitrarily small by an appropriate choice of ϵ. Let $H(\mathscr{P} \mid \psi)$ be an arbitrary prior distribution function of $\tilde{\mathscr{P}}$ and assume that a sample $\boldsymbol{x}_n$ of size n is observed. Denote by $H(\mathscr{P} \mid \psi, \boldsymbol{x}_n)$ the posterior distribution of $\tilde{\mathscr{P}}$, and for fixed $\mathfrak{Q}$ let

$$P_n[|\tilde{\mathscr{P}} - \mathfrak{Q}| < \boldsymbol{\epsilon}] = \int_{\mathscr{P} \in E} dH(\mathscr{P} \mid \psi, \boldsymbol{x}_n) \tag{2.3.31}$$

denote the posterior probability of the set

$$E = \{\mathscr{P} \mid |\mathscr{P} - \mathfrak{Q}| < \boldsymbol{\epsilon}\} \subset \mathcal{S}_{KN}. \tag{2.3.32}$$

When we say that the posterior probability mass tends, as $n \to \infty$, to concentrate at $\mathfrak{Q}$, the true state of nature, with probability one, we mean that, for any $\epsilon > 0$,

$$\lim_{n \to \infty} P_n[|\tilde{\mathscr{P}} - \mathfrak{Q}| < \boldsymbol{\epsilon}] = 1, \tag{2.3.33}$$

the limit holding with probability one. That is to say, as $n \to \infty$, the unit mass of probability concentrates at $\mathfrak{Q}$ with probability one.

Theorem 2.3.8. Let $H(\mathscr{P} \mid \psi)$ be an arbitrary prior distribution function of $\tilde{\mathscr{P}}$. Let $\boldsymbol{x}_n$ be a sample of size n obtained from a Markov chain with alternatives under the consecutive sampling rule. Assume that the sampling strategy is such that, as $n \to \infty$, if state i is entered infinitely often, every alternative in state i is sampled infinitely often ($i = 1, \ldots, N$).

If $\mathcal{Q}$, the true state of nature, is a positive matrix, then, for any $\epsilon > 0$,

$$\lim_{n\to\infty} P_n[|\tilde{\mathcal{P}} - \mathcal{Q}| < \epsilon] = 1, \tag{2.3.34}$$

the limit holding with probability one, provided $H(\mathcal{P} \mid \psi)$ assigns positive probability to the set E defined by Eq. 2.3.32.

Proof. Since the proof is involved, we proceed in several steps.

1. Let $\mathbf{F}(n) = [f_{ij}^k(n)]$ be the transition count of the sample $\boldsymbol{x}_n$. The posterior distribution of $\tilde{\mathcal{P}}$ is $H(\mathcal{P} \mid \psi, \boldsymbol{x}_n)$, where

$$dH(\mathcal{P} \mid \psi, \boldsymbol{x}_n) = \frac{\prod_{\substack{i=1\\j=1}}^{N} \prod_{k=1}^{K} (p_{ij}^k)^{f_{ij}^k(n)}\, dH(\mathcal{P} \mid \psi)}{\int_{S_{KN}} \prod_{\substack{i=1\\j=1}}^{N} \prod_{k=1}^{K} (p_{ij}^k)^{f_{ij}^k(n)}\, dH(\mathcal{P} \mid \psi)}. \tag{2.3.35}$$

Letting

$$\mathcal{M}(n) = [m_{ij}^k(n)] = [f_{ij}^k(n) + 1] \tag{2.3.36}$$

and multiplying the numerator and denominator of Eq. 2.3.35 by the normalizing constant $k(\mathcal{M}(n))$ defined by Eq. 2.2.2, we have

$$dH(\mathcal{P} \mid \psi, \boldsymbol{x}_n) = \frac{f_{M\beta}^{(K,N)}(\mathcal{P} \mid \mathcal{M}(n))\, dH(\mathcal{P} \mid \psi)}{\int_{S_{KN}} f_{M\beta}^{(K,N)}(\mathcal{P} \mid \mathcal{M}(n))\, dH(\mathcal{P} \mid \psi)}. \tag{2.3.37}$$

2. Let

$$\nu_i^k(n) = \sum_{j=1}^{N} f_{ij}^k(n),$$
$$k = 1, \ldots, K_i, \quad i = 1, \ldots, N, \quad n = 1, 2, \ldots, \tag{2.3.38}$$

denote the number of times that alternative k is used in state i in a sample of size n. As $n \to \infty$, at least one of the states of the chain is entered infinitely often. Lemma 2.3.7 and the hypotheses of the theorem imply that, with probability one, every state is entered infinitely often. Thus, under the assumed sampling strategy, $\nu_i^k(n) \to \infty$ as $n \to \infty$ with probability one ($k = 1, \ldots, K_i$; $i = 1, \ldots, N$). The mean of the distribution $f_{M\beta}^{(K,N)}(\mathcal{P} \mid \mathcal{M}(n))$ is $\bar{\mathcal{P}}(n) = [\bar{p}_{ij}^k(n)]$, where

$$\bar{p}_{ij}^k(n) = \frac{f_{ij}^k(n) + 1}{\nu_i^k(n) + N},$$
$$k = 1, \ldots, K_i, \quad i, j = 1, \ldots, N, \quad n = 1, 2, \ldots. \tag{2.3.39}$$

Thus, if $\mathcal{Q} = [q_{ij}^k]$, Lemma 2.3.6 implies that, with probability one,

$$\lim_{n\to\infty} \bar{p}_{ij}^k(n) = q_{ij}^k > 0, \qquad k = 1, \ldots, K_i, \quad i, j = 1, \ldots, N. \tag{2.3.40}$$

3. We now show that, as $n \to \infty$, the probability mass of $f_{M\beta}^{(K,N)}(\mathscr{P} \mid \mathcal{M}(n))$ tends, with probability one, to concentrate at $\mathfrak{Q}$. If $\tilde{\mathscr{P}}$ is a random matrix with the density function $f_{M\beta}^{(K,N)}(\mathscr{P} \mid \mathcal{M}(n))$, the marginal variance of $\tilde{p}_{ij}^k$ is

$$V_{ij}^k(n) = \frac{\bar{p}_{ij}^k(n)[1 - \bar{p}_{ij}^k(n)]}{\nu_i^k(n) + N + 1} \leqslant \frac{\frac{1}{4}}{\nu_i^k(n) + N + 1},$$

$$k = 1, \ldots, K_i, \quad i, j = 1, \ldots, N, \quad n = 1, 2, \ldots. \tag{2.3.41}$$

Thus, with probability one,

$$\lim_{n\to\infty} V_{ij}^k(n) = 0, \qquad k = 1, \ldots, K_i, \quad i, j = 1, \ldots, N. \tag{2.3.42}$$

Let $\epsilon' > 0$ and δ $(0 < \delta < 1)$ be given. Define the set $E \subset \mathrm{S}_{KN}$ as in Eq. 2.3.32 and let

$$P[|\tilde{\mathscr{P}} - \mathfrak{Q}| < \epsilon' \mid \mathcal{M}(n)] = \int_{\mathscr{P}\in E} f_{M\beta}^{(K,N)}(\mathscr{P} \mid \mathcal{M}(n))\, d\mathscr{P}. \tag{2.3.43}$$

Since

$$\{\mathscr{P} \mid |\mathscr{P} - \mathfrak{Q}| < \epsilon'\} = \bigcap_{i,j,k} \{\mathscr{P} \mid |p_{ij}^k - q_{ij}^k| < \epsilon'\},$$

De Morgan's law yields

$$\{\mathscr{P} \mid |\mathscr{P} - \mathfrak{Q}| < \epsilon'\}^c = \bigcup_{i,j,k} \{\mathscr{P} \mid |p_{ij}^k - q_{ij}^k| \geqslant \epsilon'\},$$

where c denotes the set complement. Then

$$1 - P[|\tilde{\mathscr{P}} - \mathfrak{Q}| < \epsilon' \mid \mathcal{M}(n)] \leqslant \sum_{i,j,k} P[|\tilde{p}_{ij}^k - q_{ij}^k| \geqslant \epsilon' \mid \mathcal{M}(n)]. \tag{2.3.44}$$

The marginal variance of $\tilde{p}_{ij}^k$ is

$$V_{ij}^k(n) = \int_{\mathrm{S}_{KN}} (p_{ij}^k - \bar{p}_{ij}^k(n))^2 f_{M\beta}^{(K,N)}(\mathscr{P} \mid \mathcal{M}(n))\, d\mathscr{P}$$

$$= -(\bar{p}_{ij}^k(n) - q_{ij}^k)^2 + \int_{\mathrm{S}_{KN}} (p_{ij}^k - q_{ij}^k)^2 f_{M\beta}^{(K,N)}(\mathscr{P} \mid \mathcal{M}(n))\, d\mathscr{P}. \tag{2.3.45}$$

Let

$$e_{ij}^k = \{\mathscr{P} \mid |p_{ij}^k - q_{ij}^k| \geqslant \epsilon'\} \subset \mathrm{S}_{KN},$$

$$k = 1, \ldots, K_i, \quad i, j = 1, \ldots, N. \tag{2.3.46}$$

Then

$$\int_{\mathrm{S}_{KN}} (p_{ij}^k - q_{ij}^k)^2 f_{M\beta}^{(K,N)}(\mathscr{P} \mid \mathcal{M}(n))\, d\mathscr{P}$$

$$\geqslant \int_{\mathscr{P}\in e_{ij}^k} (p_{ij}^k - q_{ij}^k)^2 f_{M\beta}^{(K,N)}(\mathscr{P} \mid \mathcal{M}(n))\, d\mathscr{P}$$

$$\geqslant \epsilon'^2 P[|\tilde{p}_{ij}^k - q_{ij}^k| \geqslant \epsilon' \mid \mathcal{M}(n)], \tag{2.3.47}$$

and, using Eq. 2.3.45,

$$P[|\tilde{p}_{ij}^k - q_{ij}^k| \geqslant \epsilon' \mid \mathcal{M}(n)] \leqslant \frac{1}{\epsilon'^2}[V_{ij}^k(n) + (\bar{p}_{ij}^k(n) - q_{ij}^k)^2],$$

$$k = 1, \ldots, K_i, \quad i, j = 1, \ldots, N, \quad n = 1, 2, \ldots. \quad (2.3.48)$$

By Eqs. 2.3.40 and 2.3.42, there exists an integer n^* such that, for all $n > n^*$,

$$\frac{1}{\epsilon'^2}[V_{ij}^k(n) + (\bar{p}_{ij}^k(n) - q_{ij}^k)^2] < \frac{\delta}{KN},$$

$$k = 1, \ldots, K_i, \quad i, j = 1, \ldots, N, \quad (2.3.49)$$

with probability one. Thus, for $n > n^*$, the inequality of Eq. 2.3.44 becomes

$$1 - P[|\tilde{\mathcal{P}} - \mathcal{Q}| < \epsilon' \mid \mathcal{M}(n)] < \delta, \qquad n > n^*, \qquad (2.3.50)$$

and

$$P[|\tilde{\mathcal{P}} - \mathcal{Q}| < \epsilon' \mid \mathcal{M}(n)] > 1 - \delta, \qquad n > n^*, \qquad (2.3.51)$$

with probability one. Since δ is arbitrary,

$$\lim_{n\to\infty} P[|\tilde{\mathcal{P}} - \mathcal{Q}| < \epsilon' \mid \mathcal{M}(n)] = 1, \qquad (2.3.52)$$

the limit holding with probability one, and the probability mass of $f_{M\beta}^{(K,N)}(\mathcal{P} \mid \mathcal{M}(n))$ tends to concentrate at $\mathcal{Q}$ as asserted.

4. Again defining E as in Eq. 2.3.32 and letting E^c be the complement of E in $\mathcal{S}_{KN}$, we have, from Eq. 2.3.37,

$$P_n[|\tilde{\mathcal{P}} - \mathcal{Q}| < \epsilon] = \int_{\mathcal{P}\in E} dH(\mathcal{P} \mid \psi, x_n)$$

$$= \frac{\int_{\mathcal{P}\in E} f_{M\beta}^{(K,N)}(\mathcal{P} \mid \mathcal{M}(n))\, dH(\mathcal{P} \mid \psi)}{\int_{\mathcal{P}\in E} f_{M\beta}^{(K,N)}(\mathcal{P} \mid \mathcal{M}(n))\, dH(\mathcal{P} \mid \psi) + \int_{\mathcal{P}\in E^c} f_{M\beta}^{(K,N)}(\mathcal{P} \mid \mathcal{M}(n))\, dH(\mathcal{P} \mid \psi)}. \qquad (2.3.53)$$

Let $\delta(n)$ be the maximum of the continuous function $f_{M\beta}^{(K,N)}(\mathcal{P} \mid \mathcal{M}(n))$ on the compact set E^c. Equation 2.3.52 implies that $\lim_{n\to\infty} \delta(n) = 0$, with probability one. Thus,

$$P_n[|\tilde{\mathcal{P}} - \mathcal{Q}| < \epsilon] \geqslant \frac{\int_{\mathcal{P}\in E} f_{M\beta}^{(K,N)}(\mathcal{P} \mid \mathcal{M}(n))\, dH(\mathcal{P} \mid \psi)}{\delta(n) + \int_{\mathcal{P}\in E} f_{M\beta}^{(K,N)}(\mathcal{P} \mid \mathcal{M}(n))\, dH(\mathcal{P} \mid \psi)} > 0, \qquad (2.3.54)$$

and, with probability one,

$$\lim_{n\to\infty} P_n[|\tilde{\mathscr{P}} - \mathfrak{Q}| < \epsilon] = 1. \qquad \text{Q.E.D.}$$

Theorem 2.3.9. Let $H(\mathscr{P} \mid \psi)$ be an arbitrary prior distribution function of $\tilde{\mathscr{P}}$. Let $\boldsymbol{x}_n$ be a sample of size n obtained from a Markov chain with alternatives under the ν-step sampling rule. Assume that, when the system is observed in state i, the sampling rule is restricted to policies from $\Sigma_i \subset \Sigma$ and to transition intervals from the finite set $I_i = \{\nu_1, \ldots, \nu_{m_i}\}$, such that, as $n \to \infty$, if state i is observed infinitely often, every policy in Σ_i and every transition interval in I_i are used infinitely often ($i = 1, \ldots, N$). If $\mathfrak{Q}$, the true state of nature, is a positive matrix, then for any $\epsilon > 0$,

$$\lim_{n\to\infty} P_n[|\tilde{\mathscr{P}} - \mathfrak{Q}| < \epsilon] = 1, \tag{2.3.55}$$

the limit holding with probability one, provided $H(\mathscr{P} \mid \psi)$ assigns positive probability to the set E defined by Eq. 2.3.32.

Proof. Let K_i be the total number of ordered pairs $(\boldsymbol{\sigma}, \nu)$, where $\boldsymbol{\sigma} \in \Sigma_i$ and $\nu \in I_i$ ($i = 1, \ldots, N$), and let $K = \sum_{i=1}^{N} K_i$. When in state i, let k index the possible policy and transition interval combinations $(\boldsymbol{\sigma}, \nu)$. For $\boldsymbol{\sigma} \in \Sigma_i$ and $\nu \in I_i$, let

$$\pi_{ij}^k = p_{ij}^{(\nu)}(\boldsymbol{\sigma}), \qquad k = 1, \ldots, K_i, \quad i, j = 1, \ldots, N, \tag{2.3.56}$$

and define the $K \times N$ matrix $\boldsymbol{\Pi} = [\pi_{ij}^k]$. Clearly, $\boldsymbol{\Pi}$ is a generalized stochastic matrix. If the index k corresponds to the pair $(\boldsymbol{\sigma}, \nu)$, let $f_{ij}^k(n)$ be the number of times a transition occurred from state i to state j in the sample $\boldsymbol{x}_n$ over the transition interval ν when the system was governed by the policy $\boldsymbol{\sigma}$. Then the posterior distribution of $\tilde{\mathscr{P}}$ is $H(\mathscr{P} \mid \psi, \boldsymbol{x}_n)$, where

$$\begin{aligned} dH(\mathscr{P} \mid \psi, \boldsymbol{x}_n) &= \frac{\prod_{\substack{i=1\\j=1}}^{N} \prod_{k=1}^{K_i} (\pi_{ij}^k)^{f_{ij}^k(n)}\, dH(\mathscr{P} \mid \psi)}{\int_{S_{KN}} \prod_{\substack{i=1\\j=1}}^{N} \prod_{k=1}^{K_i} (\pi_{ij}^k)^{f_{ij}^k(n)}\, dH(\mathscr{P} \mid \psi)} \\ &= \frac{f_{M\beta}^{(K,N)}(\boldsymbol{\Pi} \mid \mathcal{M}(n))\, dH(\mathscr{P} \mid \psi)}{\int_{S_{KN}} f_{M\beta}^{(K,N)}(\boldsymbol{\Pi} \mid \mathcal{M}(n))\, dH(\mathscr{P} \mid \psi)}, \end{aligned} \tag{2.3.57}$$

where $\mathcal{M}(n) = [f_{ij}^k(n) + 1]$. The proof of the theorem from this point is identical to the proof of Theorem 2.3.8. Q.E.D.

We remark that the assumptions in Theorems 2.3.8 and 2.3.9 concerning policies which are used infinitely often are not restrictive. It will usually be possible, after a finite amount of sampling, to eliminate from further consideration those policies which will be used only a finite number of times in an optimal sampling strategy. Examples of such elimination of policies by dominance arguments will be given in Chap. 5. In any case, the theorems given here apply to the marginal distribution of those alternative rows of $\tilde{\mathscr{P}}$ which are observed infinitely often.

2.4. SOME GENERAL PROPERTIES OF CLOSED FAMILIES OF DISTRIBUTIONS

Let $\mathcal{H}$ be a family of distributions indexed by $\psi \in \Psi$ which is closed under an arbitrary sampling rule. Some general properties of $\mathcal{H}$ are derived in this section. The symbol $\ell(\boldsymbol{x}_n \mid \mathscr{P})$ will be used throughout for the likelihood of a sample of size n, conditional on $\tilde{\mathscr{P}} = \mathscr{P}$, under the given sampling rule.

Theorem 2.4.1. Let $\tilde{\mathscr{P}}$ have a discrete prior distribution,

$$P[\tilde{\mathscr{P}} = \mathscr{P}_i] = \alpha_i, \qquad \mathscr{P}_i \in \mathcal{S}_{KN}, \quad i = 1, 2, \ldots, m, \tag{2.4.1}$$

where $\alpha_i \geqslant 0$, $\sum_{i=1}^{m} \alpha_i = 1$. For a fixed integer m, let $\mathcal{H}_m$ be the family of all such discrete distributions, indexed by $\alpha = (\alpha_1, \alpha_2, \ldots, \alpha_m)$. Then $\mathcal{H}_m$ is closed under all sampling rules.

Proof. Let $\ell(\boldsymbol{x}_n \mid \mathscr{P})$ be the likelihood function for an arbitrary sampling rule. If $\boldsymbol{\alpha}'$ is the prior distribution of $\tilde{\mathscr{P}}$, the posterior probability of $\mathscr{P}_i$ is

$$\alpha_i'' = \frac{\ell(\boldsymbol{x}_n \mid \mathscr{P}_i)\alpha_i'}{\sum_{i=1}^{m} \ell(\boldsymbol{x}_n \mid \mathscr{P}_i)\alpha_i'} \qquad i = 1, 2, \ldots, m. \tag{2.4.2}$$

Since $\alpha_i'' \geqslant 0$ and $\sum_{i=1}^{m} \alpha_i'' = 1$, $\boldsymbol{\alpha}'' = (\alpha_1'', \alpha_2'', \ldots, \alpha_m'') \in \mathcal{H}_m$. Q.E.D.

This theorem, while almost trivial, is of considerable importance for the practical solution of Bayesian decision problems in a Markov chain. In many cases it may be feasible to place positive probability on only a finite set of points of $\mathcal{S}_{KN}$ and to solve the corresponding discrete problem, thus considerably simplifying the computations.† We shall not emphasize

† See Silver [38], Chap. 2.

this consideration any further since most of our theorems are stated in terms of Stieltjes integrals and, hence, are applicable to discrete, continuous, and mixed prior distributions.

Theorem 2.4.2. Let $\mathcal{H} = \{H(\mathscr{P} \mid \psi) \mid \psi \in \Psi\}$ be a family of distribution functions of $\tilde{\mathscr{P}}$ closed under a given sampling rule and, for a fixed policy $\boldsymbol{\sigma}$, let $\mathcal{F}_{\boldsymbol{\sigma}} = \{F_{\boldsymbol{\sigma}}(\mathscr{P} \mid \psi) \mid \psi \in \Psi'\}$, where $\Psi' \subset \Psi$, be the corresponding family of marginal distribution functions of the $N \times N$ stochastic matrix $\tilde{\mathbf{P}}(\boldsymbol{\sigma})$. If the sampling rule is such that for $n = 1, 2, \ldots,$ it is possible to observe a sample of size n under the fixed policy $\boldsymbol{\sigma}$, and if the likelihood of any sample observed under the policy $\boldsymbol{\sigma}$ does not depend on elements of $\tilde{\mathscr{P}}$ not in $\tilde{\mathbf{P}}(\boldsymbol{\sigma})$, then $\mathcal{F}_{\boldsymbol{\sigma}}$ is also closed under the given sampling rule.

Proof. Let $\ell(\boldsymbol{x}_n \mid \mathscr{P})$ be the likelihood function corresponding to the given sampling rule and let $\ell_{\boldsymbol{\sigma}}(\boldsymbol{x}_n \mid \mathbf{P})$ be the likelihood of the sample $\boldsymbol{x}_n$ from the Markov chain governed by $\mathbf{P}(\boldsymbol{\sigma})$. The hypotheses of the theorem imply that

$$\ell_{\boldsymbol{\sigma}}(\boldsymbol{x}_n \mid \mathbf{P}) = \ell(\boldsymbol{x}_n \mid \mathscr{P}) \tag{2.4.3}$$

for all samples $\boldsymbol{x}_n$ from the chain governed by $\mathbf{P}(\boldsymbol{\sigma})$. Let $\mathcal{K}_{\boldsymbol{\sigma}}$ be the range set of the $(K - N) \times N$ generalized stochastic matrix formed by deleting from $\tilde{\mathscr{P}}$ all rows $\tilde{\boldsymbol{p}}_i^k$ such that $k = \sigma_i$ $(i = 1, \ldots, N)$. Then, if $F_{\boldsymbol{\sigma}}(\mathbf{P} \mid \psi')$ is the marginal prior distribution of $\tilde{\mathbf{P}}(\boldsymbol{\sigma})$ and if the sample $\boldsymbol{x}_n$ is observed, the posterior distribution of $\tilde{\mathbf{P}}(\boldsymbol{\sigma})$ is $F_{\boldsymbol{\sigma}}(\mathbf{P} \mid \psi', \boldsymbol{x}_n)$, where

$$\begin{aligned} dF_{\boldsymbol{\sigma}}(\mathbf{P} \mid \psi', \boldsymbol{x}_n) &= \frac{\ell_{\boldsymbol{\sigma}}(\boldsymbol{x}_n \mid \mathbf{P})\, dF_{\boldsymbol{\sigma}}(\mathbf{P} \mid \psi')}{\int_{\mathcal{S}_N} \ell_{\boldsymbol{\sigma}}(\boldsymbol{x}_n \mid \mathbf{P}l\, dF_{\boldsymbol{\sigma}}(\mathbf{P} \mid \psi')} \\ &= \frac{\int_{\mathcal{K}_{\boldsymbol{\sigma}}} \ell(\boldsymbol{x}_n \mid \mathscr{P})\, dH(\mathscr{P} \mid \psi')}{\int_{\mathcal{S}_{KN}} \ell(\boldsymbol{x}_n \mid \mathscr{P})\, dH(\mathscr{P} \mid \psi')} \\ &= \int_{\mathcal{K}_{\boldsymbol{\sigma}}} dH(\mathscr{P} \mid \psi'') = dF_{\boldsymbol{\sigma}}(\mathbf{P} \mid \psi''), \end{aligned} \tag{2.4.4}$$

for all $\psi' \in \Psi$, where ψ'' is defined by Eq. 2.1.2. Thus, $F_{\boldsymbol{\sigma}}(\mathbf{P} \mid \psi', \boldsymbol{x}_n) \in \mathcal{F}_{\boldsymbol{\sigma}}$ and $\mathcal{F}_{\boldsymbol{\sigma}}$ is closed under the sampling rule. Q.E.D.

The next theorem deals with the continuity of the expectation

$$\bar{g}(\psi) = \int g(\mathscr{P})\, dH(\mathscr{P} \mid \psi)$$

when regarded as a function of ψ, where $g(\mathscr{P})$ is any integrable function of $\mathscr{P}$.

A distribution function $H(\mathscr{P} \mid \psi)$ is said to be *continuous in* ψ at a point $\mathscr{P} \in \mathcal{S}_{KN}$ if, for any $\epsilon > 0$, there exists a $\delta > 0$ such that, for any fixed ψ, $|H(\mathscr{P} \mid \psi) - H(\mathscr{P} \mid \psi')| < \epsilon$ whenever $\|\psi - \psi'\| < \delta$. A point $\mathscr{P}_0 \in \mathcal{S}_{KN}$ is said to be a *continuity point* of $H(\mathscr{P} \mid \psi)$ if $H(\mathscr{P} \mid \psi)$ is a continuous function of $\mathscr{P}$ at $\mathscr{P}_0$ for all values of ψ.

Definition. Let $\mathcal{H}$ be a family of distribution functions indexed by $\psi \in \Psi$. $\mathcal{H}$ is said to be a *family of distribution functions continuous in* ψ if, whenever $H(\mathscr{P} \mid \psi) \in \mathcal{H}$, $H(\mathscr{P} \mid \psi)$ is a continuous function of ψ at each of its continuity points $\mathscr{P}$.

Theorem 2.4.3. Let $\mathcal{H}$ be a family of distribution functions indexed by $\psi \in \Psi$ which is continuous in ψ and let $g(\mathscr{P})$ be any integrable function of $\mathscr{P}$ defined on a set $S \subset \mathcal{S}_{KN}$. If $\bar{g}(\psi)$ is a function of ψ defined by the integral

$$\bar{g}(\psi) = \int_S g(\mathscr{P})\, dH(\mathscr{P} \mid \psi), \qquad \psi \in \Psi, \tag{2.4.5}$$

then $\bar{g}(\psi)$ is continuous on Ψ.

Proof. Let ψ be fixed and let $\{\psi_n\}$ be any sequence of points of Ψ which converges to ψ, where $\psi_n \neq \psi$ $(n = 1, 2, \ldots)$. Let $H(\mathscr{P} \mid \psi_n)$ be the corresponding sequence of distribution functions from $\mathcal{H}$. Since $\mathcal{H}$ is continuous in ψ,

$$\lim_{n\to\infty} H(\mathscr{P} \mid \psi_n) = H(\mathscr{P} \mid \psi) \tag{2.4.6}$$

at every continuity point of $H(\mathscr{P} \mid \psi)$ and, by the Helly-Bray theorem,†

$$\lim_{n\to\infty} \int_S g(\mathscr{P})\, dH(\mathscr{P} \mid \psi_n) = \int_S g(\mathscr{P})\, dH(\mathscr{P} \mid \psi). \tag{2.4.7}$$

Thus, for every sequence $\{\psi_n\}$ which converges to ψ, $\{\bar{g}(\psi_n)\} \to \bar{g}(\psi)$ and, therefore, $\bar{g}(\psi)$ is continuous at ψ. Q.E.D.

Corollary 2.4.4. Let $\mathcal{H} = \{H(\mathscr{P} \mid \psi) \mid \psi \in \Psi\}$ be a family of distribution functions indexed by $\psi \in \Psi$ which is continuous in ψ and, for a fixed policy $\boldsymbol{\sigma}$, let $\mathcal{F}_{\boldsymbol{\sigma}}$ be the corresponding family of marginal distribution functions $F_{\boldsymbol{\sigma}}(\mathbf{P} \mid \psi)$. Then $\mathcal{F}_{\boldsymbol{\sigma}}$ is a family of distributions continuous in ψ.

Proof. In Theorem 2.4.3, let $g(\mathscr{P}) = 1$, $\mathscr{P} \in \mathcal{S}_{KN}$ and, for fixed $\mathbf{P}(\boldsymbol{\sigma}) \in \mathcal{S}_N$, let

$$S = \{\mathcal{Q} \mid \mathcal{Q} \in \mathcal{S}_{KN};\ q_{ij}^{\sigma_i} \leqslant p_{ij}^{\sigma_i} \quad (i, j = 1, \ldots, N)\}. \tag{2.4.8}$$

† See, for example, Loève [28], pp. 180–182.

Then Eq. 2.4.5 becomes

$$F_\sigma(\mathbf{P} \mid \psi) = \int_S dH(\mathbf{Q} \mid \psi), \tag{2.4.9}$$

and $F_\sigma(\mathbf{P} \mid \psi)$ is a continuous function of ψ at $\mathbf{P}$ for any $\mathbf{P} \in \mathcal{S}_N$. Q.E.D.

Corollary 2.4.5. Let $\mathcal{H} = \{H(\mathscr{P} \mid \psi) \mid \psi \in \Psi\}$ be a family of distributions indexed by ψ. Suppose that, for every $H(\mathscr{P} \mid \psi) \in \mathcal{H}$, a corresponding density function $h(\mathscr{P} \mid \psi)$ exists and that $h(\mathscr{P} \mid \psi)$ is a continuous function of ψ for every $\mathscr{P} \in \mathcal{S}_{KN}$. Then $\mathcal{H}$ is a family of distributions continuous in ψ.

Proof. The corollary follows immediately from a well-known theorem of integral calculus which states that, if $h(\mathbf{Q} \mid \psi)$ is continuous in ψ, then

$$H(\mathscr{P} \mid \psi) = \int_S h(\mathbf{Q} \mid \psi)\, d\mathbf{Q}$$

is a continuous function of ψ, where, for a fixed $\mathscr{P} \in \mathcal{S}_{KN}$,

$$S = \{\mathbf{Q} \mid \mathbf{Q} \in \mathcal{S}_{KN};\ q_{ij}^k \leqslant p_{ij}^k,\ (k = 1, \ldots, K_i;\ i, j = 1, \ldots, N)\}.$$

Q.E.D.

It is clear from Eqs. 2.2.1 and 2.2.2 that the matrix beta density function $f_{M\beta}^{(K,N)}(\mathscr{P} \mid \mathcal{M})$ is a continuous function of the $K \times N$ matrix $\mathcal{M}$ and, therefore, that the family of matrix beta distributions is continuous in the parameter $\mathcal{M}$.

Chapter 3

ADAPTIVE CONTROL PROBLEMS

3.1. DISCOUNTED PROCESSES

Consider a Markov chain with alternatives in which the process, assumed to operate indefinitely, is *sampled* after each transition; that is, the decision maker knows the state of the process after each transition. Information about $\tilde{\mathscr{P}}$ is gathered in this manner and the decision maker may alter the current policy at any time, as dictated by his state of knowledge about $\tilde{\mathscr{P}}$. Such a process is an *adaptive control process.*

It is assumed that any sampling costs are included in the transition reward (or utility) matrix, $\mathfrak{R} = [r_{ij}^k]$. This implies that either the sampling costs are negligible when compared with the transition rewards or that the process is operated in such a manner that a sampling cost must be incurred after each transition. Models in which the decision maker may choose to sample or not to sample will be considered in Chap. 5.

When future rewards are discounted to a present value, we shall speak of a *discounted adaptive control process.* It is this class of problems that will be discussed, for the most part, in this chapter. The interval between two consecutive transitions is assumed to be constant and can be taken as the time unit. Let β be the present value of a unit reward earned one unit of time in the future ($0 \leqslant \beta < 1$). Since the present value of the maximum possible reward on the nth transition in the future decreases as β^n, it is clear that the total discounted reward earned over an infinite period under any sequence of policies is finite. The axioms of Bayesian decision theory imply that the decision maker, if he is to act in a manner consistent with his utility function and his judgment about the state of nature, should act so as to maximize the expected total discounted reward over an infinite period. We shall therefore define the *discounted adaptive control problem* to be the problem of selecting a sequence of policies which maximize this quantity.

In the next section the discounted adaptive control problem is formulated in terms of a set of simultaneous functional equations. It is shown in the following section that there exists a unique bounded set of solutions to these equations. In Sec. 3.4 a method of successive approximations is described which converges monotonically and uniformly to this unique set of solutions, and the question of policy convergence is considered. The concept of recursive computation is then introduced and a numerical example is presented. The chapter concludes with a discussion of the problems involved in treating undiscounted adaptive control processes in a Markov chain.

A specific form of the discounted adaptive control problem—the two-armed-bandit problem—was studied by Bellman [7] in 1956, using dynamic programming and a beta prior distribution. The method was generalized by Bellman and Kalaba [8] and is summarized by Bellman in Chap. 16 of his *Adaptive Control Processes* [6]. Bellman's method of solution is based upon the use of successive approximations.

Cozzolino [13] applied Bellman's formulation of the two-armed-bandit problem to the case of a two-state Markov chain with two alternatives in each state, assuming a matrix beta prior distribution. He mapped decision regions in the parameter space of the prior distribution for the special case of one unknown transition probability vector. Cozzolino et al. [14] have suggested various heuristic treatments of the discounted adaptive control problem, basing their results on simulation studies. Freimer [18, 19] has obtained a solution of the discounted adaptive control problem in the case of quadratic cost functions by reducing the stochastic formulation to a deterministic one in terms of certainty equivalents.

The functional equations formulated in this chapter generalize the results of these authors and, in spirit, follow Bellman's derivation [6]. Our contribution to the treatment of this problem consists of the following:

1. Proof of the existence of a unique bounded set of continuous solutions to these functional equations.
2. Derivation of a method of successive approximations which converges monotonically and uniformly to this unique set of solutions.
3. Introduction of recursive computation techniques for the numerical solution of the discounted adaptive control problem.

3.2. FORMULATION

Let the prior distribution of $\tilde{\mathscr{P}}$, $H(\mathscr{P} \mid \psi)$, be a member of a family $\mathscr{H}$, indexed by $\psi \in \Psi$. The ordered pair (i, ψ), where $i = 1, \ldots, N$ and $\psi \in \Psi$, can be regarded as the generalized state of the system. Here i is the physical state of the system and ψ summarizes—or, more precisely, indexes—the decision maker's state of knowledge about $\tilde{\mathscr{P}}$. Since the process is to be sampled consecutively, it must be assumed that $\mathcal{H}$ is closed under the consecutive sampling rule in order that we may meaningfully refer to ψ as indexing the decision maker's state of knowledge as sampling progresses.

Let $v_i(\psi)$ denote the supremum of the expected discounted reward over an infinite period when the system starts from the generalized state (i, ψ). If $R = \max_{i,j,k} \{r_{ij}^k\}$, the discounted total reward under any sampling strategy is bounded by

$$\sum_{n=0}^{\infty} \beta^n R = \frac{R}{1-\beta} \tag{3.2.1}$$

and, therefore, $v_i(\psi)$ exists for $i = 1, \ldots, N$ and all $\psi \in \Psi$. It will be shown at the conclusion of this section that $v_i(\psi)$ is attained under an optimal sampling strategy and, hence, can be regarded as the maximum expected discounted reward when the system starts from (i, ψ).

If, when in state (i, ψ), it is decided to choose the kth alternative and the system makes a transition to state j, the supremum of the posterior expected discounted reward is

$$r_{ij}^k + \beta v_j(T_{ij}^k(\psi)). \tag{3.2.2}$$

The probability of the sample outcome j, unconditional with regard to the prior distribution of $\tilde{\mathscr{P}}$, given that the system is in state (i, ψ) and that alternative k is in use, is

$$\bar{p}_{ij}^k(\psi) = \int_{S_{KN}} p_{ij}^k \, dH(\mathscr{P} \mid \psi), \tag{3.2.3}$$

the marginal prior expectation of $\tilde{p}_{ij}^k$. Let

$$\bar{q}_i^k(\psi) = \sum_{j=1}^{N} \bar{p}_{ij}^k(\psi) r_{ij}^k$$

$$k = 1, \ldots, K_i, \quad i = 1, \ldots, N, \quad \psi \in \Psi, \tag{3.2.4}$$

denote the mean one-step transition reward when the system is in state (i, ψ) and alternative k is used. Then, regarding each $v_i(\psi)$ as a function of ψ defined on Ψ $(i = 1, \ldots, N)$, the supremum of the discounted expected reward when starting from (i, ψ) must satisfy the following set of simultaneous functional equations:

$$v_i(\psi) = \max_{1 \leqslant k \leqslant K_i} \left\{ \bar{q}_i^k(\psi) + \beta \sum_{j=1}^{N} \bar{p}_{ij}^k(\psi) v_j(T_{ij}^k(\psi)) \right\},$$

$$i = 1, \ldots, N, \quad \psi \in \Psi, \quad 0 \leqslant \beta < 1. \tag{3.2.5}$$

We now consider the existence of the maximum expected discounted reward over an infinite period. In order to do this, it is necessary to define precisely the notion of a *sampling strategy* for an adaptive control process.

Let the policies $\boldsymbol{\sigma} \in \Sigma$ be indexed by the integers 0 through $J - 1$, where J is the number of elements in the finite set Σ. Thus,

$$\Sigma = \{\boldsymbol{\sigma}_0, \boldsymbol{\sigma}_1, \ldots, \boldsymbol{\sigma}_{J-1}\}.$$

Suppose the system starts from the generalized state (i_0, ψ) and that alternative k has been selected in state i_0. We can, before the first transition occurs, decide which alternative to use in each state j for the second transition. This consists of the choice of a policy $\boldsymbol{\sigma}_{\alpha_1}$, and is denoted $d_1(i_0, k) = \alpha_1$, a decision function with range $\{0, 1, \ldots, J - 1\}$.

More generally, before any transitions have occurred, we can prescribe a policy to be used immediately after the nth transition ($n = 1, 2, \ldots$). Let $\boldsymbol{x}_{n-1} = (i_0, i_1, \ldots, i_{n-1})$ be a possible sample history of the first $n - 1$ transitions and let $\boldsymbol{s}_{n-1} = (k, \boldsymbol{\sigma}_{\alpha_1}, \ldots, \boldsymbol{\sigma}_{\alpha_{n-1}})$ be the sequence of policies under which the sample $\boldsymbol{x}_{n-1}$ occurred, together with $\boldsymbol{\sigma}_{\alpha_{n-1}}$, the policy under which the nth transition will occur. The policy history $\boldsymbol{s}_{n-1}$ is determined by evaluating the decision functions $d_1(i_0, k), d_2(\boldsymbol{x}_1, \boldsymbol{s}_1), \ldots, d_{n-1}(\boldsymbol{x}_{n-2}, \boldsymbol{s}_{n-2})$ at $i_0, \boldsymbol{x}_1 = (i_0, i_1), \ldots, \boldsymbol{x}_{n-2} = (i_0, i_1, \ldots, i_{n-2})$. Conditional on the Markov chain having arrived in state i_{n-1} with sample history $\boldsymbol{x}_{n-1}$ and policy history $\boldsymbol{s}_{n-1}$, we may select an alternative for use in state j after the nth transition for each of the N states to which the nth transition may bring the system. This consists of the selection of a policy $\boldsymbol{\sigma}_{\alpha_n} \in \Sigma$, and is denoted by $d_n(\boldsymbol{x}_{n-1}, \boldsymbol{s}_{n-1}) = \alpha_n$, a function with range $\{0, \ldots, J - 1\}$. Since there are $N^{(n-1)}$ different sample histories $\boldsymbol{x}_{n-1}$ which start from a fixed state i_0, it is necessary to specify $N^{(n-1)}$ values of the nth-level decision function $d_n(\boldsymbol{x}_{n-1}, \boldsymbol{s}_{n-1})$. The specification of a complete set of decision functions $d_n(\boldsymbol{x}_{n-1}, \boldsymbol{s}_{n-1})$ for $n = 1, 2, 3, \ldots$ and for all possible sample histories, together with the choice of an initial alternative in state i_0, constitutes a *sampling strategy d*. Let D_i denote the set of all possible sampling strategies when the system starts in state i.

In the following theorem it is shown that $v_i(\psi)$, a least upper bound, is attained for some strategy $d^* \in D_i$. This is done by mapping the space of strategies D_i onto a compact subset of the real line and showing that the corresponding mapping of $v_i(\psi, d)$, the expected discounted reward under strategy d, is continuous on this set.

Theorem 3.2.1. Let $v_i(\psi, d)$ be the total expected discounted reward in a Markov chain with alternatives when the process starts from the generalized state (i, ψ) and the sampling strategy d is used. Let

$$v_i(\psi) = \sup_{d \in D_i} \{v_i(\psi, d)\}. \tag{3.2.6}$$

Then there is a strategy $d^* \in D_i$ such that

$$v_i(\psi) = v_i(\psi, d^*). \tag{3.2.7}$$

Proof. We proceed in steps.

1. For $n = 1, 2, 3, \ldots$ let $\boldsymbol{x}_n = (i_0, i_1, \ldots, i_n)$, where $i_\alpha \in \{1, \ldots, N\}$, $\alpha = 0, 1, \ldots, n$. To each sequence $\boldsymbol{x}_n$ let there correspond the N-ary number

$$z(\boldsymbol{x}_n) = \sum_{\alpha=0}^{n} i_\alpha N^{-(\alpha+1)} = 0.i_0 i_1 \cdots i_n. \tag{3.2.8}$$

For fixed n and $i_0 = i$ we may then order the $N^{(n-1)}$ different nth-level decision functions $d_n(\boldsymbol{x}_{n-1}, \boldsymbol{s}_{n-1})$ as follows: $d_n(\boldsymbol{x}_{n-1}, \boldsymbol{s}_{n-1}) < d_n(\boldsymbol{x}'_{n-1}, \boldsymbol{s}'_{n-1})$ if and only if $z(\boldsymbol{x}_{n-1}) < z(\boldsymbol{x}'_{n-1})$.

2. Consider a strategy $d \in D_i$. Let the value of the jth member of the $\mu(n) = N^{(n-1)}$ decision functions $d_n(\boldsymbol{x}_{n-1}, \boldsymbol{s}_{n-1})$ in d be denoted

$$d_{nj} \in \{0, 1, \ldots, J-1\} \; (n = 1, 2, \ldots)$$

and assume that the indexing is such that

$$d_{n1} < d_{n2} < \cdots < d_{n\mu(n)} \qquad n = 1, 2, \ldots, \tag{3.2.9}$$

with respect to the ordering introduced in step 1. This can be done since the $\mu(n)$ possible sample histories $\boldsymbol{x}_{n-1}$ which lead to the nth-level decision functions are all distinct. The strategy d can then be displayed as the ordered pair

$$d = (k, \delta), \tag{3.2.10}$$

where k is the initial alternative selected in state i and δ is the sequence

$$\begin{aligned} \delta &= (d_{11}, d_{21}, d_{22}, \ldots) \\ &= (\delta_1, \delta_2, \delta_3, \ldots). \end{aligned} \tag{3.2.11}$$

Letting Δ denote the set of all possible sequences δ, we have

$$v_i(\psi) = \max_{1 \leq k \leq K_i} \sup_{\delta \in \Delta} \{v_i(\psi; k, \delta)\}, \tag{3.2.12}$$

where, if $d = (k, \delta)$, $v_i(\psi;\ k, \delta) = v_i(\psi, d)$.

To each $\delta \in \Delta$ let there correspond the J-ary number

$$y(\delta) = \sum_{\alpha=1}^{\infty} \delta_\alpha J^{-\alpha} = 0.\delta_1 \delta_2 \delta_3 \cdots, \tag{3.2.13}$$

where $\delta_\alpha \in \{0, 1, \ldots, J-1\}$ for $\alpha = 1, 2, \ldots$. If $\delta = \{0, 0, 0, \ldots\}$, then $y(\delta) = 0$ and if $\delta = \{J-1, J-1, J-1, \ldots\}$, then

$$y(\delta) = (J-1)\sum_{\alpha=1}^{\infty} J^{-\alpha} = \frac{(J-1)J^{-1}}{1 - J^{-1}} = 1. \tag{3.2.14}$$

Thus, for any $\delta \in \Delta$, $0 \leqslant y(\delta) \leqslant 1$. Moreover, it is easily seen that the mapping Eq. 3.2.13 is a one-to-one mapping of the set Δ onto the closed interval [0, 1]. For fixed ψ, i, and k, let $w_i^k(\psi, y)$ be a function defined on [0, 1] by the relation

$$w_i^k(\psi, y(\delta)) = v_i(\psi; k, \delta),$$
$$k = 1, \ldots, K_i, \quad i = 1, \ldots, N, \quad \delta \in \Delta, \quad \psi \in \Psi. \tag{3.2.15}$$

Then Eq. 3.2.12 can be written as

$$v_i(\psi) = \max_{1 \leqslant k \leqslant K_i} \sup_{0 \leqslant y \leqslant 1} \{w_i^k(\psi, y)\}. \tag{3.2.16}$$

3. We now show that, for fixed k, $w_i^k(\psi, y)$ is continuous in y. Let

$$R^* = \max_{i,j\,k} \{|r_{ij}^k|\}, \tag{3.2.17a}$$

and

$$r^* = \min_{i,j,k} \{|r_{ij}^k|\}. \tag{3.2.17b}$$

Let $\epsilon > 0$ be given and choose a positive integer n such that,

$$\beta^{n+1} \frac{R^* - r^*}{1 - \beta} < \epsilon. \tag{3.2.18}$$

For a fixed $y \in [0, 1]$, let y' be any number such that $0 \leqslant y' \leqslant 1$ and, if $\nu = \sum_{k=1}^{n} N^{(k-1)}$, $|y - y'| < J^{-\nu}$. Then, if $y = y(\delta)$ and $y' = y'(\delta')$, we have

$$\delta_\alpha = \delta'_\alpha, \qquad \alpha = 1, 2, \ldots, \nu, \tag{3.2.19}$$

and, since both strategies use the same decision functions for the first n transitions,

$$|w_i^k(\psi, y) - w_i^k(\psi, y')| \leqslant \sum_{\alpha=n+1}^{\infty} \beta^\alpha (R^* - r^*)$$
$$= \beta^{n+1} \frac{R^* - r^*}{1 - \beta} < \epsilon. \tag{3.2.20}$$

Thus, $w_i^k(\psi, y)$ is a continuous function of y on the compact set [0, 1] and, for each k, there exists a $y_k^* \in [0, 1]$ such that

$$w_i^k(\psi, y_k^*) = \sup_{0 \leqslant y \leqslant 1} \{w_i^k(\psi, y)\}. \tag{3.2.21}$$

4. Letting $\delta^*(k)$ denote the inverse image of $y_k^* = y_k^*(\delta^*)$,

$$v_i(\psi) = \max_{1 \leqslant k \leqslant K_i} \{v_i(\psi, k, \delta^*(k))\}, \tag{3.2.22}$$

and there exists a strategy $d^* = (k^*, \delta^*(k^*))$ such that

$$v_i(\psi) = v_i(\psi, d^*). \qquad \text{Q.E.D.} \tag{3.2.23}$$

3.3. EXISTENCE AND UNIQUENESS OF $v_i(\psi)$

To show the existence of a unique bounded set of continuous solutions to the functional Eqs. 3.2.5, we shall make use of the method of successive approximations. Let the functions $v_i(n, \psi)$ be defined recursively as follows:

$$v_i(n+1, \psi) = \max_{1 \leqslant k \leqslant K_i} \left\{ \bar{q}_i^k(\psi) + \beta \sum_{j=1}^{N} \bar{p}_{ij}^k(\psi) v_j(n, T_{ij}^k(\psi)) \right\},$$

$$i = 1, \ldots, N, \quad n = 0, 1, 2, \ldots, \quad \psi \in \Psi, \quad 0 \leqslant \beta < 1, \quad (3.3.1)$$

and

$$v_i(0, \psi) = V_i(\psi), \qquad i = 1, \ldots, N, \quad \psi \in \Psi, \qquad (3.3.2)$$

where $\{V_i(\psi)\}$ is a set of bounded terminal functions.

It will be convenient to introduce some additional notation. Let

$$S_i^k(v, n, \psi) = \bar{q}_i^k(\psi) + \beta \sum_{j=1}^{N} \bar{p}_{ij}^k(\psi) v_j(n, T_{ij}^k(\psi)),$$

$$k = 1, \ldots, K_i, \quad i = 1, \ldots, N, \quad n = 0, 1, 2, \ldots, \quad \psi \in \Psi \quad (3.3.3)$$

and

$$S_i^k(v, \infty, \psi) = q_i^k(\psi) + \beta \sum_{j=1}^{N} \bar{p}_{ij}^k(\psi) v_j(T_{ij}^k(\psi)),$$

$$k = 1, \ldots, K_i, \quad i = 1, \ldots, N, \quad \psi \in \Psi. \quad (3.3.4)$$

Equation 3.3.1 may then be written as

$$v_i(n+1, \psi) = \max_{i \leqslant k \leqslant K_i} \{S_i^k(v, n, \psi)\},$$

$$i = 1, \ldots, N, \quad n = 0, 1, 2, \ldots, \quad \psi \in \Psi, \quad (3.3.5)$$

and, similarly, Eq. 3.2.5 becomes

$$v_i(\psi) = \max_{1 \leqslant k \leqslant K_i} \{S_i^k(v, \infty, \psi)\}, \qquad i = 1, \ldots, N, \quad \psi \in \Psi. \quad (3.3.6)$$

The first result is a lemma which will be used in subsequent proofs.

Lemma 3.3.1. If V is a bound for the terminal functions $V_i(\psi)$,

$$|V_i(\psi)| \leqslant V, \qquad i = 1, \ldots, N, \quad \psi \in \Psi, \qquad (3.3.7)$$

and if

$$R^* = \max_{i,j,k} \{|r_{ij}^k|\}, \qquad (3.3.8)$$

then the functions $v_i(n, \psi)$ are bounded,

$$|v_i(n, \psi)| \leqslant \beta^n V + \frac{1 - \beta^n}{1 - \beta} R^*,$$

$$i = 1, \ldots, N, \quad n = 0, 1, 2, \ldots, \quad \psi \in \Psi, \quad 0 \leqslant \beta < 1. \quad (3.3.9)$$

Proof. The proof is inductive. Equation 3.3.9 obviously holds for $n = 0$. Assume it holds for n. Then, if $k = \alpha$ maximizes the right side of Eq. 3.3.1,

$$|v_i(n+1, \psi)| \leqslant |\bar{q}_i^\alpha(\psi)| + \beta \sum_{j=1}^{N} \bar{p}_{ij}^\alpha(\psi)\, |v_j(n, T_{ij}^\alpha(\psi)|$$

$$\leqslant R^* + \beta\left[\beta^n V + \frac{1-\beta^n}{1-\beta} R^*\right]$$

$$= \beta^{n+1} V + \frac{1-\beta^{n+1}}{1-\beta} R^*. \qquad \text{Q.E.D.} \qquad (3.3.10)$$

Theorem 3.3.2. If the set of functions $\{v_i(n, \psi)\}$ is defined by Eqs. 3.3.1 and 3.3.2, then the limits

$$\lim_{n\to\infty} v_i(n, \psi) = v_i(\psi), \qquad i = 1, \ldots, N, \quad \psi \in \Psi, \qquad (3.3.11)$$

exist and $\{v_i(\psi)\}$ is a set of solutions to Eq. 3.2.5. Moreover, the convergence is uniform in ψ.

Proof. It will be established inductively that, for arbitrary positive integers n and m,

$$|v_i(n, \psi) - v_i(m, \psi)| \leqslant (\beta^n + \beta^m)V + \frac{|\beta^n - \beta^m|}{1-\beta} R^*,$$

$$i = 1, \ldots, N, \quad n, m = 0, 1, 2, \ldots, \quad \psi \in \Psi, \quad (3.3.12)$$

where V is a bound on the terminal functions. Because $0 \leqslant \beta < 1$, it then follows by the Cauchy criterion that $\lim_{n\to\infty} v_i(n, \psi)$ exists for $i = 1, \ldots, N$. That the limiting functions satisfy Eq. 3.2.5 follows by allowing n to go to ∞ in Eq. 3.3.1. Uniform convergence of the sequence of functions $\{v_i(n, \psi)\}$ follows by noting that the bound in Eq. 3.3.12 is independent of ψ.

To establish Eq. 3.3.12, we proceed as follows: Using the formulation of Eq. 3.3.5, for any fixed $\psi \in \Psi$, let

$$v_i(n, \psi) = S_i^\alpha(v, n-1, \psi) = \max_{1\leqslant k\leqslant K_i} \{S_i^k(v, n-1, \psi)\},$$

$$v_i(m, \psi) = S_i^\delta(v, m-1, \psi) = \max_{1\leqslant k\leqslant K_i} \{S_i^k(v, m-1, \psi)\}.$$

Then

$$v_i(n, \psi) - v_i(m, \psi) = S_i^\alpha(v, n-1, \psi) - S_i^\delta(v, m-1, \psi)$$
$$\leqslant S_i^\alpha(v, n-1, \psi) - S_i^\alpha(v, m-1, \psi),$$

and, similarly,

$$v_i(n, \psi) - v_i(m, \psi) \geqslant S_i^\delta(v, n-1, \psi) - S_i^\delta(v, m-1, \psi).$$

Let k^* index the larger of $|S_i^\alpha(v, n-1, \psi) - S_i^\alpha(v, m-1, \psi)|$ and $|S_i^\delta(v, n-1, \psi) - S_i^\delta(v, m-1, \psi)|$. Then

$$|v_i(n, \psi) - v_i(m, \psi)| \leqslant |S_i^{k^*}(v, n-1, \psi) - S_i^{k^*}(v, m-1, \psi)|$$
$$\leqslant \beta \sum_{j=1}^{N} \bar{p}_{ij}^{k^*}(\psi)\, |v_j(n-1, T_{ij}^{k^*}(\psi)) - v_j(m-1, T_{ij}^{k^*}(\psi))|$$
$$i = 1, \ldots, N, \quad n, m = 1, 2, \ldots, \quad \psi \in \Psi. \quad (3.3.13)$$

Assuming that $n \geqslant m$, Lemma 3.3.1 implies the inequality

$$|v_i(n-m, \psi) - v_i(0, \psi)| \leqslant (1 + \beta^{n-m})V + \frac{1 - \beta^{n-m}}{1 - \beta} R^*. \quad (3.3.14)$$

An inductive argument, using Eqs. 3.3.13 and 3.3.14, shows that

$$|v_i(n, \psi) - v_i(m, \psi)| \leqslant (\beta^m + \beta^n)V + \frac{\beta^m - \beta^n}{1 - \beta} R^*. \quad (3.3.15)$$

A similar argument in the case $n < m$ yields Eq. 3.3.12. Q.E.D.

Theorem 3.3.3. There exists a unique set of bounded functions $\{v_i(\psi)\}$ which satisfies the set of equations

$$v_i(\psi) = \max_{1 \leqslant k \leqslant K_i} \left\{ \bar{q}_i^k(\psi) + \beta \sum_{j=1}^{N} \bar{p}_{ij}^k(\psi) v_j(T_{ij}^k(\psi)) \right\},$$
$$i = 1, \ldots, N, \quad \psi \in \Psi, \quad 0 \leqslant \beta < 1. \quad (3.3.16)$$

Proof. Theorem 3.3.2 established the existence of at least one set of functions $\{v_i(\psi)\}$ which satisfy Eq. 3.3.16. Lemma 3.3.1 implies that this set of functions is bounded:

$$|v_i(\psi)| = \lim_{n \to \infty} |v_i(n, \psi)| \leqslant \frac{R^*}{1 - \beta}, \qquad i = 1, \ldots, N, \quad \psi \in \Psi. \quad (3.3.17)$$

To establish uniqueness, assume that there exist two sets of bounded functions, $\{v_i(\psi)\}$ and $\{w_i(\psi)\}$, which satisfy Eq. 3.3.16. For any i and an arbitrary $\psi \in \Psi$, let

$$v_i(\psi) = S_i^\alpha(v, \infty, \psi),$$
$$w_i(\psi) = S_i^\delta(w, \infty, \psi).$$

Then, arguing as in the proof of Theorem 3.3.2,

$$S_i^\delta(v, \infty, \psi) - S_i^\delta(w, \infty, \psi) \leqslant v_i(\psi) - w_i(\psi) \leqslant S_i^\alpha(v, \infty, \psi) - S_i^\alpha(w, \infty, \psi). \quad (3.3.18)$$

Letting k^* index the larger of $|S_i^\alpha(v, \infty, \psi) - S_i^\alpha(w, \infty, \psi)|$ and $|S_i^\delta(v, \infty, \psi) - S_i^\delta(w, \infty, \psi)|$,

$$|v_i(\psi) - w_i(\psi)| \leqslant \beta \sum_{j=1}^{N} \bar{p}_{ij}^{k}(\psi)\, |v_i(T_{ij}^{k^*}(\psi)) - w_i(T_{ij}^{k^*}(\psi))|,$$
$$i = 1, \ldots, N, \quad \psi \in \Psi. \quad (3.3.19)$$

Since $v_i(\psi)$ and $w_i(\psi)$ are both bounded functions of ψ, there exists a number, $M > 0$, such that

$$|v_i(\psi) - w_i(\psi)| < M, \qquad i = 1, \ldots, N, \quad \psi \in \Psi. \quad (3.3.20)$$

Repeated application of Eq. 3.3.19 then yields the inequality

$$|v_i(\psi) - w_i(\psi)| < \beta^n M,$$
$$n = 0, 1, 2, \ldots, \quad i = 1, \ldots, N, \quad \psi \in \Psi. \quad (3.3.21)$$

Since $0 \leqslant \beta < 1$, it then follows that

$$v_i(\psi) = w_i(\psi), \qquad i = 1, \ldots, N, \quad \psi \in \Psi. \quad (3.3.22)$$

Q.E.D.

Theorem 3.3.4. If $\{v_i(\psi)\}$ is the unique bounded set of functions which satisfy Eq. 3.2.5, and if $\bar{p}_{ij}^k(\psi)$ is a continuous function of ψ ($k = 1, \ldots, K_i$; $i, j = 1, \ldots, N$), then $v_i(\psi)$ is a continuous function of ψ ($i = 1, \ldots, N$).

Proof. Consider the functions $v_i(n, \psi)$ defined by Eqs. 3.3.1 and 3.3.2. Choosing a set of terminal functions $\{V_i(\psi)\}$ each member of which is continuous on Ψ, it follows inductively that $v_i(n, \psi)$ is continuous ($i = 1, \ldots, N$; $n = 0, 1, 2, \ldots$). By Theorem 3.3.2, $\{v_i(n, \psi)\} \to v_i(\psi)$ uniformly and, therefore, $v_i(\psi)$ is continuous. Q.E.D.

3.4. SOLUTION BY SUCCESSIVE APPROXIMATIONS

The functions $v_i(n, \psi)$ defined by Eqs. 3.3.1 and 3.3.2 can be used as successive approximations in the numerical calculation of $v_i(\psi)$ at some fixed generalized state (i, ψ). In this section we derive conditions under which the sequence of functions $\{v_i(n, \psi)\}$ converges monotonically and find a bound for the error of the nth approximant $e_i(n, \psi) = v_i(\psi) - v_i(n, \psi)$. The section concludes with a proof that the optimal sampling strategy of the n-step problem defined by Eqs. 3.3.1 and 3.3.2 converges to an optimal sampling strategy for the infinite horizon problem defined by Eq. 3.2.5.

Theorem 3.4.1. Let the terminal functions of Eq. 3.3.2 be constants,

$$V_i(\psi) = V_i, \qquad i = 1, \ldots, N, \quad \psi \in \Psi. \tag{3.4.1}$$

Let

$$v^* = \min_i \{V_i\}, \qquad V^* = \max_i \{V_i\}, \tag{3.4.2}$$

and

$$r = \min_{i,j,k} \{r_{ij}^k\}, \qquad R = \max_{i,j\,k} \{r_{ij}^k\}. \tag{3.4.3}$$

If

$$V^* - \beta v^* \leqslant r, \tag{3.4.4}$$

then, for $i = 1, \ldots, N$, the functions $v_i(n, \psi)$ defined by Eqs. 3.3.1 and 3.3.2 form a monotone increasing sequence which converges uniformly to $v_i(\psi)$, the unique bounded solution of Eq. 3.2.5. Similarly, if

$$v^* - \beta V^* \geqslant R, \tag{3.4.5}$$

then the functions $v_i(n, \psi)$ form a monotone decreasing sequence which converges uniformly to $v_i(\psi)$.

Proof. We will first show inductively that, if Eq. 3.4.4 holds, the sequences $\{v_i(n, \psi)\}$ are monotone increasing for each $i = 1, \ldots, N$ and each $\psi \in \Psi$. Uniform convergence of $\{v_i(n, \psi)\}$ to $v_i(\psi)$ has already been demonstrated. If Eq. 3.4.4 is satisfied, then

$$\begin{aligned} v_i(1, \psi) - v_i(0, \psi) &= \max_{1 \leqslant k \leqslant K_i} \left\{ \bar{q}_i^k(\psi) + \beta \sum_{j=1}^N \bar{p}_{ij}^k(\psi) V_j \right\} - V_i \\ &\geqslant r + \beta v^* - V^* \geqslant 0, \\ &\qquad i = 1, \ldots, N, \quad \psi \in \Psi. \end{aligned} \tag{3.4.6}$$

Assume that $v_i(n, \psi) - v_i(n-1, \psi) \geqslant 0$ for $i = 1, \ldots, N$ and $\psi \in \Psi$. Then, if

$$v_i(n+1, \psi) = S_i^\alpha(v, n, \psi)$$

and

$$v_i(n, \psi) = S_i^\delta(v, n-1, \psi),$$

The inductive hypothesis implies that

$$\begin{aligned} v_i(n+1, \psi) - v_i(n, \psi) &= S_i^\alpha(v, n, \psi) - S_i^\delta(v, n-1, \psi) \\ &\geqslant S_i^\delta(v, n, \psi) - S_i^\delta(v, n-1, \psi) \\ &= \beta \sum_{j=1}^N \bar{p}_{ij}^\delta(\psi)[v_j(n, T_{ij}^\delta(\psi)) - v_j(n-1, T_{ij}^\delta(\psi))] \geqslant 0, \\ &\qquad i = 1, \ldots, N, \quad \psi \in \Psi, \end{aligned} \tag{3.4.7}$$

proving the induction. If Eq. 3.4.5 holds,

$$\begin{aligned} v_i(1, \psi) - v_i(0, \psi) &\leqslant R + \beta V^* - v^* \leqslant 0, \\ &\qquad i = 1, \ldots, N, \quad \psi \in \Psi. \end{aligned} \tag{3.4.8}$$

That $v_i(n+1, \psi) \leqslant v_i(n, \psi)$ is then easily established by induction in a manner similar to that displayed in Eq. 3.4.7. Q.E.D.

Let the error of the nth approximant be defined as

$$e_i(n, \psi) = v_i(\psi) - v_i(n, \psi),$$
$$i = 1, \ldots, N, \quad n = 0, 1, 2, \ldots, \quad \psi \in \Psi. \quad (3.4.9)$$

If $\{v_i(n, \psi)\}$ is a sequence of functions which converges monotonically to $v_i(\psi)$, then $\{e_i(n, \psi)\}$ is a sequence of functions which converges monotonically to zero. In this case, if $\epsilon > 0$ is an error bound which is acceptable to the decision maker and if $n = n^*$ is the smallest positive integer such that

$$|e_i(n, \psi)| \leqslant \epsilon, \quad (3.4.10)$$

then $v_i(n^*, \psi)$ is an acceptable approximation to $v_i(\psi)$, and the sampling strategy resulting in $v_i(n^*, \psi)$ is an acceptable approximation to the first n^* levels of an optimal sampling strategy.

It is not necessary to require that the successive approximants $v_i(n, \psi)$ converge monotonically to $v_i(\psi)$ and, in fact, a nonmonotonic sequence $\{v_i(n, \psi)\}$ may converge more rapidly than a monotonic sequence. Theorem 3.4.3 provides a bound for $e_i(n, \psi)$ assuming nothing about monotonicity. A lemma is first required.

Lemma 3.4.2. Let r and R be defined by Eq. 3.4.3. Then $v_i(\psi)$, the solution of Eq. 3.2.5, has the bounds

$$\frac{r}{1-\beta} \leqslant v_i(\psi) \leqslant \frac{R}{1-\beta},$$
$$i = 1, \ldots, N, \quad \psi \in \Psi, \quad 0 \leqslant \beta < 1. \quad (3.4.11)$$

Proof. The mean reward per transition under any policy has the bounds

$$r \leqslant \bar{q}_i^k(\psi) \leqslant R, \qquad k = 1, \ldots, K_i, \quad i = 1, \ldots, N, \quad \psi \in \Psi. \quad (3.4.12)$$

Since the expected discounted reward over an infinite period under any strategy is the sum of the expected rewards at each transition, the reward of the nth transition being weighted by β^n, the maximum total reward has the bounds

$$r \sum_{n=0}^{\infty} \beta^n \leqslant v_i(\psi) \leqslant R \sum_{n=0}^{\infty} \beta^n, \qquad i = 1, \ldots, N, \quad \psi \in \Psi, \quad (3.4.13)$$

from which Eq. 3.4.11 follows. Q.E.D.

Theorem 3.4.3. Let $\{v_i(n, \psi)\}$ be a sequence of successive approximations defined by Eqs. 3.3.1 and 3.3.2, with constant terminal reward functions,

$$V_i(\psi) = V_i, \qquad i = 1, \ldots, N, \quad \psi \in \Psi. \tag{3.4.14}$$

Let v^*, V^*, r, and R be defined by Eqs. 3.4.2 and 3.4.3. Then the error of the nth approximant has the bound

$$|e_i(n, \psi)| \leqslant \beta^n \left(\max\left\{\frac{R}{1-\beta} - v^*, V^* - \frac{r}{1-\beta}\right\}\right),$$

$$i = 1, \ldots, N, \quad n = 0, 1, 2, \ldots, \quad \psi \in \Psi, \quad 0 \leqslant \beta < 1. \tag{3.4.15}$$

Proof. The proof is inductive. For $n = 0$,

$$e_i(0, \psi) = v_i(\psi) - V_i.$$

Suppose $v_i(\psi) \geqslant V_i$. Then, by Lemma 3.4.2,

$$|e_i(0, \psi)| = v_i(\psi) - V_i \leqslant \frac{R}{1-\beta} - v^*,$$

$$i = 1, \ldots, N, \quad \psi \in \Psi. \tag{3.4.16}$$

If, on the other hand, $v_i(\psi) < V_i$, Lemma 3.4.2 implies that

$$|e_i(0, \psi)| = V_i - v_i(\psi) \leqslant V^* - \frac{r}{1-\beta},$$

$$i = 1, \ldots, N, \quad \psi \in \Psi. \tag{3.4.17}$$

Therefore, in either case,

$$|e_i(0, \psi)| \leqslant \max\left\{\frac{R}{1-\beta} - v^*, V^* - \frac{r}{1-\beta}\right\},$$

$$i = 1, \ldots, N, \quad \psi \in \Psi. \tag{3.4.18}$$

It is to be noted that at least one of the two terms, $R/(1 - \beta) - v^*$ and $V^* - r/(1 - \beta)$, is nonnegative, for, if not, we have the contradiction

$$V^* < \frac{r}{1-\beta} \leqslant \frac{R}{1-\beta} < v^* \leqslant V^*.$$

Having established that Eq. 3.4.15 is valid for $n = 0$, assume it holds for n. Let

$$v_i(\psi) = S_i^{\alpha}(v, \infty, \psi),$$
$$v_i(n + 1, \psi) = S_i^{\delta}(v, n, \psi).$$

Then

$$S_i^{\delta}(v, \infty, \psi) - S_i^{\delta}(v, n, \psi) \leqslant e_i(n + 1, \psi) \leqslant S_i^{\alpha}(v, \infty, \psi) - S_i^{\alpha}(v, n, \psi). \tag{3.4.19}$$

Let k^* index the larger of $|S_i^\alpha(v, \infty, \psi) - S_i^\alpha(v, n, \psi)|$ and $|S_i^\delta(v, \infty, \psi) - S_i^\delta(v, n, \psi)|$. Then

$$|e_i(n+1, \psi)| \leqslant |S_i^{k^*}(v, \infty, \psi) - S_i^{k^*}(v, n, \psi)|$$
$$\leqslant \beta \sum_{j=1}^{N} \bar{p}_{ij}^{k^*}(\psi)\, |e_j(n, T_{ij}^{k^*}(\psi))|$$
$$\leqslant \beta^{n+1}\left(\max\left\{\frac{R}{1-\beta} - v^*, V^* - \frac{r}{1-\beta}\right\}\right). \tag{3.4.20}$$

Q.E.D.

Corollary 3.4.4. Let the terminal functions $V_i(\psi)$ be constants,

$$V_i(\psi) = V_i, \qquad i = 1, \ldots, N, \quad \psi \in \Psi. \tag{3.4.21}$$

Then, if

$$V^* - \beta v^* \leqslant r, \tag{3.4.22}$$

the error of the nth approximant has the bounds

$$0 \leqslant e_i(n, \psi) \leqslant \beta^n\left(\frac{R}{1-\beta} - v^*\right),$$
$$i = 1, \ldots, N \quad n = 0, 1, 2, \ldots, \quad \psi \in \Psi, \quad 0 \leqslant \beta < 1. \tag{3.4.23}$$

Similarly, if

$$v^* - \beta V^* \geqslant R, \tag{3.4.24}$$

$e_i(n, \psi)$ has the bounds

$$\beta^n\left(\frac{r}{1-\beta} - V^*\right) \leqslant e_i(n, \psi) \leqslant 0,$$
$$i = 1, \ldots, N, \quad n = 0, 1, 2, \ldots, \quad \psi \in \Psi, \quad 0 \leqslant \beta < 1. \tag{3.4.25}$$

Proof. If Eq. 3.4.22 is satisfied, Theorem 3.4.1 implies that $e_i(n, \psi) \geqslant 0$. Moreover, Eq. 3.4.22 implies that $v^*(1-\beta) \leqslant R$ and $V^*(1-\beta) \leqslant r$, hence, $R/(1-\beta) - v^* \geqslant V^* - r/(1-\beta)$. Equation 3.4.15 then yields the upper inequality of Eq. 3.4.23. Similarly, if Eq. 3.4.24 is satisfied, then $V^*(1-\beta) \geqslant r$ and $v^*(1-\beta) \geqslant R$, hence, $V^* - r/(1-\beta) \geqslant R/(1-\beta) - v^*$. The bounds of Eq. 3.4.25 then follow from Theorem 3.4.1 and Eq. 3.4.15. Q.E.D.

Let there correspond to the nth approximant $v_i(n, \psi)$, defined by Eqs. 3.3.1 and 3.3.2, the n-step optimal sampling strategy $d^*(n)$. At least one such optimal strategy exists since there is a finite number of different sampling strategies for the n-step problem; there may be more than one

n-step optimal strategy. The next theorem demonstrates that, as $n \to \infty$, any n-step optimal strategy ultimately lies in the set of optimal sampling strategies for the adaptive control problem of Eq. 3.2.5. It is possible that an n-step optimal strategy may never converge to a single optimal strategy for the infinite-horizon problem; however, it can be stated that as $n \to \infty$ every n-step optimal strategy becomes arbitrarily close to some optimal strategy for the infinite-horizon problem in a sense to be defined in the next paragraph. Because the expected discounted reward over an infinite period is the same for all optimal sampling strategies, this weaker form of asymptotic behavior of $d^*(n)$ is adequate for our purposes.

Let the generalized state (i, ψ) be fixed. To every n-step sampling strategy $d(n)$ there corresponds an ordered pair (k_n, y_n), where $k_n \in \{1, \ldots, K_i\}$ and $y_n \in [0, 1]$ is defined by Eq. 3.2.13 with $\delta_\alpha = 0$ for $\alpha > \sum_{k=1}^{n} N^{(k-1)}$. Let $d' = (k', y')$ be a sampling strategy for the infinite-horizon model of Eq. 3.2.5 and let $\Delta \subset D_i$ be a set of such sampling strategies. Then we say that, as $n \to \infty$, $d(n)$ *ultimately lies in* Δ if, given $\epsilon > 0$, there is a positive integer ν such that, for every $n > \nu$, there is a sampling strategy $d'_n = (k'_n, y'_n) \in \Delta$ such that $k_n = k'_n$ and $|y_n - y'_n| < \epsilon$. We do not require that d'_n be the same strategy for all $n > \nu$. This definition implies that, given an arbitrarily large positive integer μ, there exists an integer ν such that, for every $n > \nu$, the values of the decision functions on the first μ levels of $d(n)$ are equal to the values of the decision functions on the first μ levels of some $d'_n \in \Delta$.

Theorem 3.4.5. Let the generalized state (i, ψ) be fixed and let $\Delta_i(\psi) \subset D_i$ denote the set of optimal sampling strategies for the adaptive control problem of Eq. 3.2.5. If $d^*(n)$ is an n-step optimal sampling strategy for the problem defined by Eqs. 3.3.1 and 3.3.2, then, as $n \to \infty$, $d^*(n)$ ultimately lies in $\Delta_i(\psi)$.

Proof. Let k_n denote the initial alternative selected in the n-step optimal sampling strategy $d^*(n)$ and let $\mathcal{K}_i(\psi)$ be the set of alternatives in state i which are initial selections for an optimal strategy in $\Delta_i(\psi)$. We first show that for ν sufficiently large, $k_n \in \mathcal{K}_i(\psi)$ for all $n > \nu$.

Using the notation of Eqs. 3.3.3 and 3.3.4,

$$v_i(n, \psi) = S_i^{k_n}(v, n - 1, \psi), \tag{3.4.26}$$

and, for any $k \in \mathcal{K}_i(\psi)$ and $\alpha \notin \mathcal{K}_i(\psi)$,

$$v_i(\psi) = S_i^k(v, \infty, \psi) > S_i^\alpha(v, \infty, \psi). \tag{3.4.27}$$

If the decision problem is nontrivial, then at least one such α exists.

Assume that $\{k_n\}$ does not ultimately remain in $\mathcal{K}_i(\psi)$. Then there exists a subsequence $\{k_{n_\nu}\}$ such that

$$k_{n_\nu} \notin \mathcal{K}_i(\psi), \qquad \nu = 1, 2, \ldots. \tag{3.4.28}$$

Let ϵ be chosen such that

$$0 < \epsilon < \min_{\alpha \notin \mathcal{K}_i(\psi)} \{|v_i(\psi) - S_i^\alpha(v, \infty, \psi)|\}. \tag{3.4.29}$$

Since $\lim_{\nu \to \infty} v_i(n_\nu, \psi) = v_i(\psi)$, we have, by Eq. 3.4.26.

$$|v_i(\psi) - S_i^{k_{n\nu}}(v, n_\nu - 1, \psi)| < \frac{\epsilon}{2} \tag{3.4.30}$$

for all ν sufficiently large. But, using Eqs. 3.3.3 and 3.3.4,

$$\lim_{n \to \infty} S_i^k(v, n - 1, \psi) = S_i^k(v, \infty, \psi), \qquad k = 1, \ldots, K_i, \tag{3.4.31}$$

and there exists an integer ν such that

$$|S_i^{k_{n\nu}}(v, n_\nu - 1, \psi) - S_i^{k_{n\nu}}(v, \infty, \psi)| < \frac{\epsilon}{2}. \tag{3.4.32}$$

Thus, combining Eqs. 3.4.30 and 3.4.32, there exists an integer ν such that $k_{n_\nu} \notin \mathcal{K}_i(\psi)$ and

$$|v_i(\psi) - S_i^{k_{n\nu}}(v, \infty, \psi)| < \epsilon, \tag{3.4.33}$$

contradicting Eq. 3.4.29. It follows that, for sufficiently large ν, $k_n \in \mathcal{K}_i(\psi)$ for all $n > \nu$.

Let a positive integer μ be given. From the initial generalized state (i, ψ) there are a finite number of generalized states (j, ψ') which can be reached in μ transitions. With each (j, ψ') is associated a set of alternatives $\mathcal{K}_j(\psi')$ which are used in an optimal sampling strategy of $\Delta_i(\psi)$ when the system is in (j, ψ'). The above proof shows that, for n sufficiently large, the alternative used by $d^*(n)$ when in (j, ψ') lies in $\mathcal{K}_j(\psi')$. Because the optimal strategies in the infinite-horizon problem depend only on the generalized state of the system and not on the history of the system before entering that state, there is a positive integer ν such that, for every $n > \nu$, the decision functions on the first μ levels of $d^*(n)$ have the same values as the corresponding decision functions in some optimal strategy $d_n \in \Delta_i(\psi)$. Hence $d^*(n)$ ultimately lies in $\Delta_i(\psi)$. Q.E.D.

When $\mathscr{P}$ is known to the decision maker and the number of physical states is finite, Howard [22] has demonstrated the existence of stationary optimal policies for the infinite-horizon problem. These stationary policies prescribe an alternative to be used in each state i independently of the number of transitions which have elapsed. Because, in general, the decision maker's state of knowledge ψ changes with each transition, stationary optimal policies in this sense do not exist when there is uncertainty about $\mathscr{P}$. It is possible to construct a theory of stationary policies by considering the infinite-state Markov process with states (i, ψ), but, in such a process, the probability that the system ever returns to (i, ψ) is generally zero. Stationary policies are therefore not useful to the decision maker and will not be considered further here.

3.5. RECURSIVE COMPUTATION

Equations 3.3.1 and 3.3.2 are typical of a class of recursive equations which appear throughout this book. It is to be noted that, although these equations resemble a classical iterative formula for successive approximations, $v_i(n, \psi)$ is computed not in terms of $v_j(n-1, \psi)$ but in terms of $v_j(n-1, T^k_{ij}(\psi))$. Computation of $v_i(n, \psi)$ for a specific value of (i, ψ) involves the evaluation of between $(k_1N)^n$ and $(k_2N)^n$ terminal values $V_j(\psi')$, where $k_1 = \min_i \{K_i\}$ and $k_2 = \max_i \{K_i\}$.

One way to compute $v_i(n, \psi)$ is to start by evaluating and storing all required values of $V_j(\psi) = v_j(0, \psi)$, then to compute and store all required values of $v_j(1, \psi)$, using the results of the previous computation of $v_j(0, \psi)$. In general, for $\nu = 1, 2, \ldots, n-1$, $v_j(\nu, \psi)$ is computed in terms of a grid of values of $v_j(\nu - 1, \psi)$ and is stored for use at the next stage in computing $v_j(\nu + 1, \psi)$.

Since the number of terminal values $V_j(\psi)$ needed grows exponentially with n, it is clear that considerable storage capacity is required. For even moderately large n, tape or disk storage must be used. Moreover, a fairly complex indexing routine must be programmed in order to use storage space efficiently.

An alternative approach is to evaluate $v_i(n, \psi)$ recursively. With the use of this method, computation starts with the nth level rather than the zeroth level. In general, at the $(\nu + 1)$th level of computation the computational subroutine starts to evaluate $v_j(\nu + 1, \psi)$ for some pair (j, ψ). This level of computation is suspended when a value at the νth level, $v_k(\nu, \psi')$, is required. Key portions of the $(\nu + 1)$th level of computation are stored on a push-down list, and the program enters the νth level of computation to evaluate $v_j(\nu, \psi')$. Recursion is halted at the zeroth level when $V_j(\psi)$ is computed. The results of lower level computations are then fed back, in succession, to higher levels. Having obtained the value of $v_k(\nu, \psi')$ in this manner, the $(\nu + 1)$th level of computation reclaims its partially completed calculations from the pushdown list and completes them. This succession of events continues until $v_i(n, \psi)$ is evaluated.

The storage requirements for recursive calculation of $v_i(n, \psi)$ consist only of the space needed for storage of intermediate computations on the push-down list and, therefore, increase linearly with n. Thus, the recursive method has the advantage of requiring considerably less storage than the first method described. Since specific values of $v_j(\nu, \psi)$ for $\nu = 0, 1, \ldots, n - 1$ may have to be recalculated many times in the recursive method, we are essentially trading running time for storage. However, it should be noted that, if the first method requires tape handling, the recursive method may reduce over-all running time.

The general theory of recursive computation is described by McCarthy [29]. Programming languages of the ALGOL family [32] are capable of recursive computations, as are most list-processing languages; it is possible to do recursive programming in FORTRAN II [4]. The recursive programs which were written for this book used the MAD language [3].

Utilizing the recursive method, a program was written to evaluate Eqs. 3.3.1 and 3.3.2 for specific pairs (i, ψ) when $\tilde{\mathscr{P}}$ has the matrix beta distribution. This program is contained in Appendix B. Some numerical results obtained from the program are presented in the next section.

3.6. NUMERICAL EXAMPLE

Consider a two-state Markov chain with two alternatives in each state. Let the reward matrix be

$$\mathscr{R} = \begin{bmatrix} 10 & 4 \\ 4 & 6 \\ 14 & 3 \\ 8 & 16 \end{bmatrix}, \quad \begin{matrix} \left.\begin{matrix} k = 1 \\ k = 2 \end{matrix}\right\} i = 1, \\ \left.\begin{matrix} k = 1 \\ k = 2 \end{matrix}\right\} i = 2. \end{matrix} \tag{3.6.1}$$

Assume that the prior distribution of $\tilde{\mathscr{P}}$ is a matrix beta distribution with parameter

$$\mathscr{M} = \begin{bmatrix} 0.0741 & 0.0370 \\ 1.0078 & 0.3360 \\ 0.5586 & 3.9099 \\ 0.1888 & 0.1132 \end{bmatrix} \tag{3.6.2}$$

and mean

$$\bar{\mathscr{P}} = \begin{bmatrix} 0.667 & 0.333 \\ 0.750 & 0.250 \\ 0.125 & 0.875 \\ 0.625 & 0.375 \end{bmatrix}. \tag{3.6.3}$$

Letting

$$\tilde{\boldsymbol{p}} = (\tilde{p}_{11}^1, \tilde{p}_{12}^1, \tilde{p}_{11}^2, \tilde{p}_{12}^2, \tilde{p}_{21}^1, \tilde{p}_{22}^1, \tilde{p}_{21}^2, \tilde{p}_{22}^2)$$

and

$$\bar{\boldsymbol{p}} = E[\tilde{\boldsymbol{p}}],$$

the variance-covariance matrix of this distribution is

$$E[(\tilde{\boldsymbol{p}} - \bar{\boldsymbol{p}})^t(\tilde{\boldsymbol{p}} - \bar{\boldsymbol{p}})]$$

$$= \begin{bmatrix} 0.200 & -0.200 & & & & & & \\ -0.200 & 0.200 & & & & & \mathbf{0} & \\ & & 0.080 & -0.080 & & & & \\ & & -0.080 & 0.080 & & & & \\ & & & & 0.020 & -0.020 & & \\ & \mathbf{0} & & & -0.020 & 0.020 & & \\ & & & & & & 0.180 & -0.180 \\ & & & & & & -0.180 & 0.180 \end{bmatrix}. \tag{3.6.4}$$

Let the discount factor be $\beta = 0.2$.

Table 3.6.1 lists values of

$$\boldsymbol{v}(n, \mathcal{M}) = \begin{bmatrix} v_1(n, \mathcal{M}) \\ v_2(n, \mathcal{M}) \end{bmatrix}, \tag{3.6.5}$$

using the terminal functions

$$V_i(\mathcal{M}) = 0.000, \qquad i = 1, 2. \tag{3.6.6}$$

Since $r = 3 > 0$, the convergence is monotone increasing. It is seen that convergence to two decimal places has occurred by the sixth iteration. The optimal initial policy vector

$$\boldsymbol{\sigma}^*(n) = \begin{bmatrix} \sigma_1(n) \\ \sigma_2(n) \end{bmatrix} \tag{3.6.7}$$

is recorded in the third column, where $\sigma_i(n)$ is the initial decision k_n when the system starts from state i and the n-step optimal sampling strategy is $d(n) = (k_n, \delta(n))$.

Using $v(6, \mathcal{M})$ as the limiting vector $v(\mathcal{M})$, the error vector of the nth iterate, $e(n, \mathcal{M})$, was computed as

$$e(n, \mathcal{M}) = \begin{bmatrix} 10.517 \\ 13.667 \end{bmatrix} - v(n, \mathcal{M}) \tag{3.6.8}$$

and is displayed in the fourth column of Table 3.6.1. The last column of

TABLE 3.6.1

n	$v(n, \mathcal{M})$	$\sigma^*(n)$	$e(n, \mathcal{M})$	$\Delta(n)$
0	0.000 0.000	— —	10.517 13.667	20.000
1	8.002 10.999	1 2	2.515 2.668	4.000
2	10.042 13.112	1 2	0.475 0.555	0.800
3	10.418 13.562	1 2	0.099 0.105	0.160
4	10.499 13.646	1 2	0.018 0.021	0.032
5	10.514 13.664	1 2	0.003 0.003	0.006
6	10.517 13.667	1 2	0.000 0.000	0.001

$\beta = 0.2$
$V(\mathcal{M}) = \begin{matrix} 0.000 \\ 0.000 \end{matrix}$
Computation time—5 minutes.

the table contains the error bound

$$\Delta(n) = \beta^n \left(\max \left\{ \frac{R}{1 - \beta} - v^*, V^* - \frac{r}{1 - \beta} \right\} \right),$$

defined by Eq. 3.4.15. Note that the bound $\Delta(n)$ accurately predicts—in this example—the number of iterations required for two-place accuracy.

The computations shown in Table 3.6.2 are similar to those of Table 3.6.1, except that the terminal functions are

$$V_i(\mathcal{M}) = \frac{r}{1 - \beta} = 3.75, \qquad i = 1, 2. \tag{3.6.9}$$

The convergence is still monotone increasing and the error functions $e_i(n, \mathcal{M})$ are reduced to approximately two thirds of the corresponding values in Table 3.6.1. Six iterations are required in this case for two-place accuracy.

TABLE 3.6.2

n	$v(n, \mathcal{M})$	$\sigma^*(n)$	$e(n, \mathcal{M})$	$\Delta(n)$
0	3.750	—	6.767	16.250
	3.750	—	9.917	
1	8.752	1	1.765	3.250
	11.749	2	1.918	
2	10.192	1	0.325	0.650
	13.262	2	0.405	
3	10.448	1	0.069	0.130
	13.592	2	0.075	
4	10.505	1	0.012	0.026
	13.652	2	0.015	
5	10.515	1	0.002	0.005
	13.665	2	0.002	
6	10.517	1	0.000	0.001
	13.667	2	0.000	

$\beta = 0.2$
$V(\mathcal{M}) = 3.750$
$\quad\quad\quad\;\; 3.750$
Computation time—5 minutes.

In Table 3.6.3 the terminal functions are the maximum expected discounted rewards when the system is operated indefinitely under a single policy [in this case, the policy (1, 2); see Sec. 4.3],

$$V(\mathcal{M}) = \begin{bmatrix} 10.253 \\ 13.278 \end{bmatrix}.$$

Convergence is monotonic after the first iteration. The error vector is significantly reduced as compared with corresponding entries in Tables 3.6.1 and 3.6.2. Four iterations are necessary to obtain two-place accuracy in this instance.

TABLE 3.6.3

n	$v(n, \mathcal{M})$	$\sigma^*(n)$	$e(n, \mathcal{M})$	$\Delta(n)$
0	10.253 13.278	— —	0.265 0.390	9.747
1	10.254 13.276	1 2	0.264 0.392	1.949
2	10.470 13.586	1 2	0.048 0.082	0.390
3	10.507 13.652	1 2	0.011 0.016	0.078
4	10.516 13.665	1 2	0.002 0.003	0.016
5	10.517 13.667	1 2	0.001 0.001	0.003
6	10.518 13.668	1 2	0.000 0.000	0.001

$\beta = 0.2$
$V(\mathcal{M}) = \begin{matrix} 10.253 \\ 13.278 \end{matrix}$
Computation time—5 minutes.

3.7. UNDISCOUNTED PROCESSES

When the discount factor is unity, the criterion of maximizing the total expected reward over an infinite period is no longer useful since, with the possible exception of a set of sample histories of measure zero, the expected reward over an infinite period under any strategy diverges to $+\infty$ or $-\infty$. An alternative criterion is to maximize the expected rate of which the process earns rewards in the steady state (the expected *gain* of the process). This criterion is not really precise since the decision maker can, in the adaptive control process, change alternatives in any state at any time, and it is not certain that a steady state will ever be reached; nor is it obvious that it is optimal for the decision maker to allow the system to reach a steady state. Moreover, among those strategies which do lead to a steady state and which maximize the gain, there is an arbitrarily large number that are virtually equivalent—those strategies in which each alternative is sampled a large (but finite) number of times, and then a fixed policy is chosen with almost perfect information. Further remarks on this class of strategies will be made in Sec. 5.5.

Since for each $\beta \in (0, 1)$ there is a well-defined criterion leading to an optimal policy, an alternative approach to the undiscounted process is to let $\beta \to 1$ in the discounted adaptive control problem, as formulated in Eq. 3.2.5. For fixed β, let $\boldsymbol{\sigma}(\beta) = (\sigma_1(\beta), \ldots, \sigma_N(\beta))$ be an optimal initial policy, where $\sigma_i(\beta)$ is the maximizing value of k in Eq. 3.2.5 for a fixed $\psi \in \Psi$. We shall call $\boldsymbol{\sigma}(\beta)$ a *β-optimal policy*. If, for some $\delta \in (0, 1)$,

$$\boldsymbol{\sigma}(\beta) = \boldsymbol{\sigma}^*, \qquad 1 - \delta < \beta < 1, \tag{3.7.1}$$

we shall call $\boldsymbol{\sigma}^*$ an optimal initial policy for the undiscounted adaptive control problem. By prescribing a policy $\boldsymbol{\sigma}^*$ for every state (i, ψ) which can be reached from the initial state, an optimal sampling strategy for the undiscounted adaptive control problem can be constructed. The existence and nature of optimal policies as defined by Eq. 3.7.1 are matters for future investigation. Blackwell [11] and Derman [16] have used this approach to undiscounted decision problems in a Markov chain with alternatives when the transition probabilities are known with certainty.

Chapter 4

EXPECTED STEADY-STATE PROBABILITIES AND RELATED QUANTITIES

Consider a Markov chain with alternatives operated under a fixed policy $\boldsymbol{\sigma}$. Let $\tilde{\mathbf{P}}(\boldsymbol{\sigma})$ denote the $N \times N$ matrix of transition probabilities, assumed to have the prior distribution function $F_{\sigma}(\mathbf{P} \mid \psi)$. In this chapter we examine some functions of $\tilde{\mathbf{P}}$ which are of importance in decision problems, with particular attention devoted to the problem of computing the means, variances, and covariances of these quantities.

Section 4.1 deals with the n-step transition probabilities and with the expected discounted reward over n transition. Section 4.2 is concerned with the steady-state probability vector. In Sec. 4.3 we consider the expected discounted reward over an infinite number of transitions when a fixed policy $\boldsymbol{\sigma}$ is used and, in the final section, some results concerning the expected reward per transition, or process gain, are presented. These quantities are, of course, important on their own merits; the results derived here will also be applied to various terminal control models in Chap. 5.

Ideally, we should like to have the distributions of these quantities; however, it is extremely difficult to obtain useful expressions in the general case. Indeed, explicit expressions for the first and second moments are rare. Thus we consider methods for the numerical calculation of the first two moments.

Throughout this chapter it will be assumed that a specific policy $\boldsymbol{\sigma}$ is in force, that the Markov chain is governed by the $N \times N$ stochastic matrix $\tilde{\mathbf{P}} = \tilde{\mathbf{P}}(\boldsymbol{\sigma})$, and that the matrix of transition rewards is $\mathbf{R}(\boldsymbol{\sigma}) = \mathbf{R} = [r_{ij}]$. In most cases, the dependence of various functions on $\boldsymbol{\sigma}$ will not be made explicit in order to simplify the notation to some extent. It is, for the most part, assumed throughout this chapter that the prior distribution of $\tilde{\mathbf{P}}$ is a member of a family of distributions closed under consecutive sampling.

4.1. THE n-STEP TRANSITION PROBABILITY MATRIX

If $\mathbf{P}$ is a stochastic matrix governing the transitions in a Markov chain, then the probability that the system is in state j after n transitions, given that the system started in state i, is the (i, j)th element of the nth power of $\mathbf{P}$, and is denoted $p_{ij}^{(n)}$. When $\tilde{\mathbf{P}}$ is a random matrix, $\tilde{p}_{ij}^{(n)}$ is a random variable. In this section we derive general expressions for the expected value of $\tilde{p}_{ij}^{(n)}$ and the covariance of $\tilde{p}_{\alpha\beta}^{(n)}$ and $\tilde{p}_{\gamma\delta}^{(\nu)}$ and we examine a related quantity, the expected discounted reward over n transitions. Silver,† using different methods, has considered the expected value of $\tilde{p}_{ij}^{(n)}$, assuming a matrix beta prior distribution for $\tilde{\mathbf{P}}$, and has presented numerical results for a two-state process.

Theorem 4.1.1. If the prior distribution function of $\tilde{\mathbf{P}}$ is $F(\mathbf{P} \mid \psi) \in \mathcal{F}$, a family of distributions closed under consecutive sampling, and if

$$\bar{p}_{ij}^{(n)}(\psi) = \int_{S_N} p_{ij}^{(n)}\, dF(\boldsymbol{p} \mid \psi)$$

$$i, j = 1, \ldots, N, \quad \psi \in \Psi, \quad n = 1, 2, \ldots, \tag{4.1.1}$$

is the expected value of $\tilde{p}_{ij}^{(n)}$, then $\bar{p}_{ij}^{(n)}(\psi)$ can be computed recursively from the following equations:

$$\bar{p}_{ij}^{(n+1)}(\psi) = \sum_{k=1}^{N} \bar{p}_{ik}^{(n)}(T_{kj}(\psi))\bar{p}_{kj}(\psi),$$

$$i, j = 1, \ldots, N, \quad n = 1, 2, \ldots, \quad \psi \in \Psi, \tag{4.1.2a}$$

$$\bar{p}_{ij}^{(1)}(\psi) = \bar{p}_{ij}(\psi), \qquad i, j = 1, \ldots, N, \quad \psi \in \Psi. \tag{4.1.2b}$$

Proof. Since, for $n = 1, 2, \ldots,$

$$p_{ij}^{(n+1)} = \sum_{k=1}^{N} p_{ik}^{(n)} p_{kj}, \qquad \mathbf{P} \in S_N,$$

Lemma 2.3.2 yields

$$\begin{aligned}
\bar{p}_{ij}^{(n+1)}(\psi) &= \sum_{k=1}^{N} \int_{S_N} p_{ik}^{(n)} p_{kj}\, dF(\mathbf{P} \mid \psi) \\
&= \sum_{k=1}^{N} \bar{p}_{kj}(\psi) \int_{S_N} p_{ik}^{(n)}\, dF(\mathbf{P} \mid T_{kj}(\psi)) \\
&= \sum_{k=1}^{N} \bar{p}_{ik}^{(n)}(T_{kj}(\psi))\bar{p}_{kj}(\psi).
\end{aligned} \tag{4.1.3}$$

† See [38], pp. 82–87.

Since $p_{ij}^{(n)}$ is a continuous function of $\mathbf{P}$ for $i, j = 1, \ldots, N$ and $n = 1, 2, \ldots$, the integrals in Eqs. 4.1.1 and 4.1.3 exist. Q.E.D.

Theorem 4.1.2. If the prior distribution function of $\tilde{\mathbf{P}}$ is $F(\mathbf{P} \mid \psi) \in \mathcal{F}$, a family of distributions continuous in ψ, then for $i, j = 1, \ldots, N$ and $n = 1, 2, \ldots$, $\bar{p}_{ij}^{(n)}(\psi)$ is a continuous function of ψ.

Proof. The theorem follows directly from Theorem 2.4.3. Q.E.D.

Theorem 4.1.3. If $\tilde{\mathbf{P}}$ has the distribution function $F(\mathbf{P} \mid \psi) \in \mathcal{F}$, a family of distributions closed under consecutive sampling, and if

$$E[\tilde{p}_{\alpha\beta}^{(n)}\tilde{p}_{\gamma\delta}^{(\nu)} \mid \psi] = \int_{\mathcal{S}_N} p_{\alpha\beta}^{(n)} p_{\gamma\delta}^{(\nu)} \, dF(\mathbf{P} \mid \psi),$$

$$\alpha, \beta, \gamma, \delta = 1, \ldots, N, \quad n, \nu = 1, 2, \ldots, \quad \psi \in \Psi, \tag{4.1.4}$$

hen, for $n > 1$, $\nu > 1$,

$$E[\tilde{p}_{\alpha\beta}^{(n)}\tilde{p}_{\gamma\beta}^{(\nu)} \mid \psi] = \sum_{\substack{k=1\\m=1}}^{N} \bar{p}_{k\beta}(\psi)\bar{p}_{m\delta}(T_{k\beta}(\psi))E[\tilde{p}_{\alpha k}^{(n-1)}\tilde{p}_{\gamma m}^{(\nu-1)} \mid T_{m\delta}(T_{k\beta}(\psi))], \tag{4.1.5}$$

while, for $n = 1$ or $\nu = 1$,

$$E[\tilde{p}_{\alpha\beta}\tilde{p}_{\gamma\delta}^{(\nu)} \mid \psi] = \bar{p}_{\alpha\beta}(\psi)\bar{p}_{\gamma\delta}^{(\nu)}(T_{\alpha\beta}(\psi)), \tag{4.1.6}$$

$$E[\tilde{p}_{\alpha\beta}^{(n)}\tilde{p}_{\gamma\delta} \mid \psi] = p_{\alpha\beta}^{(n)}(T_{\gamma\delta}(\psi))\bar{p}_{\gamma\delta}(\psi). \tag{4.1.7}$$

Proof. The functions $p_{\alpha\beta}^{(n)}p_{\gamma\delta}^{(\nu)}$ are continuous on $\mathcal{S}_N$, hence, the integrals of Eq. 4.1.4 exist. Applying Lemma 2.3.2 twice, we obtain, for the case $n > 1$, $\nu > 1$,

$$\begin{aligned} E[\tilde{p}_{\alpha\beta}^{(n)}\tilde{p}_{\gamma\delta}^{(\nu)} \mid \psi] &= \sum_{\substack{k=1\\m=1}}^{N} \int_{\mathcal{S}_N} p_{\alpha k}^{(n-1)} p_{k\beta} p_{\gamma m}^{(\nu-1)} p_{m\delta} \, dF(\mathbf{P} \mid \psi) \\ &= \sum_{\substack{k=1\\m=1}}^{N} \bar{p}_{k\beta}(\psi)\bar{p}_{m\delta}(T_{k\beta}(\psi))E[\tilde{p}_{\alpha k}^{(n-1)}\tilde{p}_{\gamma m}^{(\nu-1)} \mid T_{m\delta}(T_{k\beta}(\psi))]. \end{aligned}$$

If $n = 1$,

$$\begin{aligned} E[\tilde{p}_{\alpha\beta}\tilde{p}_{\gamma\delta}^{(\nu)} \mid \psi] &= \int_{\mathcal{S}_N} p_{\alpha\beta} p_{\gamma\delta}^{(\nu)} \, dF(\mathbf{P} \mid \psi) \\ &= \bar{p}_{\alpha\beta}(\psi)\bar{p}_{\gamma\delta}^{(\nu)}(T_{\alpha\beta}(\psi)), \end{aligned}$$

and similarly for $\nu = 1$. Q.E.D.

Let us now consider $\bar{q}_i^{(n)}(\beta, \psi)$, the prior expected discounted reward in n transitions when the system starts in state i, β is the discount factor, and $F(\mathbf{P} \mid \psi)$ is the marginal prior distribution function of $\tilde{\mathbf{P}}$. This expectation will be required for one of the terminal control models of

Chap. 5. Let $q_i^{(n)}(\beta, \mathbf{P})$ be the corresponding expected discounted reward given that $\tilde{\mathbf{P}} = \mathbf{P}$. Then

$$q_i^{(n)}(\beta, \psi) = \int_{\mathcal{S}_N} q_i^{(n)}(\beta, \mathbf{P})\, dF(\mathbf{P} \mid \psi). \tag{4.1.8}$$

Theorem 4.1.4. If the prior distribution function of $\tilde{\mathbf{P}}$ is $F(\mathbf{P} \mid \psi) \in \mathcal{F}$, a family of distributions closed under consecutive sampling, then $\bar{q}_i^{(n)}(\beta, \psi)$ can be computed recursively from the following equations:

$$\bar{q}_i^{(n+1)}(\beta, \psi) = \sum_{k=1}^{N} \bar{p}_{ik}(\psi)[r_{ik} + \beta \bar{q}_k^{(n)}(\beta, T_{ik}(\psi))],$$

$$i = 1, \ldots, N, \quad n = 1, 2, \ldots, \quad \psi \in \Psi, \quad 0 \leqslant \beta \leqslant 1, \tag{4.1.9a}$$

$$\bar{q}_i^{(1)}(\beta, \psi) = \sum_{k=1}^{N} \bar{p}_{ik}(\psi) r_{ik}$$

$$i = 1, \ldots, N, \quad \psi \in \Psi, \quad 0 \leqslant \beta \leqslant 1, \tag{4.1.9b}$$

where $\mathbf{R} = [r_{ij}]$ is the reward matrix.

Proof. For $n = 1, 2, \ldots$ and all $\mathbf{P} \in \mathcal{S}_N$, $q_i^{(n)}(\beta, \mathbf{P})$ satisfies the following renewal equation:

$$q_i^{(n+1)}(\beta, \mathbf{P}) = \sum_{k=1}^{N} p_{ik}[r_{ik} + \beta q_k^{(n)}(\beta, \mathbf{P})], \qquad i = 1, \ldots, N.$$

Then, using Lemma 2.3.2,

$$\begin{aligned} \bar{q}_i^{(n+1)}(\beta, \psi) &= \sum_{k=1}^{N} \bar{p}_{ik}(\psi) \int_{\mathcal{S}_N} [r_{ik} + \beta q_k^{(n)}(\beta, \mathbf{P})]\, dF(\mathbf{P} \mid T_{ik}(\psi)) \\ &= \sum_{k=1}^{N} \bar{p}_{ik}(\psi)[r_{ik} + \beta \bar{q}_k^{(n)}(\beta, T_{ik}(\psi))], \end{aligned} \tag{4.1.10}$$

which is Eq. 4.1.9*a*. Since $\bar{q}_i^{(1)}(\beta, \psi)$ is $\bar{q}_i(\psi)$ as defined by Eq. 3.2.4, Eq. 4.1.9*b* follows. Q.E.D.

For the case $\beta = 1$ another method is available for evaluating $\bar{q}_i^{(n)}(1, \psi)$. In a sample of n observations, let f_{ij} be the number of transitions observed from state i to state j and let $\mathbf{F} = [f_{ij}]$, an $N \times N$ matrix, be the transition count of the sample. Prior to the observation of the sample, $\tilde{\mathbf{F}}$ is a random matrix and, given the initial state i, the number of transitions n, and the prior distribution of $\tilde{\mathbf{P}}$, we can find the distribution of $\tilde{\mathbf{F}}$, unconditional with regard to $\tilde{\mathbf{P}}$. Let $\bar{\mathbf{F}} = [\bar{f}_{ij}]$ be the mean of this unconditional sampling distribution. Then

$$\bar{q}_i^{(n)}(1, \psi) = \sum_{\substack{j=1 \\ k=1}}^{N} \bar{f}_{jk} r_{jk}. \tag{4.1.11}$$

If the prior distribution of $\tilde{\mathbf{P}}$ is the matrix beta distribution, then the distribution of $\tilde{\mathbf{F}}$, unconditional with regard to $\tilde{\mathbf{P}}$, is the beta-Whittle distribution, which is discussed in Sec. 6.5.

4.2. THE STEADY-STATE PROBABILITY VECTOR

Let $\mathbf{P}$ be an ergodic stochastic matrix. Then there is associated with $\mathbf{P}$ a unique vector of steady-state probabilities $\boldsymbol{\pi}(\mathbf{P}) = (\pi_1, \ldots, \pi_N)$, where $\pi_i = \pi_i(\mathbf{P})$ is the steady-state probability that the system is in state i $(i = 1, \ldots, N)$. The vector $\boldsymbol{\pi}$ satisfies the following system of simultaneous equations:

$$\boldsymbol{\pi} = \boldsymbol{\pi}\mathbf{P}, \tag{4.2.1a}$$

$$\sum_{i=1}^{N} \pi_i = 1. \tag{4.2.1b}$$

If $\tilde{\mathbf{P}}$ is a random matrix with an arbitrary distribution function $F(\mathbf{P} \mid \psi)$, which satisfies a mild continuity condition, we show in the following that the subset of nonergodic matrices in $\mathcal{S}_N$ is a set of measure zero. Thus, it is meaningful to speak of the random vector $\tilde{\boldsymbol{\pi}}$.

We are chiefly concerned, in this section, with the expected value, $\bar{\boldsymbol{\pi}}(\psi) = (\bar{\pi}_1(\psi), \ldots, \bar{\pi}_N(\psi))$, of $\tilde{\boldsymbol{\pi}}$. It is shown that this expectation exists and that $\lim_{n\to\infty} \bar{p}_{ij}^{(n)}(\psi) = \bar{\pi}_j(\psi)$. We then assume that $F(\mathbf{P} \mid \psi) \in \mathcal{F}$, a family of distributions closed under the consecutive sampling rule, and derive a functional equation for $\bar{\boldsymbol{\pi}}(\psi)$. Methods of successive approximations based on this equation are discussed, then some numerical results are presented. We conclude with a discussion of the covariance of $\tilde{\pi}_i$ and $\tilde{\pi}_j$.

Existence of the Moments of $\tilde{\boldsymbol{\pi}}$

Let us now consider conditions on the prior distribution of $\tilde{\mathbf{P}}$ which insure the existence of the general joint moment of the elements of $\tilde{\boldsymbol{\pi}}$,

$$E\left[\prod_{i=1}^{N} \tilde{\pi}_i^{\nu_i} \,\middle|\, \psi\right] = \int_{\mathcal{S}_N} \prod_{i=1}^{N} \pi_i^{\nu_i}\, dF(\mathbf{P} \mid \psi), \qquad \psi \in \Psi, \tag{4.2.2}$$

where the ν_i are nonnegative integers.

Let

$$\mathcal{S}_N^* = \{\mathbf{P} \mid \mathbf{P} \in \mathcal{S}_N, 0 < p_{ij} < 1 \, (i, j = 1, \ldots, N)\} \tag{4.2.3}$$

be the set of all *positive stochastic matrices* and, for $0 < \alpha < 1$, define the set

$$\mathcal{S}_N^\alpha = \{\mathbf{P} \mid \mathbf{P} \in \mathcal{S}_N, \alpha \leqslant p_{ij} \leqslant 1 - \alpha \, (i, j = 1, \ldots, N)\}. \qquad 0 < \alpha < 1 \tag{4.2.4}$$

We remark that $\mathcal{S}_N^\alpha$ is a closed and bounded, hence, compact subset of E_{N^2} and that $\mathcal{S}_N^\alpha \subset \mathcal{S}_N^* \subset \mathcal{S}_N$ for any α in the open interval (0, 1).

For fixed $\alpha \in (0, 1)$, let $S(\alpha)$ be any subset of E_{N^2} such that

$$\mathcal{S}_N - \mathcal{S}_N^\alpha \neq S(\alpha) \tag{4.2.5a}$$

and

$$\mathcal{S}_N - \mathcal{S}_N^\alpha \subset S(\alpha). \tag{4.2.5b}$$

Thus, for all $\alpha \in (0, 1)$, the boundary of $\mathcal{S}_N$ is a proper subset of $S(\alpha)$. If, for some $\alpha \in (0, 1)$, there exists a set $S(\alpha)$ satisfying Eq. 4.2.5 such that $F(\mathbf{P} \mid \psi)$, the prior distribution function of $\tilde{\mathbf{P}}$, is continuous on $S(\alpha)$, then $F(\mathbf{P} \mid \psi)$ is said to be *continuous on the boundary of* $\mathcal{S}_N$. If $\mathcal{F}$ is a family of distributions indexed by ψ, every member of which is continuous on the boundary of $\mathcal{S}_N$, then $\mathcal{F}$ is also said to be continuous on the boundary of $\mathcal{S}_N$.

The following lemma shows that continuity of $F(\mathbf{P} \mid \psi)$ on the boundary of $\mathcal{S}_N$ is a necessary and sufficient condition for the set of boundary points $\mathcal{S}_N - \mathcal{S}_N^*$ to be a set of measure zero. If $\mathbf{P} \in \mathcal{S}_N^*$, then $\mathbf{P}$ consists of a single chain with no transient states. Thus, the subset of $\mathcal{S}_N$, which includes all periodic and multiple-chain transition matrices as well as those single-chain transition matrices which have transient states, is contained within $\mathcal{S}_N - \mathcal{S}_N^*$. The import of Lemma 4.2.1 is that, provided $F(\mathbf{P} \mid \psi)$ is continuous on the boundary of $\mathcal{S}_N$, we need only consider transition matrices in $\mathcal{S}_N^*$. In this case, with probability one, $\tilde{\boldsymbol{\pi}}$ exists and, moreover, $\tilde{\boldsymbol{\pi}}_j > 0$ $(j = 1, \ldots, N)$.

Lemma 4.2.1. If $F(\mathbf{P} \mid \psi)$ is the prior distribution function of $\tilde{\mathbf{P}}$, then a necessary and sufficient condition for $\mathcal{S}_N - \mathcal{S}_N^*$ to be a set of measure zero relative to the prior distribution is that $F(\mathbf{P} \mid \psi)$ be continuous on the boundary of $\mathcal{S}_N$.

Proof. For all $\alpha \in (0, 1)$, define the sets

$$C_{ij}(\alpha) = \{\mathbf{P} \mid \mathbf{P} \in \mathcal{S}_N, 0 \leqslant p_{ij} \leqslant \alpha\}, \qquad i, j = 1, \ldots, N, 0 < \alpha < 1. \tag{4.2.6}$$

Then

$$\mathcal{S}_N - \mathcal{S}_N^* \subset \mathcal{S}_N - \mathcal{S}_N^\alpha \subset \bigcup_{i,j=1}^{N} C_{ij}(\alpha), \qquad 0 < \alpha < 1, \tag{4.2.7}$$

and, for all $\alpha \in (0, 1)$, the probability measure of the set $\mathcal{S}_N - \mathcal{S}_N^*$ has the bound

$$\int_{\mathcal{S}_N - \mathcal{S}_N^*} dF(\mathbf{P} \mid \psi) \leqslant \sum_{\substack{i=1 \\ j=1}}^{N} \int_{C_{ij}(\alpha)} dF(\mathbf{P} \mid \psi), \qquad 0 < \alpha < 1. \tag{4.2.8}$$

If $F_{ij}(p \mid \psi)$ is the marginal distribution function of $\tilde{p}_{ij}$, then

$$\int_{C_{ij}(\alpha)} dF(\mathbf{P} \mid \psi) = F_{ij}(\alpha \mid \psi), \qquad i, j = 1, \ldots, N, \quad 0 < \alpha < 1. \quad (4.2.9)$$

Assume that, for some fixed $\alpha \in (0, 1)$, there exists a set $S(\alpha)$ satisfying Eq. 4.2.5 on which $F(\mathbf{P} \mid \psi)$ is continuous. Let $\epsilon > 0$ be given. Since $F(\mathbf{P} \mid \psi)$ is continuous on $S(\alpha)$ we may choose on α' such that $0 < \alpha' < \alpha$ and

$$F_{ij}(\alpha' \mid \psi) < \frac{\epsilon}{N^2}, \qquad i, j = 1, \ldots, N. \qquad (4.2.10)$$

Then

$$\int_{\mathcal{S}_N - \mathcal{S}_N^*} dF(\mathbf{P} \mid \psi) \leqslant \sum_{\substack{i=1 \\ j=1}}^{N} F_{ij}(\alpha' \mid \psi) < \epsilon, \qquad (4.2.11)$$

and, since ϵ is arbitrary, $\mathcal{S}_N - \mathcal{S}_N^*$ is a set of measure zero, proving sufficiency.

To demonstrate necessity, it suffices to note that, if there does not exist a set $S(\alpha)$ which satisfies the conditions of the lemma, then $F(\mathbf{P} \mid \psi)$ must assign positive probability to at least one of the boundary points of $\mathcal{S}_N$. Q.E.D.

We remark that, in the case of the matrix beta distribution, the existence of a density function implies that the corresponding distribution function is continuous on E_{N^2}. Therefore, the family of matrix beta distributions is continuous on the boundary of $\mathcal{S}_N$.

Theorem 4.2.2. If the prior distribution function of $\tilde{\mathbf{P}}$, $F(\mathbf{P} \mid \psi)$, is continuous on the boundary of $\mathcal{S}_N$, then the joint moments of Eq. 4.2.2 exist for all nonnegative integers ν_i. If, furthermore, $F(\mathbf{P} \mid \psi) \in \mathcal{F}$, a family of distributions continuous in ψ, then $E[\prod_{i=1}^{N} \tilde{\pi}_i^{\nu_i} \mid \psi]$ is a continuous function of ψ.

Proof. By Lemma 4.2.1,

$$E\left[\prod_{i=1}^{N} \tilde{\pi}_i^{\nu_i} \mid \psi\right] = \int_{\mathcal{S}_N^*} \prod_{i=1}^{N} \pi_i^{\nu_i} \, dF(\mathbf{P} \mid \psi). \qquad (4.2.12)$$

Let $D_{jj}(\mathbf{P})$ be the cofactor of the jth diagonal elements of the matrix

$$\mathbf{D}(\mathbf{P}) = [\mathbf{P}^t - \mathbf{I}]. \qquad (4.2.13)$$

It can be shown† that, for all $\mathbf{P} \in \mathcal{S}_N^*$,

$$\pi_j(\mathbf{P}) = \frac{D_{jj}(\mathbf{P})}{\sum_{k=1}^{N} D_{kk}(\mathbf{P})}, \qquad j = 1, \ldots, N. \tag{4.2.14}$$

Since $D_{jj}(\mathbf{P})$ is a sum of products involving elements of $\mathbf{P}$, $\pi_j(\mathbf{P})$ is a continuous bounded function of $\mathbf{P}$ on $\mathcal{S}_N^*$ and the integral of Eq. 4.2.12 exists. When $F(\mathbf{P} \mid \psi) \in \mathcal{F}$, a family of distributions continuous in ψ, continuity of $E[\prod_{i=1}^{N} \tilde{\pi}_i^{\nu_i} \mid \psi]$ follows from Theorem 2.4.3. Q.E.D.

Theorem 4.2.2 can be proved under the weaker condition that the set of nonergodic transition probability matrices in $\mathcal{S}_N$ is a set of measure zero, but this criterion is more difficult to apply in practice than that of continuity on the boundary.

There are many problems in which it is necessary to assign positive probability to ergodic matrices on the boundary of $\mathcal{S}_N$. For example, in some random-walk models $\tilde{\mathbf{P}}$ is known to be a Jacobi matrix, that is, $\tilde{p}_{ij} = 0$ with probability one if $|i - j| > 1$. In this case the theory presented here can be applied by assigning a prior distribution to the $N \times 3$ generalized stochastic matrix $\tilde{\mathbf{P}}^*$, where the ith row of $\tilde{\mathbf{P}}^*$ consists of the elements $\tilde{p}_{i,i-1}, \tilde{p}_{ii}, \tilde{p}_{i,i+1}$. This technique can be applied to any ergodic transition probability matrix in which some elements are known to be zero.

An Ergodic Theorem

We now establish that, if $\bar{p}_{ij}^{(n)}(\psi)$ is the mean n-step transition probability defined by Eq. 4.1.1,

$$\lim_{n\to\infty} \bar{p}_{ij}^{(n)}(\psi) = \bar{\pi}_j(\psi), \qquad i, j = 1, \ldots, N, \quad \psi \in \Psi, \tag{4.2.15}$$

where $\bar{\boldsymbol{\pi}}(\psi) = (\bar{\pi}_1(\psi), \ldots, \bar{\pi}_N(\psi))$ is the expected value of $\tilde{\boldsymbol{\pi}}$. The only assumption‡ made about $F(\mathbf{P} \mid \psi)$, the prior distribution function of $\tilde{\mathbf{P}}$, is that $F(\mathbf{P} \mid \psi)$ is continuous on the boundary of $\mathcal{S}_N$. To establish Eq. 4.2.15, it must first be shown that, for any fixed $\alpha \in (0, 1)$, $\lim_{n\to\infty} p_{ij}^{(n)} = \pi_j(\mathbf{P})$ uniformly in $\mathbf{P}$ on $\mathcal{S}_N^\alpha$. This is the content of the following two lemmas.

† Singer [39]. This result was apparently first discovered by Mihoc in 1934 in his doctoral thesis (Rumanian); see Rosenblatt [34].

‡ This result can be proved under the weaker condition that the set of nonergodic matrices in $\mathcal{S}_N$ is a set of measure zero, using the bounded convergence theorem of measure theory. The proof given here brings out some interesting features of the convergence of $p_{ij}^{(n)}$ to $\pi_j(\mathbf{P})$ on $\mathcal{S}_N^*$ and does not require a knowledge of measure theory.

Lemma 4.2.3. For some fixed $\alpha \in (0, 1)$ let

$$\Delta(\mathbf{P}) = \min_{i,j} \{p_{ij}\}, \qquad \mathbf{P} \in \mathcal{S}_N^\alpha \tag{4.2.16}$$

be a function of $\mathbf{P}$ on $\mathcal{S}_N^\alpha$. Then $\Delta(\mathbf{P})$ is continuous on $\mathcal{S}_N^\alpha$.

Proof. Let $\epsilon > 0$ be given. It must be shown that, for any fixed $\mathbf{P} \in \mathcal{S}_N^\alpha$, there exists a $\delta > 0$ such that $|\Delta(\mathbf{P}) - \Delta(\mathbf{Q})| < \epsilon$ whenever $\mathbf{Q} \in \mathcal{S}_N^\alpha$ and $\|\mathbf{P} - \mathbf{Q}\| < \delta$. Let

$$p_{\underline{ij}} = \min_{i,j} \{p_{ij}\}$$

and

$$\epsilon' = p_{km} - p_{\underline{ij}} > 0, \tag{4.2.17}$$

where p_{km} is the smallest element of $\mathbf{P}$ not equal to $p_{\underline{ij}}$ (assuming, for the moment, that such an element exists). Choose $\delta = \min [\epsilon, \epsilon'/2]$. Then, for any $\mathbf{Q} \in \mathcal{S}_N^\alpha$, if $\|\mathbf{P} - \mathbf{Q}\| < \delta$, we have

$$|p_{ij} - q_{ij}| < \delta \leqslant \epsilon'/2, \qquad i, j = 1, \ldots, N,$$

and

$$p_{ij} - \epsilon'/2 < q_{ij} < p_{ij} + \epsilon'/2, \qquad i, j = 1, \ldots, N. \tag{4.2.18}$$

Let

$$S_{\underline{ij}} = \{(i, j) \mid p_{ij} \neq p_{\underline{ij}}, i, j = 1, \ldots, N\}, \tag{4.2.19}$$

assumed, for the moment, to be nonempty. Then, using Eq. 4.2.17 and the definition of p_{km},

$$p_{\underline{ij}} = p_{km} - \epsilon' \leqslant p_{ij} - \epsilon', \qquad (i, j) \in S_{\underline{ij}}. \tag{4.2.20}$$

Thus, by Eq. 4.2.18,

$$q_{\underline{ij}} < p_{\underline{ij}} + \frac{\epsilon'}{2} \leqslant p_{ij} - \frac{\epsilon'}{2} < q_{ij}, \qquad (i,j) \in S_{\underline{ij}}. \tag{4.2.21}$$

If $q_{\beta\gamma} = \min_{i,j} \{q_{ij}\}$, Eq. 4.2.21 implies that $(\beta, \gamma) \notin S_{\underline{ij}}$, and, therefore, that $p_{\underline{ij}} = p_{\beta\gamma}$. Thus,

$$|\Delta(\mathbf{P}) - \Delta(\mathbf{Q})| = |p_{\beta\gamma} - q_{\beta\gamma}| < \delta \leqslant \epsilon. \tag{4.2.22}$$

Suppose now that there is no smallest element of $\mathbf{P}$ not equal to $p_{\underline{ij}}$. Then $S_{\underline{ij}}$ is empty and $p_{ij} = 1/N$ $(i, j = 1, \ldots, N)$. Choosing $\delta = \epsilon$, $\|\mathbf{P} - \mathbf{Q}\| < \delta$ implies that

$$\left| \frac{1}{N} - q_{ij} \right| < \epsilon, \qquad i, j = 1, \ldots, N, \tag{4.2.23}$$

and, hence, that

$$|\Delta(\mathbf{P}) - \Delta(\mathbf{Q})| < \epsilon, \tag{4.2.24}$$

proving the lemma. Q.E.D.

Lemma 4.2.4. Let $\alpha \in (0, 1)$ be fixed. Then, for $i, j = 1, \ldots, N$,

$$\lim_{n\to\infty} p_{ij}^{(n)} = \pi_j(\mathbf{P}) \tag{4.2.25}$$

uniformly in $\mathbf{P}$ on $\mathcal{S}_N^\alpha$.

Proof. Let $\epsilon > 0$ be given. It must be shown that there exists a positive integer ν_α such that, if $n > \nu_\alpha$,

$$|p_{ij}^{(n)} - \pi_j(\mathbf{P})| < \epsilon \tag{4.2.26}$$

for all $\mathbf{P} \in \mathcal{S}_N^\alpha$. This will be done by showing that the sequence of functions $\{|p_{ij}^{(n)} - \pi_j(\mathbf{P})|\}$ is bounded by a sequence of functions of $\mathbf{P}$ which goes to zero uniformly on $\mathcal{S}_N^\alpha$ as $n \to \infty$. Define the functions

$$\Delta(\mathbf{P}) = \min_{i,j} \{p_{ij}\}, \qquad \mathbf{P} \in \mathcal{S}_N^\alpha \tag{4.2.27}$$

and

$$d_n(\mathbf{P}) = [1 - 2\,\Delta(\mathbf{P})]^n, \qquad n = 1, 2, \ldots, \quad \mathbf{P} \in \mathcal{S}_N. \tag{4.2.28}$$

Since $0 < \Delta(\mathbf{P}) \leqslant \frac{1}{2}$ for any $\mathbf{P} \in \mathcal{S}_N^\alpha$,

$$0 \leqslant 1 - 2\,\Delta(\mathbf{P}) < 1, \qquad \mathbf{P} \in \mathcal{S}_N^\alpha, \tag{4.2.29}$$

and

$$d_n(\mathbf{P}) \geqslant d_{n+1}(\mathbf{P}), \qquad n = 1, 2, \ldots, \quad \mathbf{P} \in \mathcal{S}_N^\alpha. \tag{4.2.30}$$

By Lemma 4.2.3 and Eqs. 4.2.29 and 4.2.30, $\{d_n(\mathbf{P})\}$ is a monotonically decreasing sequence of functions that are continuous on the compact set $\mathcal{S}_N^\alpha$, the sequence converging to the continuous function zero. Therefore,† $\{d_n(\mathbf{P})\} \to 0$ uniformly on $\mathcal{S}_N^\alpha$. It is easily established‡ that

$$|p_{ij}^{(n)} - \pi_j(\mathbf{P})| \leqslant d_n(\mathbf{P}), \qquad n = 1, 2, \ldots, \quad \mathbf{P} \in \mathcal{S}_N. \tag{4.2.31}$$

By choosing a positive integer ν_α such that $0 \leqslant d_n(\mathbf{P}) < \epsilon$ for all $n > \nu_\alpha$ and $\mathbf{P} \in \mathcal{S}_N^\alpha$, Eq. 4.2.26 is obtained. Q.E.D.

Theorem 4.2.5. Let $F(\mathbf{P} \mid \psi)$ be the prior distribution function of the random $N \times N$ stochastic matrix $\tilde{\mathbf{P}}$ and let

$$\bar{p}_{ij}^{(n)}(\psi) = \int_{\mathcal{S}_N} p_{ij}^{(n)}\, dF(\mathbf{P} \mid \psi),$$
$$i, j = 1, \ldots, N, \quad n = 1, 2, \ldots, \quad \psi \in \Psi, \tag{4.2.32}$$

$$\bar{\pi}_j(\psi) = \int_{\mathcal{S}_N} \pi_j(\mathbf{P})\, dF(\mathbf{P} \mid \psi),$$
$$= 1, \ldots, N, \quad \psi \in \Psi. \tag{4.2.33}$$

† Rudin [35], p. 136.
‡ Kemeny and Snell [26], p. 71.

Then, if $F(\mathbf{P} \mid \psi)$ is continuous on the boundary of $\mathcal{S}_N$,

$$\lim_{n\to\infty} \bar{p}_{ij}^{(n)}(\psi) = \bar{\pi}_j(\psi), \qquad i, j = 1, \ldots, N, \quad \psi \in \Psi. \tag{4.2.34}$$

Proof. Let $\epsilon > 0$ be given. For any $\alpha \in (0, 1)$,

$$|\bar{p}_{ij}^{(n)}(\psi) - \bar{\pi}_j(\psi)| \leqslant \int_{\mathcal{S}_N^\alpha} |p_{ij}^{(n)} - \pi_j(\mathbf{P})| \, dF(\mathbf{P} \mid \psi) + \int_{\mathcal{S}_N - \mathcal{S}_N^\alpha} |p_{ij}^{(n)} - \pi_j(\mathbf{P})| \, dF(\mathbf{P} \mid \psi). \tag{4.2.35}$$

Let $C_{km}(\alpha)$ be defined by Eq. 4.2.6 and let $F_{km}(p \mid \psi)$ be the marginal distribution function of $\tilde{p}_{km}$. Then, noting that $|p_{ij}^{(n)} - \pi_j(\mathbf{P})| \leqslant 1$ and using 4.2.7, the second integral of Eq. 4.2.35 has the bound

$$\int_{\mathcal{S}_N - \mathcal{S}_N^\alpha} |p_{ij}^{(n)} - \pi_j(\mathbf{P})| \, dF(\mathbf{P} \mid \psi) \leqslant \sum_{\substack{k=1 \\ m=1}}^{N} F_{km}(\alpha \mid \psi), \qquad 0 < \alpha < 1. \tag{4.2.36}$$

Since $F(\mathbf{P} \mid \psi)$ is continuous on the boundary of $\mathcal{S}_N$, there is an $\alpha' \in (0, 1)$ and a set $S(\alpha')$ satisfying Eq. 4.2.5 such that $F(\mathbf{P} \mid \psi)$ is continuous on $S(\alpha')$. In Eq. 4.2.35 let $\alpha < \alpha'$ be chosen such that $F_{km}(\alpha \mid \psi) < \epsilon/2N^2$ for $k, m = 1, \ldots, N$. Then

$$\int_{\mathcal{S}_N - \mathcal{S}_N^\alpha} |p_{ij}^{(n)} - \pi_j(\mathbf{P})| \, dF(\mathbf{P} \mid \psi) < \frac{\epsilon}{2}, \qquad n = 1, 2, \ldots. \tag{4.2.37}$$

Having fixed α, choose a positive integer ν_α such that

$$|p_{ij}^{(n)} - \pi_j(\mathbf{P})| < \frac{\epsilon}{2}$$

for all $n > \nu_\alpha$ and all $\mathbf{P} \in \mathcal{S}_N^\alpha$. Then

$$\int_{\mathcal{S}_N^\alpha} |p_{ij}^{(n)} - \pi_j(\mathbf{P})| \, dF(\mathbf{P} \mid \psi) < \frac{\epsilon}{2}, \qquad n > \nu_\alpha \tag{4.2.38}$$

and Eqs. 4.2.35, 4.2.37, and 4.2.38 yield

$$|\bar{p}_{ij}^{(n)}(\psi) - \bar{\pi}_j(\psi)| < \epsilon, \qquad n > \nu_\alpha. \tag{4.2.39}$$

Q.E.D.

Theorem 4.2.5 shows that we can approximate $\bar{\pi}_j(\psi)$ by $\bar{p}_{ij}^{(n)}(\psi)$ with the use of Eq. 4.1.2. A recursive program was written to carry out this approximation when $\tilde{\mathbf{P}}$ has a matrix beta distribution.† Some sample computations of $E[\tilde{\mathbf{P}}^n \mid \mathcal{M}]$ are displayed in Tables 4.2.1 through 4.2.3.

† See Appendix C for the MAD program listing.

We have shown at the base of each table the parameter $\mathcal{M}$ of the prior distribution of $\tilde{\mathbf{P}}$ and the mean $\overline{\mathbf{P}}$ of this distribution. The matrix $\mathbf{V}(\tilde{\mathbf{P}})$ which appears below the table has as its (i, j)th element the prior variance of $\tilde{p}_{ij}$. Silver [38] has conjectured that $\overline{\boldsymbol{\pi}}(\psi)$ can be approximated reasonably well by $\boldsymbol{\pi}(\overline{\mathbf{P}})$, the steady-state probability vector corresponding to

TABLE 4.2.1

n	$E[\tilde{\mathbf{P}}^n \mid \mathcal{M}]$
1	$\begin{bmatrix} 0.93454 & 0.06546 \\ 0.86357 & 0.13643 \end{bmatrix}$
2	$\begin{bmatrix} 0.93370 & 0.06630 \\ 0.92027 & 0.07973 \end{bmatrix}$
3	$\begin{bmatrix} 0.93297 & 0.06703 \\ 0.93096 & 0.06904 \end{bmatrix}$
4	$\begin{bmatrix} 0.93296 & 0.06704 \\ 0.93244 & 0.06756 \end{bmatrix}$
5	$\begin{bmatrix} 0.93293 & 0.06707 \\ 0.93283 & 0.06717 \end{bmatrix}$
6	$\begin{bmatrix} 0.93293 & 0.06707 \\ 0.93290 & 0.06710 \end{bmatrix}$
7	$\begin{bmatrix} 0.93293 & 0.06707 \\ 0.93292 & 0.06708 \end{bmatrix}$
8	$\begin{bmatrix} 0.93293 & 0.06707 \\ 0.93293 & 0.06707 \end{bmatrix}$

$$\mathcal{M} = \begin{bmatrix} 14.105 & 0.988 \\ 21.313 & 3.367 \end{bmatrix} \qquad \overline{\mathbf{P}} = \begin{bmatrix} 0.93454 & 0.06546 \\ 0.86357 & 0.13643 \end{bmatrix}$$

$$\boldsymbol{\pi}(\overline{\mathbf{P}}) = (0.92954 \quad 0.07046) \qquad \mathbf{V}(\tilde{\mathbf{P}}) = \begin{bmatrix} 0.0038 & 0.0038 \\ 0.0048 & 0.0048 \end{bmatrix}$$

Computation time—0.70 minute.

$\overline{\mathbf{P}}(\mathcal{M})$, the mean of the prior distribution. This approximation is also given with each table. All work was performed on an IBM 7094 computer.

In Table 4.2.1, where a 2 × 2 transition matrix is considered, it is seen that $\bar{\pi}_j(\mathcal{M})$ is obtained with three-phase accuracy for $n = 5$ and with five-place accuracy for $n = 8$. In this instance, $\bar{p}_{ij}^{(n)}(\mathcal{M})$ converges monotonically to $\bar{\pi}_j(\mathcal{M})$. The total time required to compute the eight entries of Table 4.2.1 was 0.70 minutes.

In Table 4.2.2, a 2 × 2 transition matrix is treated which has prior

TABLE 4.2.2

n	$E[\tilde{\mathbf{P}}^n \mid \mathcal{M}]$
1	$\begin{bmatrix} 0.41625 & 0.58375 \\ 0.35521 & 0.64479 \end{bmatrix}$
2	$\begin{bmatrix} 0.53220 & 0.46780 \\ 0.29321 & 0.70679 \end{bmatrix}$
3	$\begin{bmatrix} 0.43070 & 0.56930 \\ 0.38086 & 0.61914 \end{bmatrix}$
4	$\begin{bmatrix} 0.47832 & 0.52168 \\ 0.34743 & 0.65257 \end{bmatrix}$
5	$\begin{bmatrix} 0.43084 & 0.56916 \\ 0.39157 & 0.60843 \end{bmatrix}$
6	$\begin{bmatrix} 0.45896 & 0.54104 \\ 0.36973 & 0.63027 \end{bmatrix}$
7	$\begin{bmatrix} 0.42989 & 0.57011 \\ 0.39759 & 0.60241 \end{bmatrix}$
8	$\begin{bmatrix} 0.44918 & 0.55082 \\ 0.38179 & 0.61821 \end{bmatrix}$
9	$\begin{bmatrix} 0.42895 & 0.57105 \\ 0.40150 & 0.59850 \end{bmatrix}$
10	$\begin{bmatrix} 0.44333 & 0.55667 \\ 0.38931 & 0.61069 \end{bmatrix}$
11	$\begin{bmatrix} 0.42815 & 0.57185 \\ 0.40424 & 0.59576 \end{bmatrix}$
12	$\begin{bmatrix} 0.43945 & 0.56055 \\ 0.39445 & 0.60555 \end{bmatrix}$
13	$\begin{bmatrix} 0.42749 & 0.57251 \\ 0.40629 & 0.59371 \end{bmatrix}$

$$\mathcal{M} = \begin{bmatrix} 0.251 & 0.352 \\ 0.616 & 1.120 \end{bmatrix} \qquad \bar{\mathbf{P}} = \begin{bmatrix} 0.41625 & 0.58375 \\ 0.35521 & 0.64479 \end{bmatrix}$$

$$\pi(\bar{\mathbf{P}}) = (0.37830 \quad 0.62170) \qquad \mathbf{V}(\tilde{\mathbf{P}}) = \begin{bmatrix} 0.1516 & 0.1516 \\ 0.0837 & 0.0837 \end{bmatrix}$$

Computation time—5.75 minutes.

variances that are larger than those of the matrix considered in Table 4.2.1. In this instance, convergence of $\bar{p}_{ij}^{(n)}(\mathcal{M})$ to $\bar{\pi}_j(\mathcal{M})$ is much slower and is not monotonic. For $n = 13$, $\bar{p}_{11}^{(n)}(\mathcal{M})$ and $p_{21}^{(n)}(\mathcal{M})$ agree only in the first decimal place. The 13 entries of this table took a total of 5.75 minutes to compute.

Some sample computations for a three-state process are shown in Table 4.2.3. Five minutes were required to compute the first eight entries

TABLE 4.2.3

n	$E[\tilde{\mathbf{P}}^n \mid \mathcal{M}]$
2	$\begin{bmatrix} 0.60196 & 0.21244 & 0.18560 \\ 0.19754 & 0.55168 & 0.25078 \\ 0.19297 & 0.32211 & 0.48492 \end{bmatrix}$
4	$\begin{bmatrix} 0.45155 & 0.29867 & 0.24978 \\ 0.27054 & 0.43724 & 0.29222 \\ 0.26785 & 0.36814 & 0.36401 \end{bmatrix}$
6	$\begin{bmatrix} 0.38841 & 0.33563 & 0.27596 \\ 0.30102 & 0.39882 & 0.30016 \\ 0.29958 & 0.37440 & 0.32602 \end{bmatrix}$
8	$\begin{bmatrix} 0.35970 & 0.35256 & 0.28774 \\ 0.31487 & 0.38373 & 0.30140 \\ 0.31410 & 0.37405 & 0.31185 \end{bmatrix}$
9	$\begin{bmatrix} 0.35155 & 0.35691 & 0.29154 \\ 0.31896 & 0.37371 & 0.30733 \\ 0.31802 & 0.38094 & 0.30104 \end{bmatrix}$

$$\mathcal{M} = \begin{bmatrix} 18.265 & 2.102 & 3.910 \\ 2.385 & 5.168 & 10.111 \\ 1.005 & 7.612 & 1.212 \end{bmatrix}$$

$$\overline{\mathbf{P}} = \begin{bmatrix} 0.75236 & 0.08658 & 0.16106 \\ 0.13502 & 0.29257 & 0.57241 \\ 0.10225 & 0.77444 & 0.12331 \end{bmatrix}$$

$$\pi(\overline{\mathbf{P}}) = (0.32697 \quad 0.37084 \quad 0.30219)$$

$$\mathbf{V}(\tilde{\mathbf{P}}) = \begin{bmatrix} 0.0074 & 0.0031 & 0.0053 \\ 0.0063 & 0.0111 & 0.0131 \\ 0.0085 & 0.0161 & 0.0100 \end{bmatrix}$$

Computation time—5 minutes ($n = 1, \ldots, 8$);
3.26 minutes ($n = 9$).

in this case. The computation of $E[\tilde{\mathbf{P}}^n \mid \mathcal{M}]$ required 3.26 minutes. Convergence is slow and is not monotonic.

We remark that the computation time of $\bar{p}_{ij}^{(n)}(\mathcal{M})$ increases exponentially with n and linearly with N.

Successive Approximations

The numerical calculation of $\bar{\pi}_j(\psi)$ is a problem of some difficulty. To obtain an explicit formula for $\bar{\pi}_j(\psi)$ in terms of ψ is even more difficult; this general problem has not yet been solved. Silver [38], assuming a matrix beta distribution for $\tilde{\mathbf{P}}$, has calculated $\bar{\pi}_j(\mathcal{M})$ for various parameters $\mathcal{M}$ using Monte Carlo techniques. He has also shown that, for a two-state chain with one row of $\tilde{\mathbf{P}}$ known with certainty and a beta distribution on the other row, the expected value of $\tilde{\pi}_1$ is a gaussian hypergeometric function. This result is generalized in Sec. 8.5, where a series expansion of $\bar{\pi}_1(\mathcal{M})$ is obtained when the 2×2 random matrix $\tilde{\mathbf{P}}$ has the matrix beta distribution with parameter $\mathcal{M}$.

One method of computing $\bar{\pi}_j(\psi)$ is to use the ergodic theorem of the last section. A more general basis for the calculation of $\bar{\pi}_j(\psi)$ is provided in the next theorem.

Theorem 4.2.6. If $\tilde{\mathbf{P}}$ has the distribution function $F(\mathbf{P} \mid \psi) \in \mathcal{F}$, where $\mathcal{F}$ is closed under consecutive sampling and is continuous on the boundary of S_N, then the expectations $\bar{\pi}_j(\psi)$ simultaneously satisfy the functional equations

$$\bar{\pi}_j(\psi) = \sum_{k=1}^{N} \bar{\pi}_k(T_{kj}(\psi))\bar{p}_{kj}(\psi), \qquad j = 1, \ldots, N, \qquad \psi \in \Psi, \quad (4.2.40a)$$

together with

$$\sum_{j=1}^{N} \bar{\pi}_j(\psi) = 1, \qquad \psi \in \Psi, \qquad (4.2.40b)$$

$$\bar{\pi}_j(\psi) \geqslant 0, \qquad j = 1, \ldots, N, \quad \psi \in \Psi. \qquad (4.2.40c)$$

Remark. The condition of Eq. 4.2.40*b* is necessary to ensure a unique solution to Eq. 4.2.40*a*, for, if $\bar{\boldsymbol{\pi}}(\psi)$ satisfies Eq. 4.2.40*a*, $c\bar{\boldsymbol{\pi}}(\psi)$ also satisfies Eq. 4.2.40*a* for all real numbers c. Equation 4.2.40*c* ensures that the solution is a probability vector. These conditions, however, are not sufficient for uniqueness. For example, if $\bar{\mathbf{P}}(\psi)$ is a doubly stochastic matrix, $\bar{\pi}_j(\psi) = 1/N$ ($j = 1, \ldots, N$; $\psi \in \Psi$) satisfies Eq. 4.2.40 but is not generally the mean steady-state probability vector, as is shown by the case in which $\tilde{\mathbf{P}}$ takes on the values

$$\mathbf{P}_1 = \begin{bmatrix} \frac{1}{4} & \frac{3}{4} \\ \frac{1}{3} & \frac{2}{3} \end{bmatrix}, \qquad \mathbf{P}_2 = \begin{bmatrix} \frac{3}{4} & \frac{1}{4} \\ \frac{2}{3} & \frac{1}{3} \end{bmatrix},$$

each with probability $\frac{1}{2}$. In this instance $\overline{\mathbf{P}}$ is doubly stochastic and $\bar{\boldsymbol{\pi}} = (\frac{74}{143}, \frac{69}{143})$. The general problem of determining conditions under which a unique solution exists to Eq. 4.2.40*a* has not yet been solved. One set of sufficient conditions is given in Theorem 4.2.7.

Proof. For $j = 1, \ldots, N$ and $\psi \in \Psi$, using Eq. 4.2.1*a* and Lemma 2.3.2,

$$\begin{aligned}\bar{\pi}_j(\psi) &= \sum_{k=1}^{N} \int_{\mathcal{S}_N} \pi_k(\mathbf{P}) p_{kj}\, dF(\mathbf{P} \mid \psi) \\ &= \sum_{k=1}^{N} \bar{\pi}_k(T_{kj}(\psi))\bar{p}_{kj}(\psi), \qquad (4.2.41)\end{aligned}$$

which is Eq. 4.2.40*a*. Summing Eq. 4.2.33 over j yields Eq. 4.2.40*b*. The integrals involved exist by virtue of Lemma 4.2.1 and the continuity of $\pi_j(\mathbf{P})$ on $\mathcal{S}_N^*$. Equation 4.2.40*c* results since $\pi_j(\mathbf{P}) \geqslant 0$ for all $\mathbf{P} \in \mathcal{S}_N^*$. Q.E.D.

Let the vector function $\bar{\boldsymbol{\pi}}(n, \psi) = (\bar{\pi}_1(n, \psi), \ldots, \bar{\pi}_N(n, \psi))$ be defined by the equations

$$\bar{\pi}_j(n + 1, \psi) = \sum_{k=1}^{N} \bar{\pi}_k(n, T_{kj}(\psi))\bar{p}_{kj}(\psi),$$

$$j = 1, \ldots, N, \quad n = 1, 2, 3, \ldots, \quad \psi \in \Psi, \quad (4.2.42)$$

together with a terminal function $\bar{\boldsymbol{\pi}}(0, \psi) = (\bar{\pi}_1(0, \psi), \ldots, \bar{\pi}_N(0, \psi))$ which satisfies the conditions

$$\bar{\pi}_i(0, \psi) \geqslant 0, \qquad i = 1, \ldots, N, \quad \psi \in \Psi, \qquad (4.2.43a)$$

$$\sum_{i=1}^{N} \bar{\pi}_i(0, \psi) = 1, \qquad \psi \in \Psi. \qquad (4.2.43b)$$

If $\lim_{n\to\infty} \bar{\boldsymbol{\pi}}(n, \psi)$ exists, then this limit satisfies Eqs. 4.2.40*a* and 4.2.40*c*. In general, $C(n, \psi) \equiv \sum_{j=1}^{N} \bar{\pi}_j(n, \psi)$ does not equal unity and, therefore, $\lim_{n\to\infty} C(n, \psi)$ need not equal unity. However, if $\lim_{n\to\infty} \bar{\boldsymbol{\pi}}(n, \psi)$ exists, then $\lim_{n\to\infty} \bar{\boldsymbol{\pi}}(n, \psi)/C(n, \psi)$ exists and satisfies Eqs. 4.2.40*a* through 4.2.40*c*. Necessary conditions for the convergence of $\bar{\boldsymbol{\pi}}(n, \psi)$ have not yet been found; a sufficient condition is given by the following theorem.

Theorem 4.2.7. Let $\tilde{\mathbf{P}}$ have the prior distribution function $F(\mathbf{P} \mid \psi) \in \mathcal{F}$, a family of distributions closed under consecutive sampling which is continuous on the boundary of $\mathcal{S}_N$. Let $\bar{\boldsymbol{\pi}}(n, \psi)$ be defined by Eq. 4.2.42 with the constant terminal functions

$$\bar{\pi}_i(0, \psi) = p_i, \qquad i = 1, \ldots, N; \ \psi \in \Psi, \qquad (4.2.44)$$

where $\boldsymbol{p} = (p_1, \ldots, p_N)$ is a stochastic vector. Then, for $i = 1, \ldots, N$, $\lim_{n\to\infty} \pi_i(n, \psi)$ exists and is equal to $E[\tilde{\pi}_i \mid \psi]$. Moreover,

$$\sum_{i=1}^{N} \lim_{n\to\infty} \pi_i(n, \psi) = 1, \qquad \psi \in \Psi. \tag{4.2.45}$$

Thus, $\lim_{n\to\infty} \bar{\boldsymbol{\pi}}(n, \psi)$ satisfies Eq. 4.2.40.

Proof. The theorem is proved by showing that

$$\bar{\pi}_j(n, \psi) = \sum_{i=1}^{N} p_i \bar{p}_{ij}^{(n)}(\psi),$$
$$j = 1, \ldots, N, \quad n = 1, 2, 3, \ldots, \quad \psi \in \Psi, \tag{4.2.46}$$

from which it follows, by Theorem 4.2.5, that

$$\lim_{n\to\infty} \bar{\pi}_j(n, \psi) = \sum_{i=1}^{N} p_i E[\tilde{\pi}_j \mid \psi] = E[\tilde{\pi}_j \mid \psi],$$
$$j = 1, \ldots, N, \quad \psi \in \Psi. \tag{4.2.47}$$

Equation 4.2.46 is established inductively. For $n = 1$, $\bar{p}_{ij}^{(n)}(\psi) = \bar{p}_{ij}(\psi)$ and Eq. 4.2.46 holds. Assume it is true for n. Then, using Eq. 4.1.2*a*,

$$\begin{aligned}\bar{\pi}_j(n+1, \psi) &= \sum_{k=1}^{N} \bar{\pi}_k(n, T_{kj}(\psi))\bar{p}_{kj}(\psi)\\ &= \sum_{\substack{k=1\\ i=1}}^{N} p_i \bar{p}_{ik}^{(n)}(T_{kj}(\psi))\bar{p}_{kj}(\psi)\\ &= \sum_{i=1}^{N} p_i \bar{p}_{ij}^{(n+1)}(\psi),\end{aligned} \tag{4.2.48}$$

proving the assertion. From Eq. 4.2.46 it is clear that $\bar{\pi}_j(n, \psi) \geqslant 0$ ($j = 1, \ldots, N$; $n = 1, 2, \ldots$; $\psi \in \Psi$). Summing Eq. 4.2.46 over j, we have $\sum_{j=1}^{N} \bar{\pi}_j(n, \psi) = 1$ ($n = 1, 2, \ldots$; $\psi \in \Psi$), since

$$\sum_{j=1}^{N} \bar{p}_{ij}^{(n)}(\psi) = \int_{S_N} \sum_{j=1}^{N} p_{ij}^{(n)}\, dF(\mathbf{P} \mid \psi) = 1,$$
$$i = 1, \ldots, N, \quad n = 1, 2, \ldots, \quad \psi \in \Psi. \tag{4.2.49}$$

Q.E.D.

By letting $p_i = \delta_{ik}$ for some fixed index k, Eq. 4.2.46 becomes

$$\bar{\pi}_j(n, \psi) = \bar{p}_{kj}^{(n)}(\psi),$$
$$j = 1, \ldots, N, \quad n = 1, 2, 3, \ldots, \quad \psi \in \Psi, \tag{4.2.50}$$

and it is seen that the approximation of $\bar{\pi}_j(\psi)$ by $\bar{p}_{kj}^{(n)}(\psi)$ is a special case of the method of successive approximations defined by Eqs. 4.2.42 and 4.2.44.

Another approximation of interest is based on Eq. 4.2.42 and the terminal function $\bar{\boldsymbol{\pi}}(0, \psi)$ defined by

$$\bar{\pi}_i(0, \psi) = \pi_i(\bar{\mathbf{P}}(\psi)), \qquad i = 1, \ldots, N, \quad \psi \in \Psi, \qquad (4.2.51)$$

where $\boldsymbol{\pi}(\bar{\mathbf{P}}(\psi))$ is the steady-state probability vector corresponding to

TABLE 4.2.4

n	$\bar{\boldsymbol{\pi}}(n, \mathcal{M})$	$C(n, \mathcal{M})$	$\frac{1}{C(n, \mathcal{M})}\bar{\boldsymbol{\pi}}(n, \mathcal{M})$
1	(0.93301 0.06724)	1.00025	(0.93278 0.06722)
2	(0.93311 0.06713)	1.00024	(0.93289 0.06711)
3	(0.93313 0.06710)	1.00023	(0.93292 0.06708)
4	(0.93311 0.06709)	1.00020	(0.93292 0.06708)
5	(0.93310 0.06709)	1.00019	(0.93292 0.06708)
6	(0.93308 0.06709)	1.00017	(0.93292 0.06708)
7	(0.93307 0.06708)	1.00015	(0.93293 0.06707)
8	(0.93306 0.06708)	1.00014	(0.93293 0.06707)

$$\mathcal{M} = \begin{bmatrix} 14.105 & 0.988 \\ 21.313 & 3.367 \end{bmatrix} \qquad \bar{\mathbf{P}} = \begin{bmatrix} 0.93454 & 0.06546 \\ 0.86357 & 0.13643 \end{bmatrix}$$

$$\mathbf{V}(\tilde{\mathbf{P}}) = \begin{bmatrix} 0.0038 & 0.0038 \\ 0.0048 & 0.0048 \end{bmatrix}$$

Computation time—0.62 minute.

$\bar{\mathbf{P}}(\psi)$, the mean of the distribution function $F(\mathbf{P} \mid \psi)$. We have not been able to prove convergence of $\bar{\boldsymbol{\pi}}(n, \psi)$ in this case, but limited computational experience with this approximation, using a matrix beta prior distribution, suggests that convergence does occur, and in some case, is more rapid than the convergence of $\bar{p}_{kj}^{(n)}(\psi)$.

Some numerical results based on the recursive programming of Eq. 4.2.42 with the terminal functions of Eq. 4.2.51 are displayed in Tables 4.2.4 through 4.2.6. A matrix beta prior distribution was used in all cases. The MAD computer program is given in Appendix D.

A two-state process is considered in Table 4.2.4. The transition matrix has the same prior distribution as was used to compute Table 4.2.1, where it was seen that $\bar{\boldsymbol{\pi}}(\mathcal{M}) = (0.93293 \quad 0.06707)$. In Table 4.2.4 the approximation $\bar{\pi}(n, \mathcal{M})$ defined by Eq. 4.2.42 is given in column 2 and the normalizing constant $C(n, \mathcal{M}) = \bar{\pi}_1(n, \mathcal{M}) + \bar{\pi}_2(n, \mathcal{M})$ is given in column 3. In column 4 it is seen that $\lim_{n\to\infty} [1/C(n, \mathcal{M})]\bar{\pi}(n, \mathcal{M}) = \bar{\pi}(\mathcal{M})$ with three-place accuracy on the first iteration and four-place accuracy on the second iteration. The eight entries of Table 4.2.4 required 0.62 minute of computation time on an IBM 7094 machine.

TABLE 4.2.5

n	$\bar{\pi}(n, \mathcal{M})$	$C(n, \mathcal{M})$	$\frac{1}{C(n, \mathcal{M})}\bar{\pi}(n, \mathcal{M})$
1	(0.43377 0.63815)	1.07192	(0.40467 0.59533)
2	(0.44423 0.62777)	1.07200	(0.41439 0.58561)
3	(0.44447 0.62433)	1.06880	(0.41586 0.58414)
4	(0.44443 0.61940)	1.06383	(0.41776 0.58224)
5	(0.44308 0.61632)	1.05940	(0.41824 0.58176)
6	(0.44211 0.61317)	1.05528	(0.41895 0.58105)
7	(0.44088 0.61082)	1.05170	(0.41921 0.58079)
8	(0.43992 0.60858)	1.04850	(0.41957 0.58043)
9	(0.43890 0.60679)	1.04569	(0.41972 0.58028)
10	(0.43808 0.60511)	1.04319	(0.41994 0.58006)
11	(0.43725 0.60370)	1.04095	(0.42005 0.57995)
12	(0.43656 0.60238)	1.03894	(0.42020 0.57980)
13	(0.43588 0.60124)	1.03712	(0.42028 0.57972)
14	(0.43529 0.60018)	1.03547	(0.42038 0.57962)

$$\mathcal{M} = \begin{bmatrix} 0.251 & 0.352 \\ 0.616 & 1.120 \end{bmatrix} \qquad \bar{\mathbf{P}} = \begin{bmatrix} 0.41625 & 0.58375 \\ 0.35521 & 0.64479 \end{bmatrix}$$

$$\mathbf{V}(\tilde{\mathbf{P}}) = \begin{bmatrix} 0.1516 & 0.1516 \\ 0.0837 & 0.0837 \end{bmatrix}$$

Computation time—5.03 minutes ($n = 1, \ldots, 12$);
15.03 minutes ($n = 13, 14$).

In Table 4.2.5, a 2×2 transition matrix is treated which has the same prior distribution as the matrix considered in Table 4.2.2. This is a relatively loose prior distribution, and it is seen that convergence of $[1/C(n, \mathcal{M})]\bar{\pi}(n, \mathcal{M})$ is slow, although comparison with Table 4.2.2 indicates that this approximation has smaller error than the approximation $\bar{p}_{ij}^{(n)}(\mathcal{M})$. The first 12 iterations required a total of 5.03 minutes, while iterations 13 and 14 consumed 15.03 minutes, illustrating the exponential growth of the computation time with n.

A 3×3 transition matrix which has the same prior distribution used in computing Table 4.2.3 is considered in Table 4.2.6. In this case, $[1/C(n, \mathcal{M})]\bar{\pi}(n, \mathcal{M})$ again converges faster than the approximation $\bar{p}_{ij}^{(n)}(\mathcal{M})$. Two place accuracy is achieved on the first iteration, with three-place accuracy on the third iteration. The computation time for the first seven entries was 2.15 minutes; the time for entries eight and nine is not available.

TABLE 4.2.6

n	$\bar{\pi}(n, \mathcal{M})$	$C(n, \mathcal{M})$	$\frac{1}{C(n, \mathcal{M})}\bar{\pi}(n, \mathcal{M})$
1	(0.32841 0.37234 0.30058)	1.00133	(0.32797 0.37185 0.30018)
2	(0.32915 0.37145 0.30142)	1.00202	(0.32849 0.37070 0.30081)
3	(0.32963 0.37185 0.30100)	1.00248	(0.32881 0.37093 0.30026)
4	(0.32990 0.37160 0.30123)	1.00273	(0.32900 0.37059 0.30041)
5	(0.33007 0.37171 0.30110)	1.00288	(0.32912 0.37064 0.30024)
6	(0.33017 0.37162 0.30117)	1.00296	(0.32920 0.37052 0.30028)
7	(0.33023 0.37164 0.30112)	1.00299	(0.32924 0.37054 0.30022)
8	(0.33025 0.37160 0.30113)	1.00298	(0.32927 0.37050 0.30023)
9	(0.33026 0.37160 0.30110)	1.00296	(0.32929 0.37050 0.30021)

$$\mathcal{M} = \begin{bmatrix} 18.265 & 2.102 & 3.910 \\ 2.385 & 5.168 & 10.111 \\ 1.005 & 7.612 & 1.212 \end{bmatrix}$$

$$\bar{\mathbf{P}} = \begin{bmatrix} 0.75236 & 0.08658 & 0.16106 \\ 0.13502 & 0.29257 & 0.57241 \\ 0.10225 & 0.77444 & 0.12331 \end{bmatrix}$$

$$\mathbf{V}(\tilde{\mathbf{P}}) = \begin{bmatrix} 0.0074 & 0.0031 & 0.0053 \\ 0.0063 & 0.0111 & 0.0131 \\ 0.0085 & 0.0161 & 0.0100 \end{bmatrix}$$

Computation time—2.15 minutes ($n = 1, \ldots, 7$).

Variance-Covariance Matrix of $\tilde{\pi}$

Let

$$\bar{\pi}_{ij}(\psi) = \int_{\mathcal{S}_N} \pi_i(\mathbf{P})\pi_j(\mathbf{P})\, dF(\mathbf{P} \mid \psi), \qquad i, j = 1, \ldots, N, \quad \psi \in \Psi \tag{4.2.52}$$

be the expected value of $\tilde{\pi}_i\tilde{\pi}_j$ when $\tilde{\mathbf{P}}$ has the distribution function $F(\mathbf{P} \mid \psi)$. If $F(\mathbf{P} \mid \psi)$ is continuous on the boundary of $\mathcal{S}_N$, Theorem 4.2.2 implies the existence of the integral in Eq. 4.2.52. If $F(\mathbf{P} \mid \psi) \in \mathcal{F}$, a family of distributions continuous in ψ, then Theorem 2.4.3 implies that $\bar{\pi}_{ij}(\psi)$ is a continuous function of ψ. The following extension of Theorem 4.2.5 shows that $\bar{\pi}_{ij}(\psi)$ can be approximated by $E[\tilde{p}_{\alpha i}^{(n)}\tilde{p}_{\beta j}^{(\nu)} \mid \psi]$.

Theorem 4.2.8. If the prior distribution function of $\tilde{\mathbf{P}}$ is $F(\mathbf{P} \mid \psi) \in \mathcal{F}$, a family of distributions continuous on the boundary of $\mathcal{S}_N$, then

$$\lim_{\substack{n\to\infty\\ \nu\to\infty}} E[\tilde{p}_{\alpha i}^{(n)}\tilde{p}_{\beta j}^{(\nu)} \mid \psi] = \bar{\pi}_{ij}(\psi), \qquad \alpha, \beta, i, j = 1, \ldots, N, \quad \psi \in \Psi. \tag{4.2.53}$$

Proof. Let $\epsilon > 0$ be given. By Lemma 4.2.4, $\{p_{\alpha i}^{(n)}p_{\beta j}^{(\nu)}\} \to \pi_i(\mathbf{P})\pi_j(\mathbf{P})$ uniformly on $\mathcal{S}_N^\alpha$ for any $\alpha \in (0, 1)$. Arguing as in the proof of Theorem 4.2.5, we may choose n and ν sufficiently large and $\alpha > 0$ sufficiently small so that

$$\left| E[\tilde{p}_{\alpha i}^{(n)}\tilde{p}_{\beta j}^{(\nu)} \mid \psi] - \bar{\pi}_{ij}(\psi) \right| < \epsilon, \tag{4.2.54}$$

proving the theorem. Q.E.D.

The following theorem provides a basis for successive approximations to $\bar{\pi}_{ij}(\psi)$ similar to that developed on p. 72ff.

Theorem 4.2.9. If the prior distribution function of $\tilde{\mathbf{P}}$ is $F(\mathbf{P} \mid \psi) \in \mathcal{F}$, a family of distributions continuous on the boundary of $\mathcal{S}_N$ which is closed under consecutive sampling, then the product moment $\bar{\pi}_{ij}(\psi)$ satisfies the following functional equations:

$$\bar{\pi}_{ij}(\psi) = \sum_{\substack{k=1\\ m=1}}^{N} \bar{p}_{ki}(\psi)\bar{p}_{mj}(T_{ki}(\psi))\bar{\pi}_{km}(T_{mj}(T_{ki}(\psi))),$$

$$i, j = 1, \ldots, N, \quad \psi \in \Psi \tag{4.2.55a}$$

$$\sum_{\substack{i=1\\ j=1}}^{N} \bar{\pi}_{ij}(\psi) = 1, \qquad \psi \in \Psi, \tag{4.2.55b}$$

$$\bar{\pi}_{ij}(\psi) \geqslant 0, \qquad i, j = 1, \ldots, N, \quad \psi \in \Psi. \tag{4.2.55c}$$

Remark. The condition in Eq. 4.2.55*b* is necessary to ensure a unique solution to the functional Eq. 4.2.55*a*. Equation 4.2.55*c* insures that the solution is a probability vector. These conditions are not, however, sufficient for uniqueness. See the remark accompanying Theorem 4.2.6.

Proof. Since

$$\pi_i(\mathbf{P})\pi_j(\mathbf{P}) = \sum_{\substack{k=1\\ m=1}}^{N} \pi_k(\mathbf{P})\pi_m(\mathbf{P})p_{ki}p_{mj}, \qquad \mathbf{P} \in \mathcal{S}_N, \tag{4.2.56}$$

Eq. 4.2.55*a* follows from Lemma 2.3.2. Equation 4.2.55*b* follows by summing Eq. 4.2.52 over *i* and *j*. Q.E.D.

Given $\bar{\pi}_{ij}(\psi)$, $\bar{\pi}_i(\psi)$, and $\bar{\pi}_j(\psi)$, the covariance between $\tilde{\pi}_i$ and $\tilde{\pi}_j$ is computed from the relation

$$\operatorname{cov}[\tilde{\pi}_i, \tilde{\pi}_j \mid \psi] = \bar{\pi}_{ij}(\psi) - \bar{\pi}_i(\psi)\bar{\pi}_j(\psi),$$
$$i, j = 1, \ldots, N \quad \psi \in \Psi. \quad (4.2.57)$$

4.3. EXPECTED DISCOUNTED REWARD VECTOR

Consider a Markov chain operated indefinitely under a fixed policy with initial state i. If $\tilde{\mathbf{P}} = \mathbf{P}$, let $V_i(\mathbf{P})$ be the conditional expectation of the total discounted reward earned over an infinite period when the chain starts in state i, and let $V(\mathbf{P}) = (V_1(\mathbf{P}), \ldots, V_N(\mathbf{P}))$ be the corresponding vector of expected discounted rewards. Howard† has shown that, for any $\mathbf{P} \in \mathcal{S}_N$, including periodic and multiple-chain transition matrices,

$$V_i(\mathbf{P}) = \sum_{n=0}^{\infty} \beta^n \sum_{\substack{j=1 \\ k=1}}^{N} p_{ij}^{(n)} p_{jk} r_{jk},$$
$$i = 1, \ldots, N, \quad \mathbf{P} \in \mathcal{S}_N, \quad 0 \leqslant \beta < 1. \quad (4.3.1)$$

When $\tilde{\mathbf{P}}$ is a random matrix, $V(\tilde{\mathbf{P}})$ is a random vector. In this section the mean and the variance-covariance matrix of $V(\tilde{\mathbf{P}})$ are studied and expressions for elements of these unconditional expectations are found. A set of functional equations for the expected value of $V_i(\tilde{\mathbf{P}})$ is derived which is closely related to Eq. 3.2.5, which was discussed in connection with the discounted adaptive control problem. This relation is used to obtain a method of successive approximations for the numerical calculation of the expected value of $V_i(\tilde{\mathbf{P}})$. Some examples are presented on pp. 83–86.

Expected Value of V(P)

Let $\tilde{\mathbf{P}}$ have the prior distribution function $F(\mathbf{P} \mid \psi)$ and let

$$\bar{V}_i(\psi) = \int_{\mathcal{S}_N} V_i(\mathbf{P})\, dF(\mathbf{P} \mid \psi), \qquad i = 1, \ldots, N, \quad \psi \in \Psi, \quad (4.3.2)$$

be the expected value of $V_i(\tilde{\mathbf{P}})$. The first theorem shows that this expectation exists and provides a formula for $\bar{V}_i(\psi)$ in terms of the expected n-step transition probabilities $\bar{p}_{ij}^{(n)}(\psi)$ when the prior distribution belongs to a family closed under consecutive sampling. A preliminary lemma is required.

† See [22], p. 82.

Lemma 4.3.1. If $V_i(\mathbf{P})$ is defined by the infinite series Eq. 4.3.1 with $0 \leqslant \beta < 1$, then the series converges uniformly in $\mathbf{P}$ and $V_i(\mathbf{P})$ is continuous on $\mathcal{S}_N$ $(i = 1, \ldots, N)$.

Proof. For any finite n, the functions

$$w_i(n, \mathbf{P}) = \beta^n \sum_{\substack{j=1\\k=1}}^{N} p_{ij}^{(n)} p_{jk} r_{jk},$$

$$i = 1, \ldots, N, \quad n = 0, 1, 2, \ldots, \quad \mathbf{P} \in \mathcal{S}_N, \quad (4.3.3)$$

are continuous functions of $\mathbf{P}$ on $\mathcal{S}_N$. Moreover, if

$$R^* = \max_{i,j} \{|r_{ij}|\}, \quad (4.3.4)$$

the functions $w_i(n, \mathbf{P})$ are bounded on $\mathcal{S}_N$,

$$|w_i(n, \mathbf{P})| \leqslant R^*\beta^n,$$

$$i = 1, \ldots, N, \quad n = 0, 1, 2, \ldots, \quad \mathbf{P} \in \mathcal{S}_N. \quad (4.3.5)$$

Since

$$\sum_{n=0}^{\infty} R^*\beta^n = \frac{R^*}{1 - \beta} < \infty \quad (4.3.6)$$

for $0 \leqslant \beta < 1$, $\sum_{n=0}^{\infty} w_i(n, \mathbf{P})$ converges uniformly† to $V_i(\mathbf{P})$ on $\mathcal{S}_N$ and $V_i(\mathbf{P})$ is a continuous function of $\mathbf{P}$ on $\mathcal{S}_N$. Q.E.D.

Theorem 4.3.2. Let $\tilde{\mathbf{P}}$ have the prior distribution function $F(\mathbf{P} \mid \psi)$. Then the expectation $\bar{V}_i(\psi)$ defined by Eq. 4.3.2 exists. If $F(\mathbf{P} \mid \psi) \in \mathcal{F}$, a family of distributions closed under the consecutive sampling rule, then

$$\bar{V}_i(\psi) = \sum_{n=0}^{\infty} \beta^n \sum_{\substack{j=1\\k=1}}^{N} \bar{p}_{ij}^{(n)}(T_{jk}(\psi))\bar{p}_{jk}(\psi) r_{jk},$$

$$i = 1, \ldots, N, \quad \psi \in \Psi, \quad 0 \leqslant \beta < 1, \quad (4.3.7)$$

where $\bar{p}_{ij}^{(n)}(T_{jk}(\psi))$ is defined by Eq. 4.1.1.

Proof. The integral of Eq. 4.3.2 exists by virtue of the continuity of the bounded function $V_i(\mathbf{P})$ on $\mathcal{S}_N$. Since the infinite series Eq. 4.3.1 converges uniformly,

$$V_i(\psi) = \sum_{n=0}^{\infty} \beta^n \sum_{\substack{j=1\\k=1}}^{N} r_{jk} \int_{\mathcal{S}_N} p_{ij}^{(n)} p_{jk} \, dF(\mathbf{P} \mid \psi). \quad (4.3.8)$$

If $\mathcal{F}$ is closed under consecutive sampling, Lemma 2.3.2 yields Eq. 4.3.7. Q.E.D.

† See Rudin [35], p. 134.

In the section starting on p. 90 we shall discuss approximations to $\bar{V}_i(\psi)$ which are based on Eq. 4.3.7. The results of the following paragraph provide a different basis for computation of $\bar{V}_i(\psi)$.

A Functional Equation for $\bar{V}(\psi)$

We now relate $\bar{V}_i(\psi)$ to $v_i(\psi)$, the maximum expected discounted reward discussed in connection with the adaptive control problem.

Theorem 4.3.3. If $\tilde{\mathbf{P}}$ has the prior distribution function $F(\mathbf{P} \mid \psi) \in \mathcal{F}$, a family of distributions closed under consecutive sampling, then $\bar{V}(\psi) = (\bar{V}_1(\psi), \ldots, \bar{V}_N(\psi))$ satisfies the following set of simultaneous functional equations:

$$\bar{V}_i(\psi) = \bar{q}_i(\psi) + \beta \sum_{j=1}^{N} \bar{p}_{ij}(\psi)\bar{V}_j(T_{ij}(\psi)),$$
$$i = 1, \ldots, N, \quad \psi \in \Psi, \quad 0 \leqslant \beta < 1, \quad (4.3.9)$$

where $\bar{q}_i(\psi)$, the expected one-step transition reward when in state i, is defined by Eq. 3.2.4.

Proof. Letting

$$q_i(\mathbf{P}) = \sum_{k=1}^{N} p_{ik} r_{ik}, \qquad i = 1, \ldots, N, \quad \mathbf{P} \in \mathcal{S}_N, \qquad (4.3.10)$$

Eq. 4.3.1 can be written as

$$\begin{aligned} V_i(\mathbf{P}) &= \sum_{k=1}^{N} p_{ik} r_{ik} + \beta \sum_{n=0}^{\infty} \beta^n \sum_{\substack{j=1 \\ k=1}}^{N} p_{ij}^{(n+1)} p_{jk} r_{jk} \\ &= q_i(\mathbf{P}) + \beta \sum_{m=1}^{N} p_{im} \sum_{n=0}^{\infty} \beta^n \sum_{\substack{j=1 \\ k=1}}^{N} p_{mj}^{(n)} p_{jk} r_{jk} \\ &= q_i(\mathbf{P}) + \beta \sum_{m=1}^{N} p_{im} V_m(\mathbf{P}), \qquad i = 1, \ldots, N, \quad \mathbf{P} \in \mathcal{S}_N. \qquad (4.3.11) \end{aligned}$$

Thus, changing the index of summation and using Lemma 2.3.2,

$$\begin{aligned} \bar{V}_i(\psi) &= \bar{q}_i(\psi) + \beta \sum_{j=1}^{N} \int_{\mathcal{S}_N} p_{ij} V_j(\mathbf{P})\, dF(\mathbf{P} \mid \psi) \\ &= \bar{q}_i(\psi) + \beta \sum_{j=1}^{N} \bar{p}_{ij}(\psi) \bar{V}_j(T_{ij}(\psi)). \qquad (4.3.12) \end{aligned}$$

Q.E.D.

Equation 4.3.9 has the same form as Eq. 3.2.5 and may be interpreted as a discounted adaptive control equation in which there is exactly one alternative in each state. The results of Secs. 3.2 and 3.3 apply and are summarized in the following theorem which is stated without proof, since the proofs in the more general case of many alternatives in each state are given in Chap. 3.

Theorem 4.3.4. There exists a unique bounded vector function, $\bar{V}(\psi) = (\bar{V}_1(\psi), \ldots, \bar{V}_N(\psi))$, which satisfies Eq. 4.3.9. Let the sequences of functions $\{\bar{V}_i(n, \psi)\}$, $i = 1, \ldots, N$ be defined by the equations

$$\bar{V}_i(n+1, \psi) = \bar{q}_i(\psi) + \beta \sum_{j=1}^{N} \bar{p}_{ij}(\psi) V_j(n, T_{ij}(\psi)),$$

$$i = 1, \ldots, N, \quad n = 0, 1, 2, \ldots, \quad \psi \in \Psi, \quad 0 \leqslant \beta < 1. \quad (4.3.13a)$$

$$\bar{V}_i(0, \psi) = V_i(\psi), \qquad i = 1, \ldots, N, \quad \psi \in \Psi. \qquad (4.3.13b)$$

Then, provided the terminal functions $V_i(\psi)$ are bounded,

$$|V_i(\psi)| \leqslant V, \qquad i = 1, \ldots, N, \quad \psi \in \Psi, \qquad (4.3.14)$$

the sequence $\{\bar{V}_i(n, \psi)\}$ converges uniformly to $\bar{V}_i(\psi)$, the unique bounded solution of Eq. 4.3.9. If the terminal functions are constants,

$$V_i(\psi) = V_i, \qquad i = 1, \ldots, N, \quad \psi \in \Psi, \qquad (4.3.15)$$

and if $V^* = \max_i \{V_i\}$, $v^* = \min_i \{V_i\}$, $R = \max_{i,j} \{r_{ij}\}$, and $r = \min_{i,j} \{r_{ij}\}$, then the error of the nth approximant,

$$\bar{e}_i(n, \psi) = \bar{V}_i(\psi) - \bar{V}_i(n, \psi), \qquad (4.3.16)$$

has the bound

$$|\bar{e}_i(n, \psi)| \leqslant \beta^n \left[\max \left\{ \frac{R}{1-\beta} - v^*, V^* - \frac{r}{1-\beta} \right\} \right],$$

$$i = 1, \ldots, N, \quad n = 0, 1, 2, \ldots, \quad \psi \in \Psi, \quad 0 \leqslant \beta < 1. \quad (4.3.17)$$

If, furthermore,

$$V^* - \beta v^* \leqslant r, \qquad (4.3.18)$$

then $\{\bar{V}_i(n, \psi)\}$ is a monotone increasing sequence with limit $\bar{V}_i(\psi)$ and the bound of Eq. 4.3.17 becomes

$$0 \leqslant \bar{e}_i(n, \psi) \leqslant \beta^n \left(\frac{R}{1-\beta} - v^* \right),$$

$$i = 1, \ldots, N, \quad n = 0, 1, 2, \ldots, \quad \psi \in \Psi, \quad 0 \leqslant \beta < 1. \quad (4.3.19)$$

If

$$v^* - \beta V^* \geqslant R, \qquad (4.3.20)$$

then $\{\bar{V}_i(n, \psi)\}$ is a monotone decreasing sequence with limit $\bar{V}_i(\psi)$ and

$$\beta^n \left[\frac{r}{1-\beta} - V^* \right] \leqslant \bar{e}_i(n, \psi) \leqslant 0,$$

$$i = 1, \ldots, N, \quad n = 0, 1, 2, \ldots, \quad \psi \in \Psi, \quad 0 \leqslant \beta < 1. \quad (4.3.21)$$

Numerical Example

To illustrate the above results, some sample computations based on Eq. 4.3.13 are displayed in Tables 4.3.1 through 4.3.4.† These tables contain values of

$$\bar{V}(n, \mathcal{M}) = \begin{bmatrix} \bar{V}_1(n, \mathcal{M}) \\ \bar{V}_2(n, \mathcal{M}) \end{bmatrix}$$

under various policies in a two-state Markov chain with two alternatives in each state when $\tilde{\mathbf{P}}$ has a matrix beta distribution. The discount factor

TABLE 4.3.1

n	$\bar{V}(n, \mathcal{M})$	$\bar{e}(n, \mathcal{M})$	$\Delta(n)$
0	9.660 5.596	0.334 −0.052	11.904
1	9.663 5.596	0.331 −0.052	2.381
2	9.936 5.549	0.058 −0.005	0.476
3	9.982 5.544	0.012 0.000	0.095
4	9.991 5.544	0.003 0.000	0.019
5	9.993 5.544	0.001 0.000	0.004
6	9.993 5.544	0.001 0.000	0.001
7	9.994 5.544	0.000 0.000	0.000
8	9.994 5.544	0.000 0.000	0.000
9	9.994 5.544	0.000 0.000	0.000

Policy: (1, 1) $\quad \bar{V}(0, \mathcal{M}) = \begin{bmatrix} 9.660 \\ 5.596 \end{bmatrix}$

Computation time—0.56 minute.
$\beta = 0.2$

† See Appendix E for the MAD computer program listing.

is $\beta = 0.2$. The reward matrix and the prior distribution are the same as those used in computing Tables 3.6.1 through 3.6.3 for the adaptive control problem (see Eqs. 3.6.1 through 3.6.4). For each of the four possible policies $\boldsymbol{\sigma}$, the terminal functions are given by

$$\bar{V}_i(0, \mathcal{M}) = V_i(\bar{\mathbf{P}}(\boldsymbol{\sigma})), \qquad i = 1, 2,$$

the expected discounted reward starting from state i when $\tilde{\mathbf{P}}(\boldsymbol{\sigma}) = \bar{\mathbf{P}}(\boldsymbol{\sigma})$. It is seen that convergence takes place, in each case, by the seventh

TABLE 4.3.2

n	$\bar{V}(n, \mathcal{M})$	$\bar{e}(n, \mathcal{M})$	$\Delta(n)$
0	10.253 13.278	0.265 0.390	9.747
1	10.254 13.276	0.264 0.392	1.949
2	10.470 13.586	0.048 0.082	0.390
3	10.507 13.652	0.011 0.016	0.078
4	10.516 13.665	0.002 0.003	0.016
5	10.517 13.667	0.001 0.001	0.003
6	10.518 13.668	0.000 0.000	0.001
7	10.518 13.668	0.000 0.000	0.000
8	10.518 13.668	0.000 0.000	0.000
9	10.518 13.668	0.000 0.000	0.000

Policy: (1, 2) $\qquad \bar{V}(0, \mathcal{M}) = \begin{bmatrix} 10.253 \\ 13.278 \end{bmatrix}$

Computation time—0.39 minute.
$\beta = 0.2$

iteration when accuracy to the third decimal place is desired. The computation time indicated at the end of each table is the total time required to calculate all nine iterations on an IBM 7094 computer.

Also displayed in each table is the error vector,

$$\bar{e}(n, \mathcal{M}) = \begin{bmatrix} \bar{V}_1(9, \mathcal{M}) \\ \bar{V}_2(9, \mathcal{M}) \end{bmatrix} - \bar{V}(n, \mathcal{M}),$$

TABLE 4.3.3

n	$\bar{V}(n, \mathcal{M})$	$\bar{e}(n, \mathcal{M})$	$\Delta(n)$
0	5.616 5.473	−0.043 −0.059	12.027
1	5.616 5.473	−0.043 −0.059	2.405
2	5.585 5.429	−0.012 −0.015	0.481
3	5.576 5.417	−0.003 −0.003	0.096
4	5.574 5.414	−0.001 0.000	0.019
5	5.573 5.414	0.000 0.000	0.004
6	5.573 5.414	0.000 0.000	0.001
7	5.573 5.414	0.000 0.000	0.000
8	5.573 5.414	0.000 0.000	0.000
9	5.573 5.414	0.000 0.000	0.000

Policy: (2, 1) $\quad \bar{V}(0, \mathcal{M}) = \begin{bmatrix} 5.616 \\ 5.473 \end{bmatrix}$

Computation time—0.55 minute.
$\beta = 0.2$

taking $\bar{V}(\mathcal{M}) = \bar{V}(9, \mathcal{M})$. The last column of each table contains values of

$$\Delta(n) = \beta^n\left[\max\left\{\frac{R}{1-\beta} - v^*, V^* - \frac{r}{1-\beta}\right\}\right],$$

the absolute error bound of Eq. 4.3.17.

Comparing these calculations with those of Tables 3.6.1 through 3.6.3, it is seen that, in this example, the adaptive control problem and the problem of choosing a terminal policy which maximizes $\bar{V}_i(\mathcal{M})$ both have the same optimal initial policy and the same total expected reward.

TABLE 4.3.4

n	$\bar{V}(n, \mathcal{M})$	$\bar{e}(n, \mathcal{M})$	$\Delta(n)$
0	6.042 12.708	0.042 0.389	13.958
1	6.042 12.707	0.042 0.390	2.792
2	5.988 13.043	−0.012 0.054	0.558
3	5.999 13.084	−0.001 0.013	0.112
4	6.000 13.095	0.000 0.002	0.022
5	6.000 13.097	0.000 0.000	0.004
6	6.000 13.097	0.000 0.000	0.001
7	6.000 13.097	0.000 0.000	0.000
8	6.000 13.097	0.000 0.000	0.000
9	6.000 13.097	0.000 0.000	0.000

Policy: (2, 2) $\quad \bar{V}(0, \mathcal{M}) = \begin{bmatrix} 6.042 \\ 12.708 \end{bmatrix}$

Computation time—0.62 minute.
$\beta = 0.2$

Variance-Covariance Matrix

We conclude this section with a formula for the covariance of $V_i(\tilde{\mathbf{P}})$ and $V_j(\tilde{\mathbf{P}})$. This equation involves terms of the form $E[\tilde{p}_{\alpha\beta}^{(n)}\tilde{p}_{\gamma\delta}^{(\nu)} \mid \psi]$, which can be computed with the aid of Theorem 4.1.3. Approximations to cov $[V_i(\tilde{\mathbf{P}}), V_j(\tilde{\mathbf{P}}) \mid \psi]$ are considered in the section starting on p. 90.

Theorem 4.3.5. If $\tilde{\mathbf{P}}$ has the distribution function $F(\mathbf{P} \mid \psi) \in \mathcal{F}$, a family of distributions closed under consecutive sampling, then the covariance between $V_i(\tilde{\mathbf{P}})$ and $V_j(\tilde{\mathbf{P}})$ is given by

$$\operatorname{cov}[V_i(\tilde{\mathbf{P}}), V_j(\tilde{\mathbf{P}}) \mid \psi] = \sum_{\substack{n=0\\ \nu=0}}^{\infty} \beta^{n+\nu} \sum_{\alpha,\gamma,k,m=1}^{N} \bar{p}_{\alpha k}(\psi) r_{\alpha k} r_{m\gamma}$$

$$\times \{E[\tilde{p}_{i\alpha}^{(n)}\tilde{p}_{jm}^{(\nu)} \mid T_{m\gamma}(T_{\alpha k}(\psi))]\bar{p}_{m\gamma}(T_{\alpha k}(\psi)) - \bar{p}_{i\alpha}^{(n)}(T_{\alpha k}(\psi))\bar{p}_{jm}^{(\nu)}(T_{m\gamma}(\psi))\bar{p}_{m\gamma}(\psi)\},$$

$$i, j = 1, \ldots, N, \quad \psi \in \Psi, \quad 0 \leqslant \beta < 1. \tag{4.3.22}$$

Proof. The expected value of the product $V_i(\tilde{\mathbf{P}})V_j(\tilde{\mathbf{P}})$ is

$$E[V_i(\tilde{\mathbf{P}})V_j(\tilde{\mathbf{P}}) \mid \psi] = \int_{\mathcal{S}_N} \sum_{\substack{n=0\\ \nu=0}}^{\infty} w_i(n, \mathbf{P}) w_j(\nu, \mathbf{P})\, dF(\mathbf{P} \mid \psi), \tag{4.3.23}$$

where

$$w_i(n, P) = \beta^n \sum_{\substack{\alpha=1\\ k=1}}^{N} p_{i\alpha}^{(n)} p_{\alpha k} r_{\alpha k},$$

$$i = 1, \ldots, N, \quad n = 0, 1, 2, \ldots, \quad \mathbf{P} \in \mathcal{S}_N. \tag{4.3.24}$$

If

$$R^* = \max_{i,j} \{|r_{ij}|\},$$

then

$$|w_i(n, \mathbf{P}) w_j(\nu, \mathbf{P})| \leqslant (R^*)^2 \beta^{n+\nu},$$

$$i, j = 1, \ldots, N, \quad n, \nu = 0, 1, 2, \ldots, \quad \mathbf{P} \in \mathcal{S}_N. \tag{4.3.25}$$

Since

$$(R^*)^2 \sum_{\substack{n=0\\ \nu=0}}^{\infty} \beta^{n+\nu} = \frac{(R^*)^2}{(1-\beta)^2} < \infty, \qquad 0 \leqslant \beta < 1, \tag{4.3.26}$$

the double sum in the integrand of Eq. 4.2.23 converges uniformly† to $V_i(\mathbf{P})V_j(\mathbf{P})$ on $\mathcal{S}_N$. Thus,

$$E[V_i(\tilde{\mathbf{P}})V_j(\tilde{\mathbf{P}}) \mid \psi] = \sum_{\substack{n=0\\ \nu=0}}^{\infty} \beta^{n+\nu} \sum_{\alpha,\gamma,k,m=1}^{N} r_{\alpha k} r_{m\gamma} \int_{\mathcal{S}_N} p_{i\alpha}^{(n)} p_{\alpha k} p_{jm}^{(\nu)} p_{m\gamma}\, dF(\mathbf{P} \mid \psi). \tag{4.3.27}$$

† See Rudin [35], p. 134.

Applying Lemma 2.3.2 twice,

$$E[V_i(\tilde{\mathbf{P}})V_j(\tilde{\mathbf{P}}) \mid \psi]$$
$$= \sum_{\substack{n=0 \\ v=0}}^{\infty} \beta^{n+v} \sum_{\alpha,\gamma,k,m=1}^{N} \bar{p}_{\alpha k}(\psi)\bar{p}_{m\gamma}(T_{\alpha k}(\psi))r_{\alpha k}r_{m\gamma}E[\tilde{p}_{i\alpha}^{(n)}\tilde{p}_{jm}^{(v)} \mid T_{m\gamma}(T_{\alpha k}(\psi))]. \tag{4.3.28}$$

Subtracting

$$\bar{V}_i(\psi)\bar{V}_j(\psi) = \sum_{\substack{n=0 \\ v=0}}^{\infty} \beta^{n+v} \sum_{\alpha,\gamma,k,m=1}^{N} \bar{p}_{\alpha k}(\psi)\bar{p}_{m\gamma}(\psi)r_{\alpha k}r_{m\gamma}\bar{p}_{i\alpha}^{(n)}(T_{\alpha k}(\psi))\bar{p}_{jm}^{(v)}(T_{m\gamma}(\psi)) \tag{4.3.29}$$

from Eq. 4.3.28, Eq. 4.3.22 is obtained. Q.E.D.

Theorem 4.3.6. If $F(\mathbf{P} \mid \psi) \in \mathcal{F}$, a family of distributions continuous in ψ, then $\bar{V}_i(\psi)$ and cov $[V_i(\tilde{\mathbf{P}}), V_j(\tilde{\mathbf{P}}) \mid \psi]$ are continuous functions of ψ on Ψ $(i, j = 1, \ldots, N)$.

Proof. Lemma 4.3.1 implies that the bounded function $V_i(\mathbf{P})$ is integrable on $\mathcal{S}_N$. Thus, by Theorem 2.4.3, $\bar{V}_i(\psi)$ and $E[V_i(\tilde{\mathbf{P}})V_j(\tilde{\mathbf{P}}) \mid \psi]$ are continuous on Ψ. Q.E.D.

4.4. THE PROCESS GAIN

Consider a Markov chain operating in the steady state under a fixed policy. The conditional expected reward per transition, given that $\tilde{\mathbf{P}} = \mathbf{P}$, an ergodic transition matrix, is

$$g(\mathbf{P}) = \sum_{\substack{i=1 \\ j=1}}^{N} \pi_i(\mathbf{P})p_{ij}r_{ij}, \tag{4.4.1}$$

and is known as the *gain* of the process. When $\tilde{\mathbf{P}}$ is a random matrix with the distribution function $F(\mathbf{P} \mid \psi)$, which is assumed to be continuous on the boundary of $\mathcal{S}_N$, then $g(\tilde{\mathbf{P}})$ is a random variable. The mean and variance of $g(\tilde{\mathbf{P}})$ are investigated in this section, assuming that $F(\mathbf{P} \mid \psi)$ belongs to a family of distributions closed under the consecutive sampling rule.

Mean and Variance of $g(\tilde{\mathbf{P}})$

Let the expected value of $g(\tilde{\mathbf{P}})$ be

$$\bar{g}(\psi) = \int_{\mathcal{S}_N} g(\mathbf{P})\, dF(\mathbf{P} \mid \psi). \tag{4.4.2}$$

Equation 4.4.1 shows that $g(\mathbf{P})$ is continuous and bounded, hence, integrable on $\mathcal{S}_N^*$. If $F(\mathbf{P} \mid \psi)$ is continuous on the boundary of $\mathcal{S}_N$, then Lemma 4.2.1 implies the existence of the integral in Eq. 4.4.2.

Theorem 4.4.1. If $\tilde{\mathbf{P}}$ has the distribution function $F(\mathbf{P} \mid \psi) \in \mathcal{F}$, a family of distributions continuous on the boundary of $\mathcal{S}_N$ which is closed under consecutive sampling, then the expected gain $\bar{g}(\psi)$ is given by

$$\bar{g}(\psi) = \sum_{\substack{i=1\\j=1}}^{N} \bar{\pi}_i(T_{ij}(\psi))\bar{p}_{ij}(\psi)r_{ij}, \qquad \psi \in \Psi, \tag{4.4.3}$$

where $\bar{\pi}_i(\psi)$ is defined by Eq. 4.2.33.

Proof. By Eq. 4.4.1,

$$\bar{g}(\psi) = \sum_{\substack{i=1\\j=1}}^{N} r_{ij} \int_{\mathcal{S}_N} \pi_i(\mathbf{P})p_{ij}\, dF(\mathbf{P} \mid \psi). \tag{4.4.4}$$

Application of Lemma 2.3.2 yields Eq. 4.4.3. Q.E.D.

Theorem 4.4.2. If $\tilde{\mathbf{P}}$ has the distribution function $F(\mathbf{P} \mid \psi) \in \mathcal{F}$, a family of distributions continuous on the boundary of $\mathcal{S}_N$ which is closed under consecutive sampling, then the variance of $g(\tilde{\mathbf{P}})$ is

$$\begin{aligned}\operatorname{var}\,[g(\tilde{\mathbf{P}}) \mid \psi] = \sum_{i,j,k,m=1}^{N} &\bar{p}_{ij}(\psi)r_{ij}r_{km} \\ &\times [\bar{p}_{km}(T_{ij}(\psi))\bar{\pi}_{ik}(T_{km}(T_{ij}(\psi))) - \bar{p}_{km}(\psi)\bar{\pi}_i(T_{ij}(\psi))\bar{\pi}_k(T_{km}(\Psi))], \\ &\qquad \psi \in \Psi,\end{aligned} \tag{4.4.5}$$

where $\bar{\pi}_{ij}(\psi)$ is defined by Eq. 4.2.52.

Proof. The mean square of $g(\tilde{\mathbf{P}})$ is, using Lemma 2.3.2,

$$\begin{aligned}E[g^2(\tilde{\mathbf{P}}) \mid \psi] &= \sum_{i,j,k,m=1}^{N} r_{ij}r_{km} \int_{\mathcal{S}_N} \pi_i\pi_k p_{ij}p_{km}\, dF(\mathbf{P} \mid \psi) \\ &= \sum_{i,j,k,m=1}^{N} r_{ij}r_{km}\bar{p}_{ij}(\psi)\bar{p}_{km}(T_{ij}(\psi)) \int_{\mathcal{S}_N} \pi_i\pi_k\, dF(\mathbf{P} \mid T_{km}(T_{ij}(\psi))) \\ &= \sum_{i,j,k,m=1}^{N} r_{ij}r_{km}\bar{p}_{ij}(\psi)\bar{p}_{km}(T_{ij}(\psi))\bar{\pi}_{ik}(T_{km}(T_{ij}(\psi))).\end{aligned} \tag{4.4.6}$$

The existence of $E[g^2(\tilde{\mathbf{P}}) \mid \psi]$ follows from Lemma 4.2.1 and the continuity of the bounded function $\pi_i(\mathbf{P})\pi_k(\mathbf{P})p_{ij}p_{km}$ on $\mathcal{S}_N^*$. From Eq. 4.4.3, the square mean of $g(\tilde{\mathbf{P}})$ is

$$[\bar{g}(\psi)]^2 = \sum_{i,j,k,m=1}^{N} r_{ij}r_{km}\bar{p}_{ij}(\psi)\bar{p}_{km}(\psi)\bar{\pi}_i(T_{ij}(\psi))\bar{\pi}_k(T_{km}(\psi)). \tag{4.4.7}$$

Subtracting Eq. 4.4.7 from Eq. 4.4.6, Eq. 4.4.5 is obtained. Q.E.D.

Theorem 4.4.3. If $\tilde{\mathbf{P}}$ has the distribution function $F(\mathbf{P} \mid \psi) \in \mathcal{F}$, a family of distributions continuous on the boundary of $\mathcal{S}_N$ which is continuous in ψ, then the expectations $\bar{g}(\psi)$ and $\operatorname{var}\,[g(\tilde{\mathbf{P}}) \mid \psi]$ are continuous functions of ψ on Ψ.

Proof. The theorem follows immediately from Theorem 2.4.3. Q.E.D.

Approximations to the Mean and Covariance Matrix of $\mathbf{V}(\tilde{\mathbf{P}})$

The preceding results can be used to approximate the mean and the covariance matrix of the discounted reward vector $V(\tilde{\mathbf{P}})$ discussed in Sec. 4.3. We assume throughout that the prior distribution function of $\tilde{\mathbf{P}}$ is $F(\mathbf{P} \mid \psi) \in \mathcal{F}$, a family of distributions continuous on the boundary of $\mathcal{S}_N$ which is closed under consecutive sampling.

The expected value of $V_i(\tilde{\mathbf{P}})$ is $\bar{V}_i(\psi)$, which is given by Eq. 4.3.7 in terms of the mean n-step transition probabilities $\bar{p}_{ij}^{(n)}(\psi)$. Since

$$\lim_{n \to \infty} \bar{p}_{ij}^{(n)}(\psi) = \bar{\pi}_j(\psi),$$

we can replace $\bar{p}_{ij}^{(n)}(\psi)$ by $\bar{\pi}_j(\psi)$ in Eq. 4.3.7 for all n larger than some integer n^* to obtain the approximation

$$\bar{V}_i(\psi) \doteq \sum_{n=0}^{n^*} \beta^n \sum_{\substack{j=1\\k=1}}^{N} \bar{p}_{ij}^{(n)}(T_{jk}(\psi))\bar{p}_{jk}(\psi) r_{jk} + \frac{\beta^{n^*+1}}{1-\beta} \sum_{\substack{j=1\\k=1}}^{N} \bar{\pi}_j(T_{jk}(\psi))\bar{p}_{jk}(\psi) r_{jk}, \tag{4.4.8}$$

or, using Eq. 4.4.3,

$$\bar{V}_i(\psi) \doteq \sum_{n=0}^{n^*} \beta^n \sum_{\substack{j=1\\k=1}}^{N} \bar{p}_{ij}^{(n)}(T_{jk}(\psi))\bar{p}_{jk}(\psi) r_{jk} + \frac{\beta^{n^*+1}}{1-\beta} \bar{g}(\psi),$$

$$i = 1, \ldots, N, \quad n^* = 0, 1, 2, \ldots, \quad \psi \in \Psi, \quad 0 \leqslant \beta < 1. \tag{4.4.9}$$

The error incurred when the approximation 4.4.9 is used is

$$e_i(n^*, \psi) = \sum_{n=n^*+1}^{\infty} \beta^n \sum_{\substack{j=1\\k=1}}^{N} [\bar{p}_{ij}^{(n)}(T_{jk}(\psi)) - \bar{\pi}_j(T_{jk}(\psi))]\bar{p}_{jk}(\psi) r_{jk},$$

$$i = 1, \ldots, N, \quad n^* = 0, 1, 2, \ldots, \quad \psi \in \Psi, \quad 0 \leqslant \beta < 1. \tag{4.4.10}$$

Since

$$|\bar{p}_{ij}^{(n)}(T_{jk}(\psi)) - \bar{\pi}_j(T_{jk}(\psi))| \leqslant 1,$$

$$i, j = 1, \ldots, N, \quad n = 0, 1, 2, \ldots, \quad \psi \in \Psi, \tag{4.4.11}$$

$e_i(n^*, \psi)$ can be bounded by

$$|e_i(n^*, \psi)| \leqslant \frac{\beta^{n^*+1}}{1-\beta} \sum_{j=1}^{N} |\bar{q}_j(\psi)|,$$

$$i = 1, \ldots, N, \quad n^* = 0, 1, 2, \ldots, \quad \psi \in \Psi, \quad 0 \leqslant \beta < 1, \tag{4.4.12}$$

where

$$\bar{q}_j(\psi) = \sum_{k=1}^{N} \bar{p}_{jk}(\psi) r_{jk}, \qquad j = 1, \ldots, N, \quad \psi \in \Psi,$$

is the mean one-step transition reward.

The bound of Eq. 4.4.12 is conservative; tighter bounds require a tighter bound on $|\bar{p}_{ij}^{(n)}(\psi) - \bar{\pi}_j(\psi)|$ than that provided by Eq. 4.4.11. This is a problem for future investigation.

The covariance between $V_i(\tilde{\mathbf{P}})$ and $V_j(\tilde{\mathbf{P}})$ is given by Eq. 4.3.22. By Theorem 4.2.8,

$$\lim_{\substack{n\to\infty \\ \nu\to\infty}} E[\tilde{p}_{i\alpha}^{(n)}\tilde{p}_{jm}^{(\nu)} \mid \psi] = \bar{\pi}_{\alpha m}(\psi), \qquad i, j, \alpha, m = 1, \ldots, N, \quad \psi \in \Psi. \tag{4.4.13}$$

For all $n > n^*$ and $\nu > \nu^*$, let us use the approximations

$$E[\tilde{p}_{i\alpha}^{(n)}\tilde{p}_{jm}^{(\nu)} \mid T_{m\gamma}(T_{\alpha k}(\psi))] \doteq \bar{\pi}_{\alpha m}(T_{m\gamma}(T_{\alpha k}(\psi))), \tag{4.4.14}$$

$$\bar{p}_{i\alpha}^{(n)}(T_{\alpha k}(\psi))\bar{p}_{jm}^{(\nu)}(T_{m\gamma}(\psi)) \doteq \bar{\pi}_{\alpha}(T_{\alpha k}(\psi))\bar{\pi}_{m}(T_{m\gamma}(\psi)) \tag{4.4.15}$$

in Eq. 4.3.22. Using Eq. 4.4.5, we then have

$$\begin{aligned}\operatorname{cov}[V_i(\tilde{\mathbf{P}}), V_j(\tilde{\mathbf{P}}) \mid \psi] &\doteq \sum_{n=0}^{n^*}\sum_{\nu=0}^{\nu^*}\beta^{n+\nu}\sum_{\alpha,\gamma,k,m=1}^{N}\bar{p}_{\alpha k}(\psi)r_{\alpha k}r_{m\gamma} \\ &\times [E[\tilde{p}_{i\alpha}^{(n)}\tilde{p}_{jm}^{(\nu)} \mid T_{m\gamma}(T_{\alpha k}(\psi))]\bar{p}_{m\gamma}(T_{\alpha k}(\psi)) - \bar{p}_{i\alpha}^{(n)}(T_{\alpha k}(\psi))\bar{p}_{jm}^{(\nu)}(T_{m\gamma}(\psi))\bar{p}_{m\gamma}(\psi)] \\ &+ \frac{\beta^{n^*+\nu^*+2}}{(1-\beta)^2}\operatorname{var}[g(\tilde{\mathbf{P}}) \mid \psi], \qquad i, j = 1, \ldots, N, \quad \psi \in \Psi.\end{aligned} \tag{4.4.16}$$

The error involved in using Eq. 4.4.16 to approximate $\operatorname{cov}[V_i(\tilde{\mathbf{P}}), V_j(\tilde{\mathbf{P}}) \mid \psi]$ is

$$\begin{aligned}e_{ij}(n^*, \nu^*; \psi) = \sum_{\substack{n=n^*+1 \\ \nu=\nu^*+1}}^{\infty}\beta^{n+\nu}\sum_{\alpha,\gamma,k,m=1}^{N}\bar{p}_{\alpha k}(\psi)r_{\alpha k}r_{m\gamma}\,&[\{E[\tilde{p}_{i\alpha}^{(n)}\tilde{p}_{jm}^{(\nu)} \mid T_{m\gamma}(T_{\alpha k}(\psi))] \\ - \bar{\pi}_{\alpha m}(T_{m\gamma}(T_{\alpha k}(\psi)))\}\bar{p}_{m\gamma}(T_{\alpha k}(\psi)) &- \{\bar{p}_{i\alpha}^{(n)}(T_{\alpha k}(\psi))\bar{p}_{jm}^{(\nu)}(T_{m\gamma}(\psi)) \\ &- \bar{\pi}_{\alpha}(T_{\alpha k}(\psi))\bar{\pi}_{m}(T_{m\gamma}(\psi))\}\bar{p}_{m\gamma}(\psi)].\end{aligned} \tag{4.4.17}$$

A conservative bound on $e_{ij}(n^*, \nu^*; \psi)$ is

$$|e_{ij}(n^*, \nu^*; \psi)| \leqslant \frac{\beta^{n^*+\nu^*+2}}{(1-\beta)^2}\sum_{\alpha,\gamma,k,m=1}^{N}\bar{p}_{\alpha k}(\psi)\,|r_{\alpha k}|\cdot|r_{m\gamma}|\,[\bar{p}_{m\gamma}(T_{\alpha k}(\psi)) + \bar{p}_{m\gamma}(\psi)]. \tag{4.4.18}$$

An Abelian Theorem

We conclude this chapter with a theorem which relates $\bar{g}(\psi)$ to $\bar{V}_i(\psi)$. Some results from the theory of summation of divergent series are required and are summarized here without proof.†

Let $\{a_n\} = \{a_0, a_1, a_2, \ldots\}$ be a sequence of real numbers. Let

$$t_n = \frac{1}{n+1}\sum_{\nu=0}^{n}a_\nu, \qquad n = 0, 1, 2, \ldots. \tag{4.4.19}$$

† See, for example, Knopp [27].

If $\lim_{n\to\infty} t_n$ exists and is equal to t, then the sequence $\{a_n\}$ is said to be *Cesaro-summable*, or *C_1-summable*, to t. If the C_1-sum of $\{a_n\}$ exists and is equal to t, then a theorem due to Abel states that $\lim_{\beta\to 1_-} (1-\beta)\sum_{\nu=0}^{\infty} a_\nu \beta^\nu$ exists and is equal to t.

Theorem 4.4.4. Let $\tilde{\mathbf{P}}$ have the distribution function $F(\mathbf{P} \mid \psi) \in \mathcal{F}$, a family of distributions continuous on the boundary of $\mathcal{S}_N$ which is closed under the consecutive sampling rule. Let $\bar{V}_i(\psi) = \bar{V}_i(\beta, \psi)$ and $\bar{g}(\psi)$ be defined by Eqs. 4.3.2 and 4.4.2 respectively. Then

$$\lim_{\beta\to 1_-} (1-\beta)\bar{V}_i(\beta, \psi) = \bar{g}(\psi), \qquad i = 1, \ldots, N, \quad \psi \in \Psi. \tag{4.4.20}$$

Proof. We first show that the C_1-sum of the sequence $\{\bar{p}_{ij}^{(n)}(\psi)\}$ exists and is equal to $\bar{\pi}_j(\psi)$ for $j = 1, \ldots, N$ and any $\psi \in \Psi$. Let

$$t_{ij}(n, \psi) = \frac{1}{n+1}\sum_{\nu=0}^{n} \bar{p}_{ij}^{(\nu)}(\psi),$$
$$i, j = 1, \ldots, N, \quad n = 0, 1, 2, \ldots, \quad \psi \in \Psi. \tag{4.4.21}$$

Let $\epsilon > 0$ be given. Choose n^* such that, for fixed indices i and j and fixed $\psi \in \Psi$,

$$|\bar{p}_{ij}^{(n)}(\psi) - \bar{\pi}_j(\psi)| < \frac{\epsilon}{2}, \qquad n > n^*. \tag{4.4.22}$$

Then, for $n > n^*$,

$$|t_{ij}(n, \psi) - \bar{\pi}_j(\psi)| \leqslant \frac{1}{n+1}\sum_{\nu=0}^{n} |\bar{p}_{ij}^{(\nu)}(\psi) - \bar{\pi}_j(\psi)|$$
$$< \frac{1}{n+1}\sum_{\nu=0}^{n^*} |\bar{p}_{ij}^{(\nu)}(\psi) - \bar{\pi}_j(\psi)| + \frac{\epsilon}{2}. \tag{4.4.23}$$

By choosing an integer $\mu > n^*$ such that, if $n > \mu$,

$$0 \leqslant \frac{1}{n+1}\sum_{\nu=0}^{n^*} |\bar{p}_{ij}^{(\nu)}(\psi) - \bar{\pi}_j(\psi)| < \frac{\epsilon}{2}, \tag{4.4.24}$$

we have, for $n > \mu$,

$$|t_{ij}(n, \psi) - \bar{\pi}_j(\psi)| < \epsilon, \tag{4.4.25}$$

and, therefore, $\lim_{n\to\infty} t_{ij}(n, \psi) = \bar{\pi}_j(\psi)$, proving the assertion.

Using Eq. 4.3.7,

$$\lim_{\beta\to 1_-} (1-\beta)\bar{V}_i(\beta, \psi) = \sum_{\substack{j=1\\k=1}}^{N} \bar{p}_{jk}(\psi) r_{jk} \lim_{\beta\to 1_-} (1-\beta)\sum_{n=0}^{\infty} \beta^n \bar{p}_{ij}^{(n)}(T_{jk}(\psi)). \tag{4.4.26}$$

C_1-summability of $\{\bar{p}_{ij}^{(n)}(T_{jk}(\psi))\}$ to $\bar{\pi}_j(T_{jk}(\psi))$ implies that

$$\lim_{\beta \to 1_-} (1 - \beta) \sum_{n=0}^{\infty} \beta^n \bar{p}_{ij}^{(n)}(T_{jk}(\psi))$$

exists and is equal to $\bar{\pi}_j(T_{jk}(\psi))$. Thus, using Eq. 4.4.3,

$$\begin{aligned} \lim_{\beta \to 1_-} (1 - \beta) \bar{V}_i(\beta, \psi) &= \sum_{\substack{j=1 \\ k=1}}^{N} \bar{\pi}_j(T_{jk}(\psi)) \bar{p}_{jk}(\psi) r_{jk} \\ &= \bar{g}(\psi), \qquad i = 1, \ldots, N, \quad \psi \in \Psi. \qquad (4.4.27) \end{aligned}$$

Q.E.D.

Chapter 5

TERMINAL CONTROL PROBLEMS

In this chapter we consider sequential sampling models of a Markov chain with alternatives in which there is an explicit sampling cost. This leads to a distinction between sampling the process and using the process. When the process is *sampled*, the sequence of states occupied by the Markov chain during the sampling period is made known to the decision maker, who then uses this information to update his prior distribution on $\tilde{\mathscr{P}}$. During the sampling period the process earns transition rewards as specified by $\mathfrak{R}$ and sampling costs are incurred.

On the other hand, if the process is *used* over a period of n transitions, it earns transition rewards, but the decision maker is permitted to know only the initial state and the final state of the sample sequence. The only sample cost incurred is that for observing the state of the system after the nth transition.

It is reasonable to expect that, after a finite amount of sampling, the prior distribution of $\tilde{\mathscr{P}}$ will be sufficiently tight so that the best course of action for the decision maker will be to cease sampling and operate the process under some fixed terminal policy indefinitely. Hence, the models of this chapter are called *terminal control models.* In the following sections we show that such a terminal decision point occurs with probability one in an optimal sampling strategy.

Terminal control models are applicable, in general, to any Markov chain with alternatives in which rewards are earned independently of the decision maker's knowledge of the sequence of states occupied by the system and in which it is possible for him to determine the state of the system at any time, for a nonzero cost. A specific example of such a process is a Markov chain model of consumer brand-switching behavior, where a survey must be made to determine the current state of the market.

Two-action sequential sampling problems with independent, identically distributed observations have been examined from the Bayesian point of view by Wetherill [40]. A similar problem with Markov-dependent observations was considered by Bhat [9].

In Sec. 5.1 we examine model I, a discounted terminal control model in which the decision maker must sample at every transition of the process until a terminal decision point is reached. This model is formulated as a set of functional equations and it is shown that a terminal decision point is reached with probability one in an optimal sampling strategy. It is shown in Sec. 5.2 that there exists a unique solution to these equations and a method of successive approximations is introduced. This model is generalized in Sec. 5.3, where model II is introduced. Model II is a discounted terminal control model in which the decision maker can either sample or use the process until a terminal decision is made. Approximate methods of making terminal decisions are discussed in Sec. 5.4. Models of undiscounted processes are introduced in Sec. 5.5, and the chapter concludes with a brief discussion of setup costs.

5.1. DISCOUNTED PROCESSES—MODEL I

Consider a Markov chain with alternatives which has the reward matrix $\mathcal{R} = [r_{ij}^k]$. At each transition the decision maker can either sample the process or choose a terminal policy under which the system is to be operated indefinitely. Let $c_i > 0$ be the cost of observing the system and finding it in state i $(i = 1, \ldots, N)$.† The cost of any sampling strategy is, therefore, a random variable before it is executed. Assuming that the interval between transitions is constant, we may use this interval as the unit of time. Let β be the present value of a unit reward received one unit of time in the future $(0 \leqslant \beta < 1)$. We shall seek a sampling strategy which maximizes the expected total discounted reward over an infinite period.

When the decision maker chooses to sample, we clearly have a case of consecutive sampling. Thus, it is assumed that the prior distribution function of $\tilde{\mathcal{P}}$ is $H(\mathcal{P} \mid \psi) \in \mathcal{H}$, a family of distributions closed under consecutive sampling. Let (i, ψ) denote the generalized state of the system $(i = 1, \ldots, N;\ \psi \in \Psi)$ and let $v_i(\psi)$ be the supremum of the expected total discounted reward over an infinite period if the system starts from the generalized state (i, ψ). In Theorem 5.1.1 it will be shown

† Model I is easily generalized to allow the sampling cost to be c_{ij}^k, the cost of observing a transition from state i to state j under the kth alternative in state i. In this case Eq. 5.1.3 becomes

$$\bar{c}_i^k(\psi) = \sum_{j=1}^{N} \bar{p}_{ij}^k(\psi) c_{ij}^k.$$

Model II, however, requires that the sampling cost be independent of the state from which the transition originated.

that an optimal sampling strategy exists and, therefore, that $v_i(\psi)$ is the maximum expected discounted reward over an infinite period.

If, when in state (i, ψ), it is decided to sample the kth alternative and the system then makes a transition to state j, the supremum of the posterior expected reward is

$$r_{ij}^k - \beta c_j + \beta v_j(T_{ij}^k(\psi)). \tag{5.1.1}$$

The probability of the sample outcome j, unconditional with respect to the prior distribution, given that the system is in state (i, ψ) and alternative k is in use, is the prior expected value of $\tilde{p}_{ij}^k$,

$$\bar{p}_{ij}^k(\psi) = \int_{S_{KN}} p_{ij}^k \, dH(\mathbf{P} \mid \psi). \tag{5.1.2}$$

Let $\bar{q}_i^k(\psi)$ be the mean one-step transition reward defined by Eq. 3.2.4 and let

$$\bar{c}_i^k(\psi) = \sum_{j=1}^{N} \bar{p}_{ij}^k(\psi) c_j \tag{5.1.3}$$

be the expected cost of sampling alternative k when in the state (i, ψ). Then, if it is decided to sample the process on the next transition, the supremum of the prior expected reward is

$$\max_{1 \le k \le K_i} \left\{ \bar{q}_i^k(\psi) - \beta \bar{c}_i^k(\psi) + \beta \sum_{j=1}^{N} \bar{p}_{ij}^k(\psi) v_j(T_{ij}^k(\psi)) \right\},$$
$$i = 1, \ldots, N, \quad \psi \in \Psi. \tag{5.1.4}$$

Suppose, on the other hand, it is decided to cease sampling and to operate the process indefinitely under the policy $\boldsymbol{\sigma}$. Let

$$\bar{V}_i(\boldsymbol{\sigma}, \psi) = \int_{S_N} V_i(\mathbf{P}) \, dF_{\boldsymbol{\sigma}}(\mathbf{P} \mid \psi),$$
$$i = 1, \ldots, N, \quad \psi \in \Psi, \quad \boldsymbol{\sigma} \in \Sigma, \tag{5.1.5}$$

be the unconditional expected discounted reward over an infinite period† when the policy $\boldsymbol{\sigma}$ is used and the system starts from (i, ψ). Then, if it is decided to cease sampling, the maximum prior expected reward is

$$\max_{\boldsymbol{\sigma} \in \Sigma} \{\bar{V}_i(\boldsymbol{\sigma}, \psi)\}, \qquad i = 1, \ldots, N, \quad \psi \in \Psi. \tag{5.1.6}$$

The maximum exists in Eq. 5.1.6 since Σ is a finite set.

Using Eqs. 5.1.4 and 5.1.6, we have the following set of functional equations which must be satisfied by the vector function, $\boldsymbol{v}(\psi) = (v_1(\psi), \ldots, v_N(\psi))$:

$$v_i(\psi) = \max \left[\begin{array}{l} \max\limits_{1 \leqslant k \leqslant K_i} \left\{ \bar{q}_i^k(\psi) - \beta \bar{c}_i^k(\psi) + \beta \sum\limits_{j=1}^{N} \bar{p}_{ij}^k(\psi) v_j(T_{ij}^k(\psi)) \right\} \\ \max\limits_{\boldsymbol{\sigma} \in \Sigma} \{\bar{V}_i(\boldsymbol{\sigma}, \psi)\} \end{array} \right].$$
$$i = 1, \ldots, N, \quad \psi \in \Psi, \quad 0 \leqslant \beta < 1. \tag{5.1.7}$$

† See Sec. 4.3.

It is to be noted that the same symbol $v_i(\psi)$ is used in Eqs. 3.2.5 and 5.1.7 to represent two distinct functions. This has been done to simplify to some extent a necessarily complicated notation. The meaning of the symbol $v_i(\psi)$ will always be clear from its context.

We now show that an optimal sampling strategy exists, making use of the definitions and notation of Sec. 3.2†

Theorem 5.1.1. Let $v_i(\psi, d)$ be the expected total discounted reward in model I when the system starts in the generalized state (i, ψ) and the sampling strategy $d \in D_i$ is used. Let

$$v_i(\psi) = \sup_{d \in D_i} \{v_i(\psi, d)\}, \qquad i = 1, \ldots, N, \quad \psi \in \Psi. \tag{5.1.8}$$

Then there is a sampling strategy $d^* \in D_i$ such that

$$v_i(\psi) = v_i(\psi, d^*), \qquad i = 1, \ldots, N, \quad \psi \in \Psi. \tag{5.1.9}$$

Proof. Consider the adaptive control problem of Sec. 3.2. Let $\bar{D}_i$ be the set of all possible sampling strategies $\bar{d}$ in the adaptive control problem when the system starts from state i. In model I, if $d \in D_i$, it is clear that d is a possible strategy in the adaptive control problem; hence, $D_i \subset \bar{D}_i$ $(i = 1, \ldots, N)$. Suppose $\bar{d} \in \bar{D}_i$. Then $\bar{d}$ either prescribes a fixed policy $\boldsymbol{\sigma}$ for use on every transition $n > n^*$, for some integer n^*, or else not. In the first case, $\bar{d}$ is a possible strategy for model I. In the second case, $\bar{d}$ is also a possible strategy for model I, viz., a strategy in which a terminal decision point is never reached under some or all possible sample histories. Thus, $\bar{D}_i \subset D_i$ and, therefore, $\bar{D}_i = D_i$. The proof of Theorem 3.2.1 is valid for an arbitrary reward structure, provided that the reward per transition is bounded; thus, the remainder of the proof of Theorem 5.1.1 follows the proof of Theorem 3.2.1 and will not be duplicated here. Q.E.D.

We now show that, with probability one, a terminal decision point is reached in model I if an optimal sampling strategy is used. Let $\mathfrak{Q}$ denote the true state of nature; $\mathfrak{Q}$ is assumed to be positive, as defined by Eq. 2.3.26.

Theorem 5.1.2. In model I, if the true state of nature $\mathfrak{Q}$ is a positive matrix and if $H(\mathscr{P} \mid \psi) \in \mathcal{H}$, a family of distributions continuous in ψ, then, with probability one, a terminal decision point is reached in an optimal sampling strategy, provided $H(\mathscr{P} \mid \psi)$ assigns positive probability to the set E defined by Eq. 2.3.32.

† See especially pp. 38–40.

Proof. The proof is by contradiction. Assume that there is an optimal sampling strategy in which a terminal decision is never made. Then the system is operated as an adaptive control process which is sampled infinitely often under the consecutive sampling rule and at least one state i is entered infinitely often. Since at least one alternative k must be used infinitely often when in state i, Lemma 2.3.7 and the positivity of $\mathfrak{Q}$ imply that every state is entered infinitely often, and, therefore, that at least one alternative in each state is sampled infinitely often. Since the system is operating under an optimal strategy any alternative which is sampled a finite number of times is dominated by other alternatives after a finite number of transitions and can be eliminated from further consideration. Thus, we may assume, without loss of generality, that all alternatives are sampled infinitely often. By Theorem 2.3.8, the mass of the posterior distribution of $\tilde{\mathscr{P}}$ tends, with probability one, to concentrate at $\mathfrak{Q}$ as n, the number of transitions, goes to infinity. That is, for any $\epsilon > 0$, if P_n is defined by Eq. 2.3.31,

$$\lim_{n\to\infty} P_n[|\tilde{\mathscr{P}} - \mathfrak{Q}| < \epsilon] = 1, \tag{5.1.10}$$

the limit holding with probability one. Let $H(\mathscr{P} \mid \psi^*)$ be the distribution function which places the unit mass of probability on $\mathfrak{Q}$. Then, with probability one, $\psi \to \psi^*$ as $n \to \infty$. Since $\mathcal{H}$ is continuous in ψ, $\bar{p}_{ij}^k$ is continuous and Theorem 3.3.4 implies that $v_i(\psi)$ is continuous; hence, as $n \to \infty$ Eq. 5.1.7 tends to†

$$v_i(\psi^*) = \max_{1\leq k\leq K_i}\left\{\sum_{j=1}^{N} \bar{p}_{ij}^k(\psi^*)[r_{ij}^k - \beta c_j + \beta v_j(\psi^*)]\right\},$$
$$i = 1, \ldots, N. \tag{5.1.11}$$

Equation 5.1.11 is a sequential decision problem in which the decision maker is certain about the transition probabilities; this has been studied by several authors. Blackwell [11] has shown that an optimal strategy exists for Eq. 5.1.11 in which a fixed policy $\boldsymbol{\sigma} \in \Sigma$ is used at every transition. Howard [22] has shown that the expected reward under this strategy is, in the notation of this proof,

$$v_i(\psi^*) = \sum_{n=0}^{\infty} \beta^n \sum_{\substack{j=1\\k=1}}^{N} q_{ij}^{(n)}(\boldsymbol{\sigma}) q_{jk}^{\sigma_j}[r_{jk}^{\sigma_j} - \beta c_k] \qquad i = 1, \ldots, N, \tag{5.1.12}$$

where $q_{ij}^{(n)}(\boldsymbol{\sigma})$ is the (i, j)th element of $[\mathrm{Q}(\boldsymbol{\sigma})]^n$. But, as $n \to \infty$, $\bar{V}_i(\boldsymbol{\sigma}, \psi) \to \bar{V}_i(\boldsymbol{\sigma}, \psi^*)$ with probability one, since $\bar{V}_i(\boldsymbol{\sigma}, \psi)$ is continuous. Let

† The argument is valid even if the distribution which places the unit mass of probability on $\mathfrak{Q}$ is not a member of $\mathcal{H}$.

$\bar{V}_i(\boldsymbol{\sigma}^*, \psi^*) = \max_{\sigma \in \Sigma} \{\bar{V}_i(\boldsymbol{\sigma}, \psi^*)\}$. Since $c_j > 0$ $(j = 1, \ldots, N)$, Eqs. 5.1.12 and 4.3.1 imply the contradiction

$$v(\psi^*) < \sum_{n=0}^{\infty} \beta^n \sum_{\substack{j=1\\k=1}}^{N} q_{ij}^{(n)}(\boldsymbol{\sigma}) q_{jk}^{\sigma_j} r_{jk}^{\sigma_j} = \bar{V}_i(\boldsymbol{\sigma}, \psi^*)$$

$$\leqslant \bar{V}_i(\boldsymbol{\sigma}^*, \psi^*), \qquad i = 1, \ldots, N. \tag{5.1.13}$$

Therefore, with probability one, a terminal decision point is reached after a finite number of transitions. Q.E.D.

5.2. EXISTENCE AND UNIQUENESS OF SOLUTIONS—SUCCESSIVE APPROXIMATIONS

Let the sequence of vector functions $\boldsymbol{v}(n, \psi)$, where $\boldsymbol{v}(n, \psi) = (v_1(n, \psi), \ldots, v_N(n, \psi))$, be defined by the equations

$$v_i(n+1, \psi) = \max \left[\begin{array}{l} \max\limits_{1 \le k \le K_i} \left\{ \bar{q}_i^k(\psi) - \beta \bar{c}_i^k(\psi) + \beta \sum\limits_{j=1}^{N} \bar{p}_{ij}^k(\psi) v_j(n, T_{ij}^k(\psi)) \right\} \\ \max\limits_{\sigma \in \Sigma} \{\bar{V}_i(\boldsymbol{\sigma}, \psi)\} \end{array} \right],$$

$$i = 1, \ldots, N, \quad n = 1, 2, \ldots, \quad \psi \in \Psi, \quad 0 \leqslant \beta < 1, \tag{5.2.1a}$$

$$v_i(0, \psi) = \max_{\sigma \in \Sigma} \{\bar{V}_i(\boldsymbol{\sigma}, \psi)\}, \qquad i = 1, \ldots, N, \quad \psi \in \Psi. \tag{5.2.1b}$$

Using Eq. 5.2.1, it is shown in this section that there exists a unique bounded solution to Eq. 5.1.7. Equation 5.2.1 can then be used as a computational tool to approximate this unique solution and, with this application in mind, a bound on the error, $e_i(n, \psi) = v_i(\psi) - v_i(n, \psi)$, is derived. With the aid of this bound, we show that $\{\boldsymbol{v}(n, \psi)\} \to \boldsymbol{v}(\psi)$ uniformly in ψ.

Lemma 5.2.1. If $R^* = \max_{i,j,k} \{|r_{ji}^k|\}$ and $C = \max_j \{c_j\}$, then the functions $v_i(n, \psi)$ defined by Eq. 5.2.1 have the bound

$$|v_i(n, \psi)| \leqslant \frac{R^* + \beta C}{1 - \beta},$$

$$i = 1, \ldots, N, \quad n = 0, 1, 2, \ldots, \quad \psi \in \Psi, \quad 0 \leqslant \beta < 1. \tag{5.2.2}$$

Proof. By Eqs. 4.3.5 and 4.3.6,

$$|\bar{V}_i(\boldsymbol{\sigma}, \psi)| \leqslant \frac{R^*}{1 - \beta},$$

$$i = 1, \ldots, N, \quad \psi \in \Psi, \quad \boldsymbol{\sigma} \in \Sigma, \tag{5.2.3}$$

and, since $C > 0$,

$$|v_i(0, \psi)| < \frac{R^* + \beta C}{1 - \beta}, \qquad i = 1, \ldots, N, \quad \psi \in \Psi. \tag{5.2.4}$$

Assume that Eq. 5.2.2 holds for n. Then

$$|v_i(n + 1, \psi)| \leqslant \max \left[R^* + \beta C + \frac{\beta R^* + \beta^2 C}{1 - \beta}, \frac{R^*}{1 - \beta} \right]$$
$$= \frac{R^* + \beta C}{1 - \beta}. \tag{5.2.5}$$

Q.E.D.

Theorem 5.2.2. If $\boldsymbol{v}(n, \psi)$ is defined by Eq. 5.2.1, then $\{v_i(n, \psi)\}$ is a monotone increasing sequence ($i = 1, \ldots, N$; $\psi \in \Psi$) and $\lim_{n\to\infty} \boldsymbol{v}(n, \psi)$ exists and is a solution to Eq. 5.1.7.

Proof. We show inductively that $\{v_i(n, \psi)\}$ is a monotone increasing sequence. Since $v_i(0, \psi) = \max \{\bar{V}_i(\boldsymbol{\sigma}, \psi)\}$, we have $v_i(1, \psi) \geqslant v_i(0, \psi)$. Assume that $v_i(n, \psi) \geqslant v_i(n - 1, \psi)$ for $i = 1, \ldots, N$ and $\psi \in \Psi$. If $v_i(n, \psi) = \max_{\boldsymbol{\sigma}\in\Sigma} \{\bar{V}_i(\boldsymbol{\sigma}, \psi)\}$, then $v_i(n + 1, \psi) \geqslant v_i(n, \psi)$. Suppose that, for some $k \in \{1, \ldots, K_i\}$,

$$v_i(n, \psi) = \bar{q}_i^k(\psi) - \beta\bar{c}_i^k(\psi) + \beta \sum_{j=1}^{N} \bar{p}_{ij}^k(\psi) v_j(n - 1, T_{ij}^k(\psi)). \tag{5.2.6}$$

Then, since

$$v_i(n + 1, \psi) \geqslant \bar{q}_i^k(\psi) - \beta\bar{c}_i^k(\psi) + \beta \sum_{j=1}^{N} \bar{p}_{ij}^k(\psi) v_j(n, T_{ij}^k(\psi)), \tag{5.2.7}$$

we have

$$v_i(n + 1, \psi) - v_i(n, \psi)$$
$$\geqslant \beta \sum_{j=1}^{N} \bar{p}_{ij}^k(\psi)[v_j(n, T_{ij}^k(\psi)) - v_j(n - 1, T_{ij}^k(\psi))] \geqslant 0, \tag{5.2.8}$$

proving the induction. By Lemma 5.2.1, the sequence $\{v_i(n, \psi)\}$ is bounded, hence, $\lim_{n\to\infty} v_i(n, \psi)$ exists ($i = 1, \ldots, N$). That the limit is a solution of Eq. 5.1.7 is seen by letting $n \to \infty$ in Eq. 5.2.1*a*. Q.E.D.

Theorem 5.2.3. There is a unique bounded solution to Eq. 5.1.7.

Proof. It was shown in Theorem 5.2.2 that there is at least one bounded solution $\boldsymbol{v}(\psi)$ to Eq. 5.1.7. Assume that $\boldsymbol{w}(\psi) = (w_1(\psi), \ldots w_N(\psi))$ is also a bounded solution. Let

$$S_i^k(v, \infty, \psi) = \bar{q}_i^k(\psi) - \beta\bar{c}_i^k(\psi) + \beta \sum_{j=1}^{N} \bar{p}_{ij}^k(\psi) v_j(T_{ij}^k(\psi)),$$
$$k = 1, \ldots, K_i, \quad i = 1, \ldots, N, \quad \psi \in \Psi. \tag{5.2.9}$$

Assume (i, ψ) is fixed. There are four cases.

CASE 1. $v_i(\psi) = \max_{\sigma\in\Sigma} \{\bar{V}_i(\boldsymbol{\sigma}, \psi)\}$ and $w_i(\psi) = \max_{\sigma\in\Sigma} \{\bar{V}_i(\boldsymbol{\sigma}, \psi)\}$. Then $v_i(\psi) = w_i(\psi)$.

CASE 2. For some $\alpha \in \{1, \ldots, K_i\}$, $v_i(\psi) = S_i^\alpha(v, \infty, \psi)$ and $w_i(\psi) = \max_{\sigma\in\Sigma} \{\bar{V}_i(\boldsymbol{\sigma}, \psi)\}$. Then

$$0 \leqslant v_i(\psi) - w_i(\psi) \leqslant S_i^\alpha(v, \infty, \psi) - S_i^\alpha(w, \infty, \psi). \tag{5.2.10}$$

CASE 3. For some $\gamma \in \{1, \ldots, K_i\}$, $w_i(\psi) = S_i^\gamma(w, \infty, \psi)$ and $v_i(\psi) = \max_{\sigma\in\Sigma} \{\bar{V}_i(\boldsymbol{\sigma}, \psi)\}$. Then

$$S_i^\gamma(v, \infty, \psi) - S_i^\gamma(w, \infty, \psi) \leqslant v_i(\psi) - w_i(\psi) \leqslant 0. \tag{5.2.11}$$

CASE 4. For some indices a, $b \in \{1, \ldots, K_i\}$, $v_i(\psi) = S_i^a(v, \infty, \psi)$ and $w_i(\psi) = S_i^b(w, \infty, \psi)$. Then

$$S_i^b(v, \infty, \psi) - S_i^b(w, \infty, \psi) \leqslant v_i(\psi) - w_i(\psi) \leqslant S_i^a(v, \infty, \psi) - S_i^a(w, \infty, \psi). \tag{5.2.12}$$

Let k^* index the maximum of

$$|S_i^a(v, \infty, \psi) - S_i^a(w, \infty, \psi)|,$$
$$|S_i^b(v, \infty, \psi) - S_i^b(w, \infty, \psi)|,$$
$$|S_i^\alpha(v, \infty, \psi) - S_i^\alpha(w, \infty, \psi)|,$$

and

$$|S_i^\gamma(v, \infty, \psi) - S_i^\gamma(w, \infty, \psi)|,$$

Then, in all of the above cases,

$$\begin{aligned} |v_i(\psi) - w_i(\psi)| &\leqslant |S_i^{k^*}(v, \infty, \psi) - S_i^{k^*}(w, \infty, \psi)| \\ &\leqslant \beta \sum_{j=1}^N \bar{p}_{ij}^{k^*}(\psi)\, |v_j(T_{ij}^{k^*}(\psi)) - w_j(T_{ij}^{k^*}(\psi))|, \quad \psi \in \Psi. \end{aligned} \tag{5.2.13}$$

Since $v_i(\psi)$ and $w_i(\psi)$ are both bounded, there exists a number $M > 0$ such that

$$|v_i(\psi) - w_i(\psi)| < M, \qquad \psi \in \Psi.$$

Repeated application of Eq. 5.2.13 yields

$$|v_i(\psi) - w_i(\psi)| < \beta^n M, \qquad n = 0, 1, 2, \ldots, \quad \psi \in \Psi. \tag{5.2.14}$$

Since $0 \leqslant \beta < 1$, Eq. 5.2.14 implies $v_i(\psi) = w_i(\psi)$. Q.E.D.

We now derive a bound on the error of the nth approximant $v_i(n, \psi)$. Let

$$S_i^k(v, n, \psi) = \bar{q}_i^k(\psi) - \beta\bar{c}_i^k(\psi) + \beta \sum_{j=1}^N \bar{p}_{ij}^k(\psi) v_j(n, T_{ij}^k(\psi)),$$
$$k = 1, \ldots, K_i, \quad i = 1, \ldots, N, \quad n = 0, 1, 2, \ldots, \quad \psi \in \Psi. \tag{5.2.15}$$

Theorem 5.2.4. Let the error of the nth approximant $v_i(n, \psi)$ be defined as

$$e_i(n, \psi) = v_i(\psi) - v_i(n, \psi),$$
$$i = 1, \ldots, N, \quad n = 0, 1, 2, \ldots, \quad \psi \in \Psi, \quad (5.2.16)$$

where $v_i(n, \psi)$ is defined by Eq. 5.2.1 and $v_i(\psi)$ is the unique bounded solution of Eq. 5.1.7. Let R and r be defined by Eq. 3.4.3. Then $e_i(n, \psi)$ has the bounds

$$0 \leqslant e_i(n, \psi) \leqslant \beta^n \frac{R - r}{1 - \beta},$$
$$i = 1, \ldots, N, \quad n = 0, 1, 2, \ldots, \quad \psi \in \Psi, \quad 0 \leqslant \beta < 1. \quad (5.2.17)$$

Proof. By Theorem 5.2.2, $\{v_i(n, \psi)\}$ is a monotone increasing sequence with the limit $v_i(\psi)$; hence, $e_i(n, \psi) \geqslant 0$ $(n = 0, 1, 2, \ldots)$. The remainder of the inequality of Eq. 5.2.17 is proved by induction.

We first establish that $v_i(\psi) \leqslant R/(1 - \beta)$. Since $\bar{V}(\boldsymbol{\sigma}, \psi) \leqslant R \sum_{n=0}^{\infty} \beta^n = R/(1 - \beta)$ for all $\boldsymbol{\sigma} \in \Sigma$, we have

$$v_i(0, \psi) \leqslant \frac{R}{1 - \beta}, \qquad i = 1, \ldots, N, \quad \psi \in \Psi. \qquad (5.2.18)$$

Assume $v_i(n, \psi) \leqslant R/(1 - \beta)$. Then, since $c_j > 0$ $(j = 1, \ldots, N)$,

$$v_i(n + 1, \psi) \leqslant \max \left[R + \frac{\beta R}{1 - \beta}, \frac{R}{1 - \beta} \right] = \frac{R}{1 - \beta} \qquad (5.2.19)$$

and, by induction,

$$v_i(n, \psi) \leqslant \frac{R}{1 - \beta},$$
$$i = 1, \ldots, N, \quad n = 0, 1, 2, \ldots, \quad \psi \in \Psi. \quad (5.2.20)$$

Thus $v_i(\psi) = \lim_{n \to \infty} v_i(n, \psi) \leqslant R/(1 - \beta)$, proving the assertion.

Since $\bar{V}_i(\boldsymbol{\sigma}, \psi) \geqslant r/(1 - \beta)$ for all $\boldsymbol{\sigma} \in \Sigma$, we have

$$e_i(0, \psi) \leqslant \frac{R - r}{1 - \beta}, \qquad i = 1, \ldots, N, \quad \psi \in \Psi, \qquad (5.2.21)$$

and Eq. 5.2.17 holds for $n = 0$. Assume the equation is valid for n. Then, arguing as in the proof of Theorem 5.2.3, there is an index $k \in \{1, \ldots, K_i\}$ such that

$$\begin{aligned} e_i(n + 1, \psi) = |e_i(n + 1, \psi)| &\leqslant |S_i^k(v, \infty, \psi) - S_i^k(v, n, \psi)| \\ &\leqslant \beta \sum_{j=1}^{N} \bar{p}_{ij}^k(\psi)\, |e_j(n, T_{ij}^k(\psi))| \\ &\leqslant \beta^{n+1} \frac{R - r}{1 - \beta}. \qquad \text{Q.E.D.} \quad (5.2.22) \end{aligned}$$

Corollary 5.2.5. If $\mathbf{v}(n, \psi)$ is defined by Eq. 5.2.1 and $\mathbf{v}(\psi)$ is the unique bounded solution of Eq. 5.1.7, then $\{\mathbf{v}(n, \psi)\} \to \mathbf{v}(\psi)$ uniformly in ψ.

Proof. Since the error bound in Eq. 5.2.17 is independent of ψ, the corollary follows from Theorem 5.2.4. Q.E.D.

Theorem 5.2.6. If the prior distribution function of $\tilde{\mathscr{P}}$ is $H(\mathscr{P} \mid \psi) \in \mathscr{H}$, a family of distributions continuous in ψ which is closed under consecutive sampling, then $\mathbf{v}(\psi)$, the unique bounded solution of Eq. 5.1.7, is a continuous function of ψ.

Proof. Since $\mathscr{H}$ is continuous in ψ, $v_i(0, \psi) = \max_{\boldsymbol{\sigma} \in \Sigma} \{\bar{V}_i(\boldsymbol{\sigma}, \psi)\}$ is a continuous function of ψ. Moreover, $\bar{p}_{ij}^k(\psi)$ is continuous. Thus, by induction, $v_i(n, \psi)$ is continuous for $i = 1, \ldots, N$ and $n = 0, 1, 2, \ldots$. Since $\{v_i(n, \psi)\} \to v_i(\psi)$ uniformly in ψ, $v_i(\psi)$ is continuous $(i = 1, \ldots, N)$. Q.E.D.

5.3. DISCOUNTED PROCESSES—MODEL II

In considering model I it is immediately apparent that the maximum expected reward will not be decreased—and may be increased—if we stop sampling in some states while continuing to sample in others. For example, if the marginal prior distribution of $\tilde{\mathbf{p}}_i^k$ is loose, while the marginal prior distribution of the remaining $(K - 1)$ rows of $\tilde{\mathscr{P}}$ is tight, it may be profitable to sample only when the system is in state i. Model II admits this additional option.

As in Sec. 5.1, let $v_i(\psi)$ be the supremum of the expected total discounted reward over an infinite period when the system starts from the generalized state (i, ψ). It is assumed that the decision maker can sample the system, use the system over a period of n transitions, or make a terminal decision. If the system is sampled, the consecutive sampling rule is operative and if the system is used, the ν-step sampling rule is operative. Thus we shall assume that the prior distribution function of $\tilde{\mathscr{P}}$ is $H(\mathscr{P} \mid \psi) \in \mathscr{H}$, a family of distributions closed under the ν-step sampling rule. Therefore, $\mathscr{H}$ is also closed under consecutive sampling. Thus, if the decision maker is in the state (i, ψ) and chooses either to sample or to use the process, the posterior distribution of $\tilde{\mathscr{P}}$ will be a member of $\mathscr{H}$.

If it is decided to sample when in state (i, ψ), the supremum of the prior expected reward is given by Eq. 5.1.4. Suppose, on the other hand, it is decided to use the process under policy $\boldsymbol{\sigma}$ for $n > 1$ transitions. The probability that the system will be observed in state j, unconditional with regard to the prior distribution of $\tilde{\mathscr{P}}$, given that the system starts in the generalized state (i, ψ) and that n transitions are to be observed under the policy $\boldsymbol{\sigma}$, is

$$\bar{p}_{ij}^{(n)}(\boldsymbol{\sigma}, \psi) = \int_{S_N} p_{ij}^{(n)}\, dF_{\boldsymbol{\sigma}}(\mathbf{P} \mid \psi),$$
$$i, j = 1, \ldots, N, \quad n = 2, 3, \ldots, \quad \boldsymbol{\sigma} \in \Sigma, \quad \psi \in \Psi, \quad (5.3.1)$$

the (i, j)th element of the prior expected n-step transition probability matrix under policy $\boldsymbol{\sigma}$. Let $\bar{q}_{ij}^{(n)}(\boldsymbol{\sigma}, \beta, \psi)$ denote the prior expected discounted reward earned over n transitions under the policy $\boldsymbol{\sigma}$ when the system starts from (i, ψ). Both $\bar{p}_{ij}^{n}(\boldsymbol{\sigma}, \psi)$ and $\bar{q}_{i}^{(n)}(\boldsymbol{\sigma}, \beta, \psi)$ are discussed in Sec. 4.1. Let $T_{ij}(n, \boldsymbol{\sigma}, \psi)$ denote the parameter of the posterior distribution of $\tilde{\mathscr{P}}$ when the system starts from (i, ψ) and is observed in state j after n transitions under the policy $\boldsymbol{\sigma}$. The prior expected reward under these conditions is

$$\bar{q}_{i}^{(n)}(\boldsymbol{\sigma}, \beta, \psi) + \beta^n \sum_{j=1}^{N} \bar{p}_{ij}^{(n)}(\boldsymbol{\sigma}, \psi)[v_j(T_{ij}(n, \boldsymbol{\sigma}, \psi)) - c_j],$$
$$i = 1, \ldots, N, \quad n = 2, 3, \ldots, \quad \boldsymbol{\sigma} \in \Sigma, \quad \psi \in \Psi, \quad (5.3.2)$$

and, if it is decided to use the system, the supremum of the expected discounted reward is

$$\max_{\boldsymbol{\sigma} \in \Sigma} \sup_{n=2,3,\ldots} \left\{ \bar{q}_{i}^{(n)}(\boldsymbol{\sigma}, \beta, \psi) + \beta^n \sum_{j=1}^{N} \bar{p}_{ij}^{(n)}(\boldsymbol{\sigma}, \psi)[v_j(T_{ij}(n, \boldsymbol{\sigma}, \psi)) - c_j] \right\},$$
$$i = 1, \ldots, N, \quad \psi \in \Psi. \quad (5.3.3)$$

Finally, if it is decided to make a terminal decision when in the generalized state (i, ψ), the supremum of the expected total discounted reward is

$$\max_{\boldsymbol{\sigma} \in \Sigma} \{\bar{V}_i(\boldsymbol{\sigma}, \psi)\}, \qquad i = 1, \ldots, N, \quad \psi \in \Psi. \qquad (5.3.4)$$

Noting that in Eq. 5.3.3 the supremum is attained for some finite n (for otherwise, we have a terminal decision and the supremum is given by Eq. 5.3.4), we shall write max instead of sup. Then the vector function $\boldsymbol{v}(\psi) = (v_1(\psi), \ldots, v_N(\psi))$ must satisfy the following functional equation:

$$v_i(\psi) = \max \begin{bmatrix} \max\limits_{1 \leqslant k \leqslant K_i} \left\{ \bar{q}_i^k(\psi) - \beta \bar{c}_i^k(\psi) + \beta \sum\limits_{j=1}^{N} \bar{p}_{ij}^k(\psi) v_j(T_{ij}^k(\psi)) \right\} \\ \max\limits_{\boldsymbol{\sigma} \in \Sigma} \max\limits_{n=2,3,\ldots} \left\{ \bar{q}_i^{(n)}(\boldsymbol{\sigma}, \beta, \psi) + \beta^n \sum\limits_{j=1}^{N} \bar{p}_{ij}^{(n)}(\boldsymbol{\sigma}, \psi) \right. \\ \left. \times [v_j(T_{ij}(n, \boldsymbol{\sigma}, \psi)) - c_j] \right\} \\ \max\limits_{\boldsymbol{\sigma} \in \Sigma} \{\bar{V}_i(\boldsymbol{\sigma}, \psi)\} \end{bmatrix},$$
$$i = 1, \ldots, N, \quad \psi \in \Psi. \quad (5.3.5)$$

We now consider some properties of model II. These properties, for the most part, parallel those of model I and the proofs are quite similar to those of Sec. 5.2. In the following two theorems it is shown that an optimal sampling strategy exists for model II and that, under realistic conditions a terminal decision point is reached with probability one in an optimal strategy. We then demonstrate the existence of a unique bounded solution to Eq. 5.3.5, and consider a method of successive approximations, together with a bound on the error of the nth approximant.

Theorem 5.3.1. Let $v_i(\psi, d)$ be the expected total discounted reward in model II when the system starts in the generalized state (i, ψ) and the sampling strategy $d \in D_i$ is used. Let

$$v_i(\psi) = \sup_{d \in D_i} \{v_i(\psi, d)\}, \qquad i = 1, \ldots, N, \quad \psi \in \Psi. \tag{5.3.6}$$

Then there is a sampling strategy $d^* \in D_i$ such that

$$v_i(\psi) = v_i(\psi, d^*), \qquad i = 1, \ldots, N, \quad \psi \in \Psi. \tag{5.3.7}$$

Proof. Let $\bar{D}_i$ be the set of all possible sampling strategies $\bar{d}$ in the adaptive control problem. Then $D_i \subset \bar{D}_i$. Suppose $\bar{d} \in \bar{D}_i$. Then $\bar{d}$ either prescribes a fixed policy $\boldsymbol{\sigma}$ for use on every transition $n > n^*$, for some integer n^*, or else not. In either case, $\bar{d}$ is a possible strategy for model II and $\bar{D}_i \subset D_i$. Thus, $D_i = \bar{D}_i$. The remainder of the proof is analogous to the proof of Theorem 3.2.1, with appropriate modifications to the reward and cost structure. Q.E.D.

Under the most general conditions there is no assurance that a terminal decision will be made in model II. For example, the reward and cost structure might be such that the optimal sampling strategy will call for use of the process for transition intervals of successive lengths ν, $\nu + n_1$, $\nu + n_2, \ldots$, where $n_1 < n_2, \ldots$, paying decreasing sampling costs for decreasing amounts of information about the state of nature as the prior distribution gets tighter. However, as the transition interval becomes large, the expected discounted reward over that interval approaches the total expected discounted reward that results from a terminal decision. Let μ be a positive integer and let the transition intervals be chosen from the finite set $\{1, \ldots, \mu\}$. It is easily established that if μ is chosen to be sufficiently large, the maximum expected discounted reward in this restricted version of model II can be made arbitrarily close to $v_i(\psi)$. The next theorem shows that a terminal decision is made with probability one in such a restricted version of model II.

Theorem 5.3.2. In model II, if the true state of nature $\mathbf{Q}$ is a positive matrix, if $H(\mathscr{P} \mid \psi) \in \mathscr{H}$, a family of distributions continuous in ψ, and if the transition intervals are chosen from the finite set $\{1, \ldots, \mu\}$, then, with probability one, a terminal decision point is reached in an optimal sampling strategy, provided $H(\mathscr{P} \mid \psi)$ assigns positive probability to the set E defined by Eq. 2.3.32.

Proof. Assume that there is an optimal sampling strategy in which a terminal decision is never made. We shall show a contradiction. Let a decision point in the sample history be a point in time at which the state of the system is made known to the decision maker. Then the assumption is that there are an infinite number of decision points. There is at least one state i which is observed infinitely often and at least one policy $\boldsymbol{\sigma}$ and transition interval n which are used infinitely often in state i. Lemma 2.3.7 and the positivity of $\mathfrak{Q}$ imply that every state is observed infinitely often with probability one. There is a finite set of ordered pairs $(n, \boldsymbol{\sigma})$, where $n \in \{1, 2, \ldots, \mu\}$ and $\boldsymbol{\sigma} \in \Sigma$, which describe the decisions made at each decision point. We may assume, without loss of generality, that all members of this finite set are used infinitely often in the sampling strategy, since any pair $(n, \boldsymbol{\sigma})$ which is used only a finite number of times is eventually dominated. The conditions of Theorem 2.3.9 are satisfied, and, therefore, the mass of the posterior distribution tends, with probability one, to concentrate at $\mathfrak{Q}$ as ν, the number of decision points, goes to infinity. If $H(\mathscr{P} \mid \psi^*)$ is the distribution function which places the unit mass of probability on $\mathfrak{Q}$, then $\psi \to \psi^*$ as $\nu \to \infty$. Since $\mathscr{H}$ is continuous in ψ, Theorems 2.4.3 and 5.3.8 below imply that the functions in Eq. 5.3.5 are continuous, hence, as $\nu \to \infty$, Eq. 5.3.5 becomes†

$$v_i(\psi^*) = \max \begin{bmatrix} \max\limits_{1 \leq k \leq K_i} \left\{ \bar{q}_i^k(\psi^*) - \beta \bar{c}_i^k(\psi^*) + \beta \sum\limits_{j=1}^{N} \bar{p}_{ij}^k(\psi^*) v_j(\psi^*) \right\} \\ \max\limits_{\boldsymbol{\sigma} \in \Sigma} \max\limits_{n=2, \ldots, \mu} \left\{ \bar{q}_i^{(n)}(\boldsymbol{\sigma}, \beta, \psi^*) + \beta^n \sum\limits_{j=1}^{N} \bar{p}_{ij}^{(n)}(\boldsymbol{\sigma}, \psi^*)[v_j(\psi^*) - c_j] \right\} \\ \max\limits_{\boldsymbol{\sigma} \in \Sigma} \{V_i(\boldsymbol{\sigma}, \psi^*)\} \end{bmatrix}$$

$$i = 1, \ldots, N. \quad (5.3.8)$$

Writing the first two lines of Eq. 5.3.8 as one equation, the assumption that a terminal decision is not made implies that

$$v_i(\psi^*) = \max_{\boldsymbol{\sigma} \in \Sigma} \max_{n=1, \ldots, \mu} \left\{ \bar{q}_i^{(n)}(\boldsymbol{\sigma}, \beta, \psi^*) + \beta^n \sum_{j=1}^{N} \bar{p}_{ij}^{(n)}(\boldsymbol{\sigma}, \psi^*)[v_j(\psi^*) - c_j] \right\}. \quad (5.3.9)$$

† The argument remains valid when the distribution which places the unit mass of probability on $\mathfrak{Q}$ is not a member of $\mathscr{H}$.

We now construct a new set of policies as follows. Let $\boldsymbol{s} = (s_1, \ldots, s_N)$ be a policy vector, where $s_k = (n_k, \boldsymbol{\sigma}_k)$ is a choice of a transition interval $n_k \in \{1, \ldots, \mu\}$ and a policy $\boldsymbol{\sigma}_k \in \Sigma$. If the alternative s_k is selected in state i, then the system goes to state j with probability $\bar{p}_{ij}^{(n_k)}(\boldsymbol{\sigma}_k, \psi^*)$, earning the expected reward $\bar{q}_j^{(n_k)}(\boldsymbol{\sigma}_k, \beta, \psi^*) - \beta^{n_k} c_j$. If S is the set of all possible alternatives s_k, then Eq. 5.3.9 can be written as

$$v_i(\psi^*) = \max_{s_k \in S} \left\{ \sum_{j=1}^{N} \bar{p}_{ij}^{(n_k)}(\boldsymbol{\sigma}_k, \psi^*)[\bar{q}_i^{(n_k)}(\boldsymbol{\sigma}_k, \beta, \psi^*) - \beta^{n_k} c_j + \beta^{n_k} v_j(\psi^*)] \right\}. \tag{5.3.10}$$

Equation 5.3.10 has the same formal structure as Eq. 5.1.11 in the proof of Theorem 5.1.2. An argument similar to that leading to Eq. 5.1.13 shows the contradiction

$$v_i(\psi^*) < \max_{\sigma \in \Sigma} \{\bar{V}_i(\boldsymbol{\sigma}, \psi^*)\}, \qquad i = 1, \ldots, N. \tag{5.3.11}$$

Thus, with probability one, a terminal decision point is reached. Q.E.D.

Let us now consider the existence and uniqueness of solutions to the functional equation 5.3.5. Let the sequence of vector functions $\boldsymbol{v}(n, \psi)$, where $\boldsymbol{v}(n, \psi) = (v_1(n, \psi), \ldots, v_N(n, \psi))$, be defined by the following equations:

$$v_i(n+1, \psi) = \max \begin{bmatrix} \max\limits_{1 \leqslant k \leqslant K_i} \left\{ \bar{q}_i^k(\psi) - \beta \bar{c}_i^k(\psi) + \beta \sum\limits_{j=1}^{N} \bar{p}_{ij}^k(\psi) v_j(n, T_{ij}^k(\psi)) \right\} \\ \max\limits_{\sigma \in \Sigma} \max\limits_{\nu = 2, 3, \ldots, n+1} \left\{ \bar{q}_i^{(\nu)}(\boldsymbol{\sigma}, \beta, \psi) + \beta^\nu \sum\limits_{j=1}^{N} \bar{p}_{ij}^{(\nu)}(\boldsymbol{\sigma}, \psi) \right. \\ \qquad\qquad \left. \times [v_j(n, T_{ij}(\nu, \boldsymbol{\sigma}, \psi)) - c_j] \right\} \\ \max\limits_{\sigma \in \Sigma} \{\bar{V}_i(\boldsymbol{\sigma}, \psi)\} \end{bmatrix}$$

$$i = 1, \ldots, N, \quad n = 0, 1, 2, \ldots, \quad \psi \in \Psi, \quad 0 \leqslant \beta < 1, \tag{5.3.12a}$$

$$v_i(0, \psi) = \max_{\sigma \in \Sigma} \{\bar{V}(\boldsymbol{\sigma}, \psi)\}, \qquad i = 1, \ldots, N, \quad \psi \in \Psi. \tag{5.3.12b}$$

Lemma 5.3.3. If $R^* = \max\limits_{i,j,k} \{|r_{ij}^k|\}$ and $C = \max\limits_j \{c_j\}$, then the functions $v_i(n, \psi)$ defined by Eq. 5.3.12 have the bound

$$|v_i(n, \psi)| \leqslant \frac{R^* + \beta C}{1 - \beta},$$

$$i = 1, \ldots, N, \quad n = 0, 1, 2, \ldots, \quad \psi \in \Psi, \quad 0 \leqslant \beta < 1. \tag{5.3.13}$$

Proof. The proof is by induction. Equation 5.2.4 shows that Eq. 5.3.13 holds for $n = 0$. Assume it holds for n. Since $|\bar{q}_i^{(1)}(\boldsymbol{\sigma}, \beta, \psi)| = |\bar{q}_i^{\sigma_i}(\psi)| \leqslant R^*$, an induction using Eq. 4.1.9 shows that

$$|\bar{q}_i^{(\nu)}(\boldsymbol{\sigma}, \beta, \psi)| \leqslant \frac{1 - \beta^\nu}{1 - \beta} R^*,$$

$$i = 1, \ldots, N, \quad \nu = 1, 2, 3, \ldots, \quad \boldsymbol{\sigma} \in \Sigma, \quad \psi \in \Psi. \tag{5.3.14}$$

Thus, from Eq. 5.3.12a and the induction hypothesis, we have

$$\begin{aligned}
|v_i(n + 1, \psi)| &\leqslant \max \begin{bmatrix} R^* + \beta C + \beta \dfrac{R^* + \beta C}{1 - \beta} \\[2ex] \displaystyle\max_{\nu=2,3,\ldots,n+1} \left\{ \frac{1 - \beta^\nu}{1 - \beta} R^* + \beta^\nu C + \beta^\nu \frac{R^* + \beta C}{1 - \beta} \right\} \\[2ex] \dfrac{R^*}{1 - \beta} \end{bmatrix} \\
&= \max \left[\frac{R^* + \beta C}{1 - \beta}, \max_{\nu=2,\ldots,n+1} \left\{ \frac{R^* + \beta^\nu C}{1 - \beta} \right\} \right] \\
&= \frac{R^* + \beta C}{1 - \beta}.
\end{aligned} \tag{5.3.15}$$

Q.E.D.

Theorem 5.3.4. If $\boldsymbol{v}(n, \psi)$ is defined by Eq. 5.3.12, then $\{v_i(n, \psi)\}$ is a monotone increasing sequence ($i = 1, \ldots, N$) and $\lim_{n\to\infty} v_i(n, \psi)$ exists and is a solution of Eq. 5.3.5.

Proof. The proof that $\{v_i(n, \psi)\}$ is monotone increasing is inductive. Clearly, $v_i(1, \psi) \geqslant v_i(0, \psi)$ for $i = 1, \ldots, N$ and $\psi \in \Psi$. Assume that $v_i(n, \psi) \geqslant v_i(n - 1, \psi)$. If, for some $\boldsymbol{\sigma} \in \Sigma$ and some integer ν,

$$v_i(n, \psi) = \bar{q}_i^{(\nu)}(\boldsymbol{\sigma}, \beta, \psi) + \beta^\nu \sum_{j=1}^N \bar{p}_{ij}^{(\nu)}(\boldsymbol{\sigma}, \psi)[v_j(n - 1, T_{ij}(\nu, \boldsymbol{\sigma}, \psi)) - c_j], \tag{5.3.16}$$

then

$$\begin{aligned}
v_i(n + 1, \psi) - v_i(n, \psi) \geqslant \beta^\nu \sum_{j=1}^N \bar{p}_{ij}^{(\nu)}(\boldsymbol{\sigma}, \psi)[v_j(n, T_{ij}(\nu, \boldsymbol{\sigma}, \psi)) \\
- v_j(n - 1, T_{ij}(\nu, \boldsymbol{\sigma}, \psi))] \geqslant 0.
\end{aligned} \tag{5.3.17}$$

If $v_i(n, \psi) = \max_{\boldsymbol{\sigma}\in\Sigma} \{\bar{V}_i(\boldsymbol{\sigma}, \psi)\}$, then $v_i(n + 1, \psi) \geqslant v_i(n, \psi)$ and, using Eq. 5.2.8, we have, in all cases,

$$v_i(n + 1, \psi) \geqslant v_i(n, \psi), \qquad i = 1, \ldots, N, \quad \psi \in \Psi, \tag{5.3.18}$$

proving monotonicity. By Lemma 5.3.3, the sequence $\{v_i(n, \psi)\}$ is bounded and, therefore, $\lim_{n \to \infty} v_i(n, \psi)$ exists. That the limit satisfies Eq. 5.3.5 follows by letting $n \to \infty$ in Eq. 5.3.12*a*. Q.E.D.

The remaining theorems, the proofs of which parallel very closely those of corresponding theorems in Sec. 5.2, are stated without proof.

Theorem 5.3.5. There is a unique bounded solution to Eq. 5.3.5.

Theorem 5.3.6. Let the error of the nth approximant $v_i(n, \psi)$ be defined as

$$e_i(n, \psi) = v_i(\psi) - v_i(n, \psi),$$
$$i = 1, \ldots, N, \quad n = 0, 1, 2, \ldots, \quad \psi \in \Psi, \quad (5.3.19)$$

where $\boldsymbol{v}(\psi) = (v_1(\psi), \ldots, v_N(\psi))$ is the unique bounded solution of Eq. 5.3.5 and $\boldsymbol{v}(n, \psi)$ is defined by Eq. 5.3.12. Then $e_i(n, \psi)$ has the bounds

$$0 \leqslant e_i(n, \psi) \leqslant \beta^n \frac{R - r}{1 - \beta},$$
$$i = 1, \ldots, N, \quad n = 0, 1, 2, \ldots, \quad \psi \in \Psi, \quad 0 \leqslant \beta < 1, \quad (5.3.20)$$

where R and r are defined by Eq. 3.4.3.

Corollary 5.3.7. If $\boldsymbol{v}(n, \psi)$ is defined by Eq. 5.3.12 and $\boldsymbol{v}(\psi)$ is the unique bounded solution of Eq. 5.3.5, then $\{\boldsymbol{v}(n, \psi)\} \to \boldsymbol{v}(\psi)$ uniformly in ψ.

Theorem 5.3.8. If the prior distribution function of $\tilde{\mathscr{P}}$ is $H(\mathscr{P} \mid \psi) \in \mathscr{H}$, a family of distributions continuous in ψ which is closed under ν-step sampling, then $\boldsymbol{v}(\psi)$, the unique bounded solution of Eq. 5.3.5, is continuous in ψ.

The numerical solution of model II involves considerably more computation than does the solution of model I. Not only does Eq. 5.3.12, the successive approximation scheme for model II, involve evaluation of more terms than does the corresponding scheme for model I, but the requirement that $\mathscr{H}$, the family of prior distributions of $\mathscr{P}$, be closed under ν-step sampling often means that the number of parameters which must be handled in computing solutions to model II is larger than that required for solving model I. The additional complexity of model II is probably worthwhile only in the case of a prior distribution which is tight on some rows of $\tilde{\mathscr{P}}$ and loose on others and where the cost of sampling is high.

We note that, although the aim of model II is to allow the decision maker to sample only those states in which there are transition probability vectors with loose marginal prior distributions, he does not have full control over the future states in which the system may be observed. For example, suppose it is desired to sample the system only when it is in state i. Then a sampling strategy must be choosen which trades off the expected discounted earnings of the system against the need for a high probability that the system enters state i at each decision point.

We remark in this connection that a decision to use the process when in state i does not necessarily imply that the consecutive sampling alternative is dominated at future decision points when the system is found in state i. Such dominance may hold under a sample history which reduces the marginal variances of the alternative probabilities in the ith state, but there is certainly no reason to expect this to be the case under a sequence of observations which increases the marginal variances of some transition probabilities.

5.4. APPROXIMATE TERMINAL DECISIONS

In models I and II it is necessary to evaluate expressions of the form

$$\bar{V}_i(\boldsymbol{\sigma}^*, \psi) = \max_{\boldsymbol{\sigma}\in\Sigma} \{\bar{V}_i(\boldsymbol{\sigma}, \psi)\}, \tag{5.4.1}$$

where $\bar{V}_i(\boldsymbol{\sigma}, \psi)$ is the expected total discounted reward earned over an infinite period under the policy $\boldsymbol{\sigma}$ when the system starts from the generalized state (i, ψ). Since Σ may contain a large number of policies, it is desirable to find methods of solving Eq. 5.4.1 for the maximizing policy $\boldsymbol{\sigma}^*$ which avoid a direct search over all elements of Σ. This problem has not been solved, but some preliminary remarks concerning the approximation of $\boldsymbol{\sigma}^*$ are offered in this section. It will be seen that these remarks are also applicable to the problem of selecting a policy which maximizes the expected gain $\bar{g}(\boldsymbol{\sigma}, \psi)$ discussed in Sec. 4.4.

Let $V_i(\boldsymbol{\sigma}, \mathscr{P})$ be the conditional expected total discounted reward over an infinite period under policy $\boldsymbol{\sigma}$ when the system starts from state i and $\tilde{\mathscr{P}} = \mathscr{P}$. The policy which maximizes this reward can be found efficiently by means of Howard's policy iteration algorithm [22]. It was seen in the proofs of Theorems 5.1.2 and 5.3.2 that, as the number of observations in model I or model II goes to infinity, the mass of the posterior probability distribution of $\tilde{\mathscr{P}}$ tends, with probability one, to concentrate at the true state of nature. Thus, if $\bar{\mathscr{P}}$ is the mean of the distribution of $\tilde{\mathscr{P}}$, we can approximate $\boldsymbol{\sigma}^*$ by $\hat{\boldsymbol{\sigma}}$, where $\hat{\boldsymbol{\sigma}}$ is defined by

$$V_i(\hat{\boldsymbol{\sigma}}, \bar{\mathscr{P}}) = \max_{\sigma\in\Sigma} \{V_i(\boldsymbol{\sigma}, \bar{\mathscr{P}})\}. \tag{5.4.2}$$

The error of this approximation goes to zero with probability one as the number of observations of the process goes to infinity. We consider here a bound on the error,

$$e_i(\hat{\boldsymbol{\sigma}}, \psi) = \bar{V}_i(\boldsymbol{\sigma}^*, \psi) - V_i(\hat{\boldsymbol{\sigma}}, \psi). \tag{5.4.3}$$

Let the policies $\boldsymbol{\sigma}$ be indexed by j. Thus, $\Sigma = \{\boldsymbol{\sigma}_1, \ldots, \boldsymbol{\sigma}_J\}$, where J is the number of distinct policies in Σ. For a fixed index i, let $\mathcal{S}_{KN}$ be partitioned into a set of J mutually exclusive and exhaustive subsets S_{ij} such that, if $\mathscr{P} \in S_{ij}$, then

$$V_i(\boldsymbol{\sigma}_j, \mathscr{P}) = \max_{\boldsymbol{\sigma}\in\Sigma} \{V_i(\boldsymbol{\sigma}, \mathscr{P})\}. \tag{5.4.4}$$

If $H(\mathscr{P} \mid \psi)$ is the prior distribution function of $\tilde{\mathscr{P}}$, let

$$P_{ij}(\psi) = \int_{S_{ij}} dH(\mathscr{P} \mid \psi), \qquad j = 1, \ldots, J, \quad \psi \in \Psi, \tag{5.4.5}$$

denote the prior probability that $\tilde{\mathscr{P}} \in S_{ij}$. Since the sets S_{ij} partition $\mathcal{S}_{KN}$,

$$\sum_{j=1}^{J} P_{ij}(\psi) = 1, \qquad \psi \in \Psi, \quad i = 1, \ldots, N. \tag{5.4.6}$$

Let $\bar{V}_{ij}(\boldsymbol{\sigma}, \psi)$ be the conditional expected value of $V_i(\boldsymbol{\sigma}, \tilde{\mathscr{P}})$, given that $\tilde{\mathscr{P}} \in S_{ij}$:

$$\bar{V}_{ij}(\boldsymbol{\sigma}, \psi) = \frac{1}{P_{ij}(\psi)} \int_{S_{ij}} V_i(\boldsymbol{\sigma}, \mathscr{P})\, dH(\mathscr{P} \mid \psi),$$
$$j = 1, \ldots, J, \quad \boldsymbol{\sigma} \in \Sigma, \quad \psi \in \Psi. \tag{5.4.7}$$

We note that Eq. 5.4.4 implies

$$\bar{V}_{ij}(\boldsymbol{\sigma}_j, \psi) \geqslant \bar{V}_{ij}(\boldsymbol{\sigma}, \psi), \qquad j = 1, \ldots, J, \quad \boldsymbol{\sigma} \in \Sigma, \quad \psi \in \Psi. \tag{5.4.8}$$

Let $R(\boldsymbol{\sigma})$ and $r(\boldsymbol{\sigma})$ be the maximum and minimum transition rewards when the policy $\boldsymbol{\sigma} = (\sigma_1, \ldots, \sigma_N)$ is used,

$$R(\boldsymbol{\sigma}) = \max_{i,j} \{r_{ij}^{\sigma_i}\}, \qquad \boldsymbol{\sigma} \in \Sigma, \tag{5.4.9a}$$

$$r(\boldsymbol{\sigma}) = \max_{i,j} \{r_{ij}^{\sigma_i}\}, \qquad \boldsymbol{\sigma} \in \Sigma, \tag{5.4.9b}$$

and let r and R be defined by Eq. 3.4.3. By Eq. 4.3.1

$$V_i(\boldsymbol{\sigma}, \mathscr{P}) = \sum_{n=0}^{\infty} \beta^n \sum_{\substack{j=1\\k=1}}^{N} p_{ij}^{(n)}(\boldsymbol{\sigma}) p_{jk}^{\sigma_j} r_{jk}^{\sigma_j},$$
$$\boldsymbol{\sigma} \in \Sigma, \quad \mathscr{P} \in \mathcal{S}_{KN}, \quad 0 \leqslant \beta < 1, \tag{5.4.10}$$

and, therefore,

$$\frac{r}{1-\beta} \leqslant \frac{r(\boldsymbol{\sigma})}{1-\beta} \leqslant \bar{V}_i(\boldsymbol{\sigma}, \psi) \leqslant \frac{R(\boldsymbol{\sigma})}{1-\beta} \leqslant \frac{R}{1-\beta},$$
$$\boldsymbol{\sigma} \in \Sigma, \quad \psi \in \Psi, \quad 0 \leqslant \beta < 1, \tag{5.4.11}$$

$$\frac{r(\boldsymbol{\sigma})}{1-\beta} \leqslant \bar{V}_{ij}(\boldsymbol{\sigma}, \psi) \leqslant \frac{R(\boldsymbol{\sigma})}{1-\beta},$$
$$j = 1, \ldots, J, \quad \boldsymbol{\sigma} \in \Sigma, \quad \psi \in \Psi, \quad 0 \leqslant \beta < 1. \tag{5.4.12}$$

Lemma 5.4.1. For $j = 1, \ldots, J$, the following inequality is valid:

$$\bar{V}_{ij}(\boldsymbol{\sigma}_j, \psi)P_{ij}(\psi) \leqslant \bar{V}_i(\boldsymbol{\sigma}_j, \psi) - (1 - P_{ij}(\psi))\frac{r(\boldsymbol{\sigma}_j)}{1-\beta},$$
$$j = 1, \ldots, J, \quad \psi \in \Psi, \quad 0 \leqslant \beta < 1. \quad (5.4.13)$$

Proof. Since the sets S_{ij} partition $\mathcal{S}_{KN}$, we have, using Eq. 5.4.12,

$$\begin{aligned}\bar{V}_i(\boldsymbol{\sigma}_j, \psi) &= \bar{V}_{ij}(\boldsymbol{\sigma}_j, \psi)P_{ij}(\psi) + \sum_{k \neq j} \bar{V}_{ij}(\boldsymbol{\sigma}_j, \psi)P_{ik}(\psi) \\ &\geqslant \bar{V}_{ij}(\boldsymbol{\sigma}_j, \psi)P_{ij}(\psi) + (1 - P_{ij}(\psi))\frac{r(\boldsymbol{\sigma}_j)}{1-\beta}. \quad (5.4.14)\end{aligned}$$

Equation 5.4.13 is a rearrangement of Eq. 5.4.14. Q.E.D.

Lemma 5.4.2. For any policy $\boldsymbol{\sigma} \in \Sigma$ and any index $j \in \{1, \ldots, J\}$, the expected discounted reward under the policy $\boldsymbol{\sigma}$ has the upper bound

$$\bar{V}_i(\boldsymbol{\sigma}, \psi) \leqslant \bar{V}_i(\boldsymbol{\sigma}_j, \psi) + \frac{1 - P_{ij}(\psi)}{1-\beta}(R - r(\boldsymbol{\sigma}_j)),$$
$$j = 1, \ldots, J, \quad \boldsymbol{\sigma} \in \Sigma, \quad \psi \in \Psi, \quad 0 \leqslant \beta < 1. \quad (5.4.15)$$

Proof. We have, using Eqs. 5.4.11, 5.4.8, and Lemma 5.4.1,

$$\begin{aligned}\bar{V}_i(\boldsymbol{\sigma}, \psi) &= \bar{V}_{ij}(\boldsymbol{\sigma}, \psi)P_{ij}(\psi) + \sum_{k \neq j} \bar{V}_{ik}(\boldsymbol{\sigma}, \psi)P_{ik}(\psi) \\ &\leqslant \bar{V}_{ij}(\boldsymbol{\sigma}, \psi)P_{ij}(\psi) + (1 - P_{ik}(\psi))\frac{R}{1-\beta} \\ &\leqslant \bar{V}_{ij}(\boldsymbol{\sigma}_j, \psi)P_{ij}(\psi) + (1 - P_{ij}(\psi))\frac{R}{1-\beta} \\ &\leqslant \bar{V}_i(\boldsymbol{\sigma}_j, \psi) + \frac{1 - P_{ij}(\psi)}{1-\beta}(R - r(\boldsymbol{\sigma}_j)). \qquad \text{Q.E.D.} \quad (5.4.16)\end{aligned}$$

Theorem 5.4.3. Let $e_i(\boldsymbol{\sigma}_j, \psi)$ be defined by

$$e_i(\boldsymbol{\sigma}_j, \psi) = \bar{V}_i(\boldsymbol{\sigma}^*, \psi) - \bar{V}_i(\boldsymbol{\sigma}_j, \psi),$$
$$j = 1, \ldots, J, \quad i = 1, \ldots, N, \quad \psi \in \Psi, \quad (5.4.17)$$

where $\boldsymbol{\sigma}^*$ is the maximizing terminal policy defined by Eq. 5.4.1. Then $e_i(\boldsymbol{\sigma}_j, \psi)$ has the bounds

$$0 \leqslant e_i(\boldsymbol{\sigma}_j, \psi) \leqslant \frac{1 - P_{ij}(\psi)}{1-\beta}(R - r(\boldsymbol{\sigma}_j)),$$
$$i = 1, \ldots, N, \quad j = 1, \ldots, J, \quad \psi \in, \Psi, \quad 0 \leqslant \beta < 1. \quad (5.4.18)$$

Proof. By Eq. 5.4.1, $\bar{V}_i(\boldsymbol{\sigma}^*, \psi) \geqslant \bar{V}_i(\boldsymbol{\sigma}_j, \psi)$ and $e_i(\boldsymbol{\sigma}_j, \psi) \geqslant 0$. The upper half of the inequality follows from Eq. 5.4.15. Q.E.D.

In order to bound $e_i(\boldsymbol{\sigma}_j, \psi)$, using Eq. 5.4.18, it is necessary to evaluate $P_{ij}(\psi)$. This problem has not been completely solved, chiefly because there is no satisfactory method of finding the boundaries of the set S_{ij}. Moreover, S_{ij} is not necessarily a connected set, which further complicates the problem. The probability $P_{ij}(\psi)$ can be estimated by using numerical or Monte Carlo techniques.

If $g(\boldsymbol{\sigma}, \tilde{\mathscr{P}})$ is the gain of a Markov chain with alternatives when operated in the steady state under the policy $\boldsymbol{\sigma}$, and if $\bar{g}(\boldsymbol{\sigma}, \psi)$ is the corresponding expected value when $\tilde{\mathscr{P}}$ has the distribution function $H(\mathscr{P} \mid \psi)$, then, as we shall see in the next section, it is often necessary to evaluate expressions of the form

$$\bar{g}(\boldsymbol{\sigma}^*, \psi) = \max_{\boldsymbol{\sigma} \in \Sigma} \{\bar{g}(\boldsymbol{\sigma}, \psi)\}. \tag{5.4.19}$$

If $\bar{\mathscr{P}}$ is the mean of the distribution $H(\mathscr{P} \mid \psi)$, we may wish to approximate $\boldsymbol{\sigma}^*$ by $\hat{\boldsymbol{\sigma}}$, defined by the expression

$$g(\hat{\boldsymbol{\sigma}}, \bar{\mathscr{P}}) = \max_{\boldsymbol{\sigma} \in \Sigma} \{g(\boldsymbol{\sigma}, \bar{\mathscr{P}})\}. \tag{5.4.20}$$

There are efficient algorithms for the solution of Eq. 5.4.20 [16, 22]. Let the error of the approximation $\boldsymbol{\sigma}_j$ be defined as

$$e(\boldsymbol{\sigma}_j, \psi) = \bar{g}(\boldsymbol{\sigma}^*, \psi) - \bar{g}(\boldsymbol{\sigma}_j, \psi),$$
$$j = 1, \ldots, J, \quad \psi \in \Psi. \tag{5.4.21}$$

A bound on $e(\boldsymbol{\sigma}_j, \psi)$ similar to that of Eq. 5.4.18 is easily derived.

Let $\mathbb{S}^*_{KN}$ be the set of all positive $K \times N$ generalized stochastic matrices and let $\mathbb{S}^*_{KN}$ be partitioned into J sets S_j where, if $\mathscr{P} \in S_j$, then

$$g(\boldsymbol{\sigma}_j, \mathscr{P}) = \max_{\boldsymbol{\sigma} \in \Sigma} \{g(\boldsymbol{\sigma}, \mathscr{P})\}. \tag{5.4.22}$$

If $H(\mathscr{P} \mid \psi)$ is the prior distribution function of $\tilde{\mathscr{P}}$, let

$$P_j(\psi) = \int_{S_j} dH(\mathscr{P} \mid \psi), \qquad j = 1, \ldots, J, \quad \psi \in \Psi, \tag{5.4.23}$$

be the prior probability that $\tilde{\mathscr{P}} \in S_j$. Let

$$\bar{g}_j(\boldsymbol{\sigma}, \psi) = \frac{1}{P_j(\psi)} \int_{S_j} g(\boldsymbol{\sigma}, \mathscr{P})\, dH(\mathscr{P} \mid \psi),$$
$$j = 1, \ldots, J, \quad \boldsymbol{\sigma} \in \Sigma, \quad \psi \in \Psi, \tag{5.4.24}$$

be the conditional expectation of $g(\boldsymbol{\sigma}, \tilde{\mathscr{P}})$ given that $\tilde{\mathscr{P}} \in S_j$. Then, by Eq. 5.4.22,

$$\bar{g}_j(\boldsymbol{\sigma}_j, \psi) \geqslant \bar{g}_j(\boldsymbol{\sigma}, \psi), \qquad j = 1, \ldots, J, \quad \boldsymbol{\sigma} \in \Sigma, \quad \psi \in \Psi. \tag{5.4.25}$$

If $R(\boldsymbol{\sigma})$ and $r(\boldsymbol{\sigma})$ are defined by Eq. 5.4.9 and R and r are defined by Eq. 3.4.3, Eq. 4.4.1 implies the inequalities

$$r \leqslant \bar{g}(\boldsymbol{\sigma}, \psi) \leqslant R, \qquad \boldsymbol{\sigma} \in \Sigma, \quad \psi \in \Psi, \tag{5.4.26}$$

$$r(\boldsymbol{\sigma}) \leqslant \bar{g}_j(\boldsymbol{\sigma}, \psi) \leqslant R(\boldsymbol{\sigma}), \qquad j = 1, \ldots, J, \quad \boldsymbol{\sigma} \in \Sigma, \quad \psi \in \Psi. \tag{5.4.27}$$

Lemma 5.4.4. For $j = 1, \ldots, J$,

$$\bar{g}_j(\boldsymbol{\sigma}_j, \psi)P_j(\psi) \leqslant \bar{g}(\boldsymbol{\sigma}_j, \psi) - (1 - P_j(\psi))r(\boldsymbol{\sigma}_j), \qquad j = 1, \ldots, J, \quad \psi \in \Psi. \tag{5.4.28}$$

Proof. Using Eq. 5.4.27,

$$\begin{aligned} \bar{g}(\boldsymbol{\sigma}_j, \psi) &= \bar{g}_j(\boldsymbol{\sigma}_j, \psi)P_j(\psi) + \sum_{k \neq j} \bar{g}_k(\boldsymbol{\sigma}_j, \psi)P_k(\psi) \\ &\geqslant \bar{g}_j(\boldsymbol{\sigma}_j, \psi)P_j(\psi) + (1 - P_j(\psi))r(\boldsymbol{\sigma}_j). \end{aligned} \quad 5.4.29)$$

Q.E.D.

Lemma 5.4.5. For any policy $\boldsymbol{\sigma} \in \Sigma$ and any $j \in \{1, \ldots, J\}$,

$$\bar{g}(\boldsymbol{\sigma}, \psi) \leqslant \bar{g}(\boldsymbol{\sigma}_j, \psi) + (1 - P_j(\psi))(R - r(\boldsymbol{\sigma}_j)), \qquad j = 1, \ldots, J, \quad \boldsymbol{\sigma} \in \Sigma, \quad \psi \in \Psi. \tag{5.4.30}$$

Proof. By Eqs. 5.4.26, 5.4.25, and Lemma 5.4.4,

$$\begin{aligned} \bar{g}(\boldsymbol{\sigma}, \psi) &= \bar{g}_j(\boldsymbol{\sigma}, \psi)P_j(\psi) + \sum_{k \neq j} \bar{g}_k(\boldsymbol{\sigma}, \psi)P_k(\psi) \\ &\leqslant \bar{g}_j(\boldsymbol{\sigma}_j, \psi)P_j(\psi) + (1 - P_j(\psi))R \\ &\leqslant \bar{g}(\boldsymbol{\sigma}_j, \psi) + (1 - P_j(\psi))(R - r(\boldsymbol{\sigma}_j)). \end{aligned} \tag{5.4.31}$$

Q.E.D.

Theorem 5.4.6. The error function $e(\boldsymbol{\sigma}_j, \psi)$ defined by Eq. 5.4.21 has the bound

$$0 \leqslant e(\boldsymbol{\sigma}_j, \psi) \leqslant (1 - P_j(\psi))(R - r(\boldsymbol{\sigma}_j)), \qquad j = 1, \ldots, J, \quad \psi \in \Psi. \tag{5.4.32}$$

Proof. The theorem follows directly from Eqs. 5.4.19 and 5.4.30.

Q.E.D.

5.5. UNDISCOUNTED PROCESSES

We have commented in Sec. 3.7 on the lack of a clear criterion for making decisions in an adaptive control model with no discounting. These remarks apply as well to undiscounted terminal models. One criterion we may use is to consider the class of sampling strategies which maximize the expected steady-state gain of the process, then to choose from this class the strategy which maximizes the expected reward over the transient period which precedes the terminal decision. This criterion is made precise in this section, where models III and IV, the undiscounted analogues of models I and II, are introduced. No analysis of these models has been carried out.

Model III

In model III it is assumed that the process will be sampled consecutively until a terminal decision point is reached, at which time a terminal policy is selected and the system is operated under this policy over a finite terminal operation period.

Let $v_i(\psi; \nu)$ be the supremum of the expected reward over a period whose terminal operation phase lasts for ν transitions when the system starts in state i and the prior distribution of $\tilde{\mathscr{P}}$ is $H(\mathscr{P} \mid \psi) \in \mathcal{H}$, a family of distributions closed under consecutive sampling. If, when in state (i, ψ), it is decided to sample at least once more, the supremum of the prior expected reward is given by Eq. 5.1.4 with $\beta = 1$.

Since we shall be concerned with large values of ν, we assume that, when it is decided to cease sampling, a terminal policy will be selected which maximizes the steady-state gain of the system $\bar{g}(\boldsymbol{\sigma}, \psi)$. Therefore, when it is decided to cease sampling, the supremum of the expected reward over the terminal period is

$$\max_{\boldsymbol{\sigma} \in \Sigma} \{\nu \bar{g}(\boldsymbol{\sigma}, \psi)\}. \tag{5.5.1}$$

Thus, under the assumptions of model III, $v_i(\psi; \nu)$ must satisfy the following functional equations:

$$v_i(\psi; \nu) = \max \begin{bmatrix} \max\limits_{1 \le k \le K_i} \left\{ \bar{q}_i^k(\psi) - \bar{c}_i^k(\psi) + \sum\limits_{j=1}^{N} \bar{p}_{ij}^k(\psi) v_j(T_{ij}^k(\psi); \nu) \right\} \\ \max\limits_{\boldsymbol{\sigma} \in \Sigma} \{\nu \bar{g}(\boldsymbol{\sigma}, \psi)\} \end{bmatrix},$$

$$i = 1, \ldots, N, \quad \psi \in \Psi, \quad \nu = 1, 2, 3, \ldots. \tag{5.5.2}$$

The arguments of Secs. 5.1 and 5.2 required that the discount factor β be less than unity and, therefore, are not directly applicable to model III. The existence and properties of solutions to Eq. 5.5.2 are matters for future investigation.

Equation 5.5.2 yields the supremum of the expected reward over a period with terminal phase of length ν and also yields a decision for the current transition interval. This decision, which is either the selection of an alternative to be sampled or a terminal policy, will be called a *ν-optimal decision.* A ν-optimal decision which is the same for all ν sufficiently large will be called an *optimal decision.* Since, for large ν, every ν-optimal decision maximizes gain and also maximizes the total reward over the sampling period, it is seen that an optimal decision, as defined here, satisfies the criterion set forth at the beginning of the section. The existence and nature of optimal decisions have not yet been investigated.

Model IV

We now assume that the decision maker can sample or use the process at any time prior to the terminal decision, independently of his past decisions. Let $v_i(\psi; \nu)$ be the supremum of the expected reward over a period with terminal operation phase of length ν when the system starts in state i with the prior distribution $H(\mathscr{P} \mid \psi)$. It is assumed that $H(\mathscr{P} \mid \psi) \in \mathcal{H}$, a family of distributions closed under ν-step sampling. Following the arguments of Sec. 5.3 and of the previous paragraph, it is seen that $v_i(\psi; \nu)$ must satisfy the following functional equation:

$$v_i(\psi; \nu) = \max \begin{bmatrix} \max\limits_{1 \le k \le K_i} \left\{ \bar{q}_i^k(\psi) - \bar{c}_i^k(\psi) + \sum\limits_{j=1}^{N} \bar{p}_{ij}^k(\psi) v_j(T_{ij}^k(\psi); \nu) \right\} \\ \max\limits_{\sigma \in \Sigma} \sup\limits_{n=2,3,\ldots} \left\{ \bar{q}_i^{(n)}(\boldsymbol{\sigma}, 1, \psi) + \sum\limits_{j=1}^{N} \bar{p}_{ij}^{(n)}(\boldsymbol{\sigma}, \psi) \right. \\ \left. \qquad \times \left[v_j(T_{ij}(n, \boldsymbol{\sigma}, \psi); \nu) - c_j \right] \right\} \\ \max\limits_{\sigma \in \Sigma} \{ \nu \bar{g}(\boldsymbol{\sigma}, \psi) \} \end{bmatrix},$$

$$i = 1, \ldots, N, \quad \psi \in \Psi, \quad \nu = 1, 2, 3, \ldots. \qquad (5.5.3)$$

The foregoing remarks concerning ν-optimal decisions and optimal decisions apply as well to model IV.

By approaching optimal decisions for the undiscounted terminal control models by means of ν-optimal decisions we have emphasized the fact that an undiscounted infinite-horizon model is an approximation to a system which runs for a long but finite period. We can equally well view the undiscounted model as an approximation to a system with a discount factor very close to unity. Thus, another approach to the solution of the undiscounted terminal control problem is to let $\beta \to 1$ in models I and II. The existence and properties of solutions obtained in this manner and their relation to solutions obtained via ν-optimal decisions have not yet been investigated.

5.6. DISCOUNTED PROCESSES WITH SETUP COSTS

In many processes which can be modeled as a Markov chain with alternatives there is a cost associated with changing alternatives in each state. Such a setup cost could include, for example, the cost of starting the operation of alternative k and of shutting down alternative j when in state i. Setup costs can easily be introduced into models I and II; we illustrate how this is done in model I for a fixed cost S which is incurred for each change of alternative made. The method is easily generalized to the case in which S is a function of the state in which the change is made and of the alternatives involved in the change, and is also applicable to the adaptive control model of Chap. 3.

Let $\boldsymbol{\sigma} = (\sigma_1, \ldots, \sigma_N)$ denote the policy under which the system is currently operating, where σ_i is the index of the alternative in use in the ith state ($\sigma_i = 1, \ldots, K_i$). We now define the generalized state of the system as $(i, \psi, \boldsymbol{\sigma})$, where i is the physical state of the system ($i = 1, \ldots, N$), ψ indexes the prior distribution of $\tilde{\mathscr{P}}$ ($\psi \in \Psi$), and $\boldsymbol{\sigma}$ is the policy currently in use ($\boldsymbol{\sigma} \in \Sigma$). Let $v_i(\psi, \boldsymbol{\sigma})$ be the supremum of the expected total discounted reward over an infinite period if the system starts in the generalized state $(i, \psi, \boldsymbol{\sigma})$. The prior distribution function of $\tilde{\mathscr{P}}$ is assumed to belong to a family of distributions closed under consecutive sampling.

If the system is in state $(i, \psi, \boldsymbol{\sigma})$ and it is decided to sample alternative k, the supremum of the expected reward is

$$(\delta_{k\sigma_i} - 1)S + \bar{q}_i^k(\psi) - \beta \bar{c}_i^k(\psi) + \beta \sum_{j=1}^{N} \bar{p}_{ij}^k(\psi) v_j(T_{ij}^k(\psi), \boldsymbol{\sigma}_i^*(k)), \quad (5.6.1)$$

where $\boldsymbol{\sigma}_i^*(k) = (\sigma_{i1}^*, \ldots, \sigma_{iN}^*)$, defined by

$$\begin{aligned} \sigma_{i\alpha}^* &= \sigma_\alpha, \qquad \alpha \neq i, \\ &= k\,, \qquad \alpha = i, \end{aligned} \quad (5.6.2)$$

is the new policy vector when alternative k is chosen in state i; δ_{ij} is the Kronecker delta. The quantities $\bar{q}_i^k(\psi)$ and $\bar{c}_i^k(\psi)$ are defined by Eq. 3.2.4 and 5.1.3 respectively.

If it is decided to cease sampling when the system is in state $(i, \psi, \boldsymbol{\sigma})$ and operate indefinitely under the policy $\boldsymbol{\sigma}' = (\sigma_1', \ldots, \sigma_N')$, the expected reward is

$$S \sum_{j=1}^{N} (\delta_{\sigma_j \sigma_j'} - 1) + \bar{V}_i(\boldsymbol{\sigma}', \psi), \quad (5.6.3)$$

where $\bar{V}_i(\boldsymbol{\sigma}', \psi)$ is the prior expected discounted reward for operating the system over an infinite period under the policy $\boldsymbol{\sigma}'$, starting from state i, when $H(\mathscr{P} \mid \psi)$ is the prior distribution of $\tilde{\mathscr{P}}$.

Thus, in model I with a fixed setup cost, $v_i(\psi, \boldsymbol{\sigma})$ must satisfy the following functional equation:

$$v_i(\psi, \boldsymbol{\sigma}) = \max \left[\begin{array}{l} \max\limits_{1 \leq k \leq K_i} \left\{ (\delta_{k\sigma_i} - 1)S + \bar{q}_i^k(\psi) - \beta \bar{c}_i^k(\psi) \right. \\ \qquad\qquad \left. + \beta \sum\limits_{j=1}^{N} \bar{p}_{ij}^k(\psi) v_j(T_{ij}^k(\psi), \boldsymbol{\sigma}_i^*(k)) \right\} \\ \max\limits_{\boldsymbol{\sigma}' \in \Sigma} \left\{ S \sum\limits_{j=1}^{N} (\delta_{\sigma_j \sigma_j'} - 1) + \bar{V}_i(\boldsymbol{\sigma}', \psi) \right\} \end{array} \right],$$

$$i = 1, \ldots, N, \quad \psi \in \Psi, \quad \boldsymbol{\sigma} \in \Sigma. \quad (5.6.4)$$

Chapter 6

DISTRIBUTION THEORY

In this chapter we introduce some probability mass functions and density functions which will be required for the next chapter, where we do the prior-posterior and preposterior analysis of a Markov chain observed under the consecutive sampling rule. The Whittle, Whittle-1, and Whittle-2 probability mass functions are defined in Sec. 6.1, and formulas for their moments are derived. The multivariate beta density function is considered in Sec. 6.2 and is used to define the matrix beta density function in Sec. 6.3. Some extensions of the matrix beta distribution are considered in Sec. 6.4, and the chapter concludes with a discussion of the beta-Whittle probability mass function.

The multivariate beta density function defined by Eq. 6.2.1 was introduced by Mauldon [30] in 1959; Mosimann [31] has studied the main properties of this distribution. The matrix beta distribution was used by Silver [38], but not under that name. The Whittle and beta-Whittle distributions are original with the present work.

6.1. THE WHITTLE DISTRIBUTION AND RELATED DISTRIBUTIONS

Let $\boldsymbol{x}_n = (x_0, x_1, \ldots, x_n)$ be a sequence of consecutive observations of the states of a Markov chain over a period of n transitions, where $x_0 = u$ is the state of the system prior to the first transition. The range set of the random variables $\tilde{x}_i$ is the set of integers which index the states of the chain, $\{1, \ldots, N\}$. It is assumed that the transitions are governed by a known $N \times N$ stochastic matrix $\mathbf{P} = [p_{ij}]$ and that the distribution of the initial state $\tilde{u}$ is a known stochastic row vector $\boldsymbol{p} = (p_1, \ldots, p_N)$.

Given a sample outcome $\boldsymbol{x}_n$, we define the statistic f_{ij} as the number of indices $m \in \{0, 1, \ldots, n-1\}$, such that $x_m = i$ and $x_{m+1} = j$ $(i, j = 1, \ldots, N)$. In other words, f_{ij} is the number of occurrences of a transition from state i to state j in the sample $\boldsymbol{x}_n$. Let $\mathbf{F} = [f_{ij}]$, an $N \times N$ matrix, be the *transition count* of the sample. Prior to the observation of $\boldsymbol{x}_n$, $\tilde{\mathbf{F}}$ and $\tilde{u}$ are random quantities whose joint distribution is studied in this section.

Let

$$f_{i\cdot} = \sum_{j=1}^{N} f_{ij}, \qquad i = 1, \ldots, N, \tag{6.1.1}$$

and

$$f_{\cdot j} = \sum_{i=1}^{N} f_{ij} \qquad j = 1, \ldots, N, \tag{6.1.2}$$

be the row and column sums of **F**. With the exception of the initial and final transitions, every transition into state i in the sample $\boldsymbol{x}_n$ must be followed by a transition out of state i. Therefore, the elements of **F** are constrained by the equations

$$f_{i\cdot} - f_{\cdot i} = \delta_{iu} - \delta_{iv}, \qquad i = 1, \ldots, N, \tag{6.1.3}$$

where $u = x_0$ is the initial state, $v = x_n$ is the final state, and δ_{ij} is the Kronecker delta.

The following lemma shows that, given a transition count **F** and an initial state u, the final state of the sample is uniquely determined. A similar derivation shows that, given **F** and v, u is uniquely determined. Lemma 6.1.5 below shows, however, that **F** does not necessarily uniquely determine both u and v.

Lemma 6.1.1. Let $u \in \{1, \ldots, N\}$ be fixed. If **F** is an $N \times N$ matrix of nonnegative integers which satisfies the equations

$$f_{i\cdot} - f_{\cdot i} = \delta_{iu} - \delta_{iv}, \qquad i = 1, \ldots, N, \tag{6.1.4}$$

for some integer $v \in \{1, \ldots, N\}$, then v is the only positive integer for which Eq. 6.1.4 is true.

Proof. The proof is by contradiction. Assume that v and w both satisfy Eq. 6.1.4. If $u \neq v$, then

$$f_{v\cdot} - f_{\cdot v} = \delta_{vu} - \delta_{vv} = -1$$

and, also,

$$f_{v\cdot} - f_{\cdot v} = \delta_{vu} - \delta_{vw} = -\delta_{vw},$$

which implies that $v = w$. If $u = v$, then

$$f_{i\cdot} - f_{\cdot i} = \delta_{iu} - \delta_{iu} = 0, \qquad i = 1, \ldots, N,$$

and

$$f_{i.} - f_{.i} = \delta_{iu} - \delta_{iw}, \qquad i = 1, \ldots, N.$$

Thus,

$$\delta_{iu} = \delta_{iw}, \qquad i = 1, \ldots, N,$$

and $w = u = v$. Q.E.D.

Let $I = \{0, 1, 2, \ldots\}$ denote the set of all nonnegative integers. For fixed $u \in \{1, \ldots, N\}$, $v \in \{1, \ldots, N\}$, $n \in \{1, 2, 3, \ldots\}$, and $\mathbf{P} \in \mathcal{S}_N$, define the following set of $N \times N$ matrices, $\mathbf{F} = [f_{ij}]$,

$$\phi_N(u, v, n, \mathbf{P}) = \Big\{\mathbf{F} \mid f_{ij} \in I, \sum_{\substack{i=1\\j=1}}^{N} f_{ij} = n,$$

$$f_{i.} - f_{.i} = \delta_{iu} - \delta_{iv}, \quad f_{ij} = 0 \text{ if } p_{ij} = 0, \quad (i, j = 1, \ldots, N)\Big\}. \tag{6.1.5}$$

Let

$$\phi_N(u, n, \mathbf{P}) = \bigcup_{v=1}^{N} \phi_N(u, v, n, \mathbf{P}),$$

$$u = 1, \ldots, N, \quad n = 1, 2, \ldots, \quad \mathbf{P} \in \mathcal{S}_N. \tag{6.1.6}$$

It is clear that $\phi_N(u, n, \mathbf{P})$ is the set of all possible transition counts $\mathbf{F}$ which can arise from a sample of n consecutive transitions in a Markov chain with transition matrix $\mathbf{P}$ and initial state u.

The Whittle Distribution

The $N \times N$ random matrix $\tilde{\mathbf{F}} = [\tilde{f}_{ij}]$ with range set $\phi_N(u, n, \mathbf{P})$ is said to have the Whittle distribution with parameter $(u, n, \mathbf{P})$ if $\tilde{\mathbf{F}}$ has the joint probability mass function

$$f_W^{(N)}(\mathbf{F} \mid u, n, \mathbf{P}) = F_{vu}^{*} \frac{\prod_{i=1}^{N} f_{i.}!}{\prod_{\substack{i=1\\j=1}}^{N} f_{ij}!} p_{ij}^{f_{ij}}, \qquad \mathbf{F} \in \phi_N(u, n, \mathbf{P}),$$

$$= 0 \qquad \text{otherwise}, \tag{6.1.7}$$

where

$$u = 1, \ldots, N, \qquad n = 1, 2, 3, \ldots, \qquad \mathbf{P} \in \mathcal{S}_N.$$

The index v is the unique solution of the equations

$$f_{i.} - f_{.i} = \delta_{iu} - \delta_{iv}, \qquad i = 1, \ldots, N,$$

and F^*_{vu} is the (v, u)th cofactor of the $N \times N$ matrix $\mathbf{F}^* = [f^*_{ij}]$ defined by

$$f^*_{ij} = \delta_{ij} - \frac{f_{ij}}{f_{i.}}, \qquad f_{i.} > 0, \tag{6.1.8a}$$

$$= \delta_{ij}, \qquad f_{i.} = 0. \tag{6.1.8b}$$

Since, in Eq. 6.1.7, there may be some $p_{ij} = 0$, we use the convention $0^0 = 1$.

We have called the mass function Eq. 6.1.7 the *Whittle distribution* because Whittle [41] was the first to show that

$$\sum_{\mathbf{F} \in \phi_N(u,n,\mathbf{P})} \prod_{\substack{i=1\\j=1}}^{N} p_{ij}^{f_{ij}} = \frac{\prod_{\substack{i=1\\j=1}}^{N} f_{ij}!}{F^*_{vu} \prod_{i=1}^{N} f_{i.}!}. \tag{6.1.9}$$

Whittle's derivation of Eq. 6.1.9 and subsequent proofs of this relation by Dawson and Good [15] and by Goodman [21] were obtained under the restriction $f_{i.} > 0$ $(i = 1, \ldots, N)$. Billingsley [10], in a particularly elegant proof of Eq. 6.1.9, did not require this restriction.

Moments of the Whittle Distribution

We now derive expressions for the means, variances, and covariances of the elements of $\tilde{\mathbf{F}}$. Before presenting these results, however, it is necessary to summarize certain facts from the theory of matrices.

Let $\mathbf{P}$ be an $N \times N$ matrix with eigenvalues $\lambda_1, \ldots, \lambda_N$, assumed to be distinct. Let $g(x)$ be an arbitrary scalar polynomial, $a_0 + a_1 x + \cdots + a_n x^n$, and let $\mathbf{g}(\mathbf{P})$ be the corresponding matrix polynomial, $a_0 \mathbf{I} + a_1 \mathbf{P} + \cdots + a_n \mathbf{P}^n$. Sylvester's theorem states that

$$\mathbf{g}(\mathbf{P}) = \sum_{k=1}^{N} g(\lambda_k) \mathbf{A}^{(k)}, \tag{6.1.10}$$

where the $N \times N$ matrices $\mathbf{A}^{(k)}$ are defined by the expression

$$\mathbf{A}^{(k)} = [a_{ij}^{(k)}] = \frac{\prod_{i \neq k} [\lambda_i \mathbf{I} - \mathbf{P}]}{\prod_{i \neq k} (\lambda_i - \lambda_k)}, \qquad k = 1, \ldots, N. \tag{6.1.11}$$

These matrices have the following properties:

$$\mathbf{A}^{(i)} \mathbf{A}^{(j)} = \mathbf{0}, \qquad i \neq j, \tag{6.1.12a}$$

$$[\mathbf{A}^{(i)}]^2 = \mathbf{A}^{(i)}, \qquad i = 1, \ldots, N. \tag{6.1.12b}$$

A formula similar to Eq. 6.1.10, called the *confluent form of Sylvester's theorem*, is available in the case of repeated eigenvalues.

If $\mathbf{P}$ is an ergodic stochastic matrix, that is, if $\mathbf{P}$ is the transition matrix of a single nonperiodic Markov chain, then exactly one eigenvalue has the value unity and all other eigenvalues have modulus less than unity. We shall adopt the convention that λ_1 is the unit root:

$$\lambda_1 = 1 \tag{6.1.13a}$$

$$|\lambda_i| < 1, \qquad i = 2, \ldots, N. \tag{6.1.13b}$$

Then the matrix $\mathbf{A}^{(1)}$ is an $N \times N$ matrix each row of which is the steady-state vector $\boldsymbol{\pi} = (\pi_1, \ldots, \pi_N)$ defined by the relation $\boldsymbol{\pi} = \boldsymbol{\pi}\mathbf{P}$.

Theorem 6.1.2. If the $N \times N$ random matrix $\tilde{\mathbf{F}}$ has the Whittle distribution with parameter $(u, n, \mathbf{P})$, then the expected value of $\tilde{f}_{ij}$ is

$$E[\tilde{f}_{ij}] = \bar{f}_{ij}(u, n) = \sum_{k=0}^{n-1} p_{ui}^{(k)} p_{ij},$$

$$i, j = 1, \ldots, N, \quad n = 1, 2, 3, \ldots, \quad u = 1, \ldots, N, \tag{6.1.14}$$

where $p_{ui}^{(k)}$ is the (u, i)th element of $\mathbf{P}^k$. If, furthermore, $\mathbf{P}$ is ergodic and the eigenvalues $\lambda_1, \ldots, \lambda_N$ of $\mathbf{P}$ are distinct, then the expected value of $\tilde{f}_{ij}$ has the spectral representation

$$\bar{f}_{ij}(u, n) = p_{ij}\left[n\pi_i + \sum_{m=2}^{N} \frac{1 - \lambda_m^n}{1 - \lambda_m} a_{ui}^{(m)}\right],$$

$$i, j = 1, \ldots, N, \quad n = 1, 2, 3, \ldots, \quad u = 1, \ldots, N, \tag{6.1.15}$$

where $\mathbf{A}^{(m)} = [a_{ij}^{(m)}]$ is defined by Eq. 6.1.11.

Proof. Let $f_{ij}(u, n)$ be the number of transitions from i to j in a sample of n transitions which has initial state u. Prior to the observation of the sample, $\tilde{f}_{ij}(u, n)$ is a random variable. If the system starts in state u and the first transition is to state k, then $\tilde{f}_{ij}(u, n)$ satisfies the equations

$$\tilde{f}_{ij}(u, n) = \delta_{ui}\delta_{kj} + \tilde{f}_{ij}(k, n-1),$$

$$n = 2, 3, \ldots, \quad k = 1, \ldots, N, \tag{6.1.16a}$$

and

$$\tilde{f}_{ij}(u, 1) = \delta_{ui}\,\delta_{kj}, \qquad k = 1, \ldots, N. \tag{6.1.16b}$$

Thus, $\tilde{f}_{ij}(u, n)$ satisfies the equations

$$\tilde{f}_{ij}(u, n) = p_{uj}\,\delta_{ui} + \sum_{k=1}^{N} p_{uk}\tilde{f}_{ij}(k, n-1), \qquad n = 2, 3, \ldots, \tag{6.1.17a}$$

$$\tilde{f}_{ij}(u, 1) = p_{uj}\,\delta_{ui}. \tag{6.1.17b}$$

We shall prove inductively that

$$\tilde{f}_{ij}(u, n) = \sum_{k=0}^{n-1} p_{ui}^{(k)} p_{ij},$$

$$i, j = 1, \ldots, N, \quad n = 1, 2, 3, \ldots, \quad u = 1, \ldots, N. \tag{6.1.18}$$

Since $\delta_{ui}p_{ij} = \delta_{ui}p_{uj}$, Eq. 6.1.17 is satisfied by Eq. 6.1.18 for $n = 1$. Assume that Eq. 6.1.18 holds for n. Then, using Eq. 6.1.17a,

$$\begin{aligned}\tilde{f}_{ij}(u, n+1) &= p_{uj}\,\delta_{ui} + \sum_{k=1}^{N} p_{uk} \sum_{m=0}^{n-1} p_{ki}^{(m)} p_{ij} \\ &= p_{uj}\,\delta_{ui} + \sum_{m=0}^{n-1} p_{ui}^{(m+1)} p_{ij} \\ &= \sum_{k=0}^{n} p_{ui}^{(k)} p_{ij},\end{aligned} \tag{6.1.19}$$

proving the induction.

If all the eigenvalues of $\mathbf{P}$ are distinct, Sylvester's theorem yields

$$p_{ui}^{(k)} = \sum_{m=1}^{N} \lambda_m^k a_{ui}^{(m)}, \qquad k = 0, 1, 2, \ldots. \tag{6.1.20}$$

If, furthermore, $\mathbf{P}$ is ergodic and $\lambda_1 = 1$ is the only eigenvalue of unit modulus, Eq. 6.1.18 can be written as

$$\begin{aligned}\tilde{f}_{ij}(u, n) &= \sum_{k=0}^{n-1} \sum_{m=1}^{N} \lambda_m^k a_{ui}^{(m)} p_{ij} \\ &= p_{ij}\left[n\pi_i + \sum_{m=2}^{N} \frac{1-\lambda_m^n}{1-\lambda_m} a_{ui}^{(m)}\right],\end{aligned}$$

$$i, j = 1, \ldots, N, \quad n = 1, 2, 3, \ldots, \quad u = 1, \ldots, N, \tag{6.1.21}$$

Q.E.D.

Theorem 6.1.3. If the $N \times N$ random matrix $\tilde{\mathbf{F}}$ has the Whittle distribution with parameter $(u, n, \mathbf{P})$, then, for $\alpha, \beta, \gamma, \delta = 1, \ldots, N$, the covariance between $\tilde{f}_{\alpha\beta}$ and $\tilde{f}_{\gamma\beta}$ is

$$\begin{aligned}\operatorname{cov}[\tilde{f}_{\alpha\beta}, \tilde{f}_{\gamma\delta}] &= \tilde{f}_{\alpha\beta}(u, n)[\delta_{\alpha\gamma}\,\delta_{\beta\delta} - \tilde{f}_{\gamma\delta}(u, n)] \\ &\quad + \sum_{k=1}^{n-1} [p_{u\alpha}^{(n-1-k)} p_{\alpha\beta} \tilde{f}_{\gamma\delta}(\beta, k) + p_{u\gamma}^{(n-1-k)} p_{\gamma\delta} \tilde{f}_{\alpha\beta}(\delta, k)] \\ &\qquad\qquad n = 2, 3, \ldots, \qquad (6.1.22a) \\ &= \delta_{\alpha u} p_{u\beta}[\delta_{\alpha\gamma}\,\delta_{\beta\delta} - \delta_{\gamma u} p_{u\delta}], \qquad n = 1. \qquad (6.1.22b)\end{aligned}$$

If $\mathbf{P}$ is ergodic and the eigenvalues of $\mathbf{P}$, $\lambda_1, \ldots, \lambda_N$, are all distinct, the covariance of $\tilde{f}_{\alpha\beta}$ and $\tilde{f}_{\gamma\beta}$ has the spectral representation

$$
\begin{aligned}
\operatorname{cov}[\tilde{f}_{\alpha\beta}, \tilde{f}_{\gamma\delta}] = {} & p_{\alpha\beta}\,\delta_{\alpha\gamma}\,\delta_{\beta\delta}\left[n\pi_\alpha + \sum_{m=2}^{N} \frac{1-\lambda_m^n}{1-\lambda_m}\, a_{u\alpha}^{(m)}\right] \\
& - p_{\alpha\beta}p_{\gamma\delta}\left\{n\sum_{m=2}^{N}\left[\frac{1-\lambda_m^n}{1-\lambda_m}(\pi_\alpha a_{u\gamma}^{(m)} + \pi_\gamma a_{u\alpha}^{(m)})\right]\right. \\
& \left. + \sum_{\substack{m=2\\ j=2}}^{N}\left(\frac{1-\lambda_m^n}{1-\lambda_m}\right)\left(\frac{1-\lambda_j^n}{1-\lambda_j}\right) a_{u\alpha}^{(m)} a_{u\gamma}^{(j)}\right\} \\
& + p_{\alpha\beta}p_{\gamma\delta}\left\{-n\pi_\alpha\pi_\gamma + \sum_{m=2}^{N} \frac{n-1-n\lambda_m+\lambda_m^n}{(1-\lambda_m)^2}\right. \\
& \times [\pi_\alpha(a_{u\gamma}^{(m)} + a_{\beta\gamma}^{(m)}) + \pi_\gamma(a_{u\alpha}^{(m)} + a_{\delta\alpha}^{(m)})] \\
& + \sum_{m=2}^{N} \frac{1-n\lambda_m^{n-1}+(n-1)\lambda_m^n}{(1-\lambda_m)^2}(a_{u\alpha}^{(m)}a_{\beta\gamma}^{(m)} + a_{u\gamma}^{(m)}a_{\delta\alpha}^{(m)}) \\
& + \sum_{m=2}^{N} \sum_{\substack{j\neq 1\\ j\neq m}} \frac{a_{u\alpha}^{(m)}a_{\beta\gamma}^{(j)} + a_{u\gamma}^{(m)}a_{\delta\alpha}^{(j)}}{1-\lambda_j} \\
& \left.\times\left[\frac{1-\lambda_m^{n-1}}{1-\lambda_m} - \frac{\lambda_j(\lambda_m^{n-1}-\lambda_j^{n-1})}{\lambda_m-\lambda_j}\right]\right\}
\end{aligned}
\tag{6.1.23}
$$

when $n > 1$.

Proof. The proof is presented in steps.

1. If $\tilde{f}_{\alpha\beta}(u, n)$ is the number of transitions from state α to state β in a sample of n transitions when the chain starts in state u, Eq. 6.1.16 and the relation $\delta_{ki}\delta_{kj} = \delta_{ij}\delta_{ki}$ imply that, if the first transition is from u to k,

$$
\begin{aligned}
\tilde{f}_{\alpha\beta}(u, n)\tilde{f}_{\gamma\beta}(u, n) &= \delta_{\alpha\gamma}\delta_{\beta\delta}\delta_{\alpha u}\delta_{\beta k} + \delta_{u\gamma}\delta_{k\delta}\tilde{f}_{\alpha\beta}(k, n-1) \\
&\quad + \delta_{u\alpha}\delta_{k\beta}\tilde{f}_{\gamma\delta}(k, n-1) + \tilde{f}_{\alpha\beta}(k, n-1)\tilde{f}_{\gamma\delta}(k, n-1), \\
&\qquad n = 2, 3, \ldots, \quad k = 1, \ldots, N, \qquad (6.1.24a) \\
&= \delta_{\alpha\gamma}\delta_{\beta\delta}\delta_{\alpha u}\delta_{\beta k}, \qquad n = 1, \quad k = 1, \ldots, N. \qquad (6.1.24b)
\end{aligned}
$$

Let

$$\sigma_{\alpha\beta\gamma\delta}(u, n) = E[\tilde{f}_{\alpha\beta}(u, n)\tilde{f}_{\gamma\delta}(u, n)]. \tag{6.1.25}$$

Then, using Eq. 6.1.24, it is seen that $\sigma_{\alpha\beta\gamma\delta}(u, n)$ satisfies the equations

$$
\begin{aligned}
\sigma_{\alpha\beta\gamma\delta}(u, n) &= \delta_{\alpha\gamma}\delta_{\beta\delta}\delta_{\alpha u}p_{u\beta} + \delta_{u\gamma}p_{u\delta}\bar{f}_{\alpha\beta}(\delta, n-1) + \delta_{u\alpha}p_{u\beta}\bar{f}_{\gamma\delta}(\beta, n-1) \\
&\quad + \sum_{k=1}^{N} p_{uk}\sigma_{\alpha\beta\gamma\delta}(k, n-1), \qquad n = 2, 3, \ldots, \qquad (6.1.26a) \\
&= \delta_{\alpha\gamma}\delta_{\beta\delta}\delta_{\alpha u}p_{u\beta}, \qquad n = 1. \qquad (6.1.26b)
\end{aligned}
$$

2. We now show that

$$\sigma_{\alpha\beta\gamma\delta}(u, n) = \delta_{\alpha\gamma}\delta_{\beta\delta}\bar{f}_{\alpha\beta}(u, n) + \sum_{k=1}^{n-1} [p_{u\alpha}^{(n-1-k)} p_{\alpha\beta}\bar{f}_{\gamma\delta}(\beta, k) + p_{u\gamma}^{(n-1-k)} p_{\gamma\delta}\bar{f}_{\alpha\beta}(\delta, k)],$$
$$u = 1, \ldots, N, \quad n = 2, 3, \ldots, \tag{6.1.27a}$$
$$= \delta_{\alpha\gamma}\delta_{\beta\delta}\bar{f}_{\alpha\beta}(u, 1), \qquad u = 1, \ldots, N, \quad n = 1, \tag{6.1.27b}$$

in which case Eq. 6.1.22 follows.

It is clear from Eq. 6.1.17*b* that Eq. 6.1.27*b* equals Eq. 6.1.26*b*. The case $n = 2, 3, \ldots$ will be proved by induction. For $n = 2$, it is easily verified that Eq. 6.1.26*a* is equal to the expression in Eq. 6.1.27*a*. Assume that Eq. 6.1.27*a* is correct for n. Then, using Eqs. 6.1.26*a* and 6.1.14,

$$\begin{aligned}
\sigma_{\alpha\beta\gamma\delta}(u, n+1) &= \delta_{\alpha\gamma}\delta_{\beta\delta}\delta_{\alpha u}p_{u\beta} + \delta_{u\gamma}p_{u\delta}\bar{f}_{\alpha\beta}(\delta, n) + \delta_{u\alpha}p_{u\beta}\bar{f}_{\gamma\delta}(\beta, n) \\
&\quad + \sum_{k=1}^{N} p_{uk}\Big\{\delta_{\alpha\gamma}\delta_{\beta\delta}\sum_{m=0}^{n-1} p_{k\alpha}^{(m)}p_{\alpha\beta} + \sum_{m=1}^{n-1}[p_{k\alpha}^{(n-1-m)}p_{\alpha\beta}\bar{f}_{\gamma\delta}(\beta, m) \\
&\quad + p_{k\gamma}^{(n-1-m)}p_{\gamma\delta}\bar{f}_{\alpha\beta}(\delta, m)]\Big\} \\
&= \delta_{\alpha\gamma}\delta_{\beta\delta}\delta_{\alpha u}p_{u\beta} + \delta_{u\gamma}p_{u\delta}\bar{f}_{\alpha\beta}(\delta, n) + \delta_{u\alpha}p_{u\beta}\bar{f}_{\gamma\delta}(\beta, n) \\
&\quad + \delta_{\alpha\gamma}\delta_{\beta\delta}\sum_{m=0}^{n-1} p_{u\alpha}^{(m+1)}p_{\alpha\beta} \\
&\quad + \sum_{m=1}^{n-1}[p_{u\alpha}^{(n-m)}p_{\alpha\beta}\bar{f}_{\gamma\delta}(\beta, m) + p_{u\gamma}^{(n-m)}p_{\gamma\delta}\bar{f}_{\alpha\beta}(\delta, m)] \\
&= \delta_{\alpha\gamma}\delta_{\beta\delta}\bar{f}_{\alpha\beta}(u, n+1) \\
&\quad + \sum_{k=1}^{n}[p_{u\alpha}^{(n-k)}p_{\alpha\beta}\bar{f}_{\gamma\delta}(\beta, k) + p_{u\gamma}^{(n-k)}p_{\gamma\delta}\bar{f}_{\alpha\beta}(\delta, k)],
\end{aligned} \tag{6.1.28}$$

proving the induction.

3. If **P** is ergodic and has distinct eigenvalues, Eqs. 6.1.15 and 6.1.20 for the spectral representations of $\bar{f}_{ij}(u, n)$ and $p_{ui}^{(k)}$ can be used in Eq. 6.1.22*a* to obtain, for $n = 2, 3, \ldots,$

$$\begin{aligned}
\operatorname{cov}[\bar{f}_{\alpha\beta}, \bar{f}_{\gamma\delta}] &= p_{\alpha\beta}\left[n\pi_\alpha + \sum_{m=2}^{N}\frac{1-\lambda_m^n}{1-\lambda_m}a_{u\alpha}^{(m)}\right] \\
&\quad \times \left(\delta_{\alpha\gamma}\delta_{\beta\delta} - p_{\gamma\delta}\left[n\pi_\gamma + \sum_{m=2}^{N}\frac{1-\lambda_m^n}{1-\lambda_m}a_{u\gamma}^{(m)}\right]\right) \\
&\quad + p_{\alpha\beta}p_{\gamma\delta}\sum_{k=1}^{n-1}\sum_{m=1}^{N}\lambda_m^{(n-1-k)}\left[a_{u\alpha}^{(m)}\left(k\pi_\gamma + \sum_{j=2}^{N}\frac{1-\lambda_j^k}{1-\lambda_j}a_{\beta\gamma}^{(j)}\right)\right. \\
&\quad \left. + a_{u\gamma}^{(m)}\left(k\pi_\alpha + \sum_{j=2}^{N}\frac{1-\lambda_j^k}{1-\lambda_j}a_{\delta\alpha}^{(j)}\right)\right].
\end{aligned} \tag{6.1.29}$$

Multiplying out Eq. 6.1.29 and using the relations

$$\sum_{k=1}^{n-1} k\lambda_m^{(n-1-k)} = \frac{n - 1 - n\lambda_m + \lambda_m^n}{(1 - \lambda_m)^2}, \qquad m = 2, \ldots, N, \quad (6.1.30)$$

$$\sum_{k=1}^{n-1} (1 - \lambda_j^k) = \frac{n - 1 - n\lambda_j + \lambda_j^n}{1 - \lambda_j}, \qquad j = 2, \ldots, N, \quad (6.1.31)$$

$$\sum_{k=1}^{n-1} \lambda_m^{(n-1-k)}(1 - \lambda_j^k) = \frac{1 - \lambda_m^{n-1}}{1 - \lambda_m} - \frac{\lambda_j(\lambda_m^{n-1} - \lambda_j^{n-1})}{\lambda_m - \lambda_j},$$

$$j, m = 2, \ldots, N, \quad j \neq m, \quad (6.1.32)$$

and

$$\sum_{k=1}^{n-1} \lambda_m^{(n-1-k)}(1 - \lambda_m^k) = \frac{1 - n\lambda_m^{n-1} + (n-1)\lambda_m^n}{1 - \lambda_m},$$

$$m = 2, \ldots, N, \quad (6.1.33)$$

Eq. 6.1.23 is obtained. Q.E.D.

In Theorems 6.1.2 and 6.1.3 the spectral representations provide an efficient method of computing the means, variances, and covariances of elements of $\tilde{\mathbf{F}}$, despite the apparent complexity of Eq. 6.1.23. This method is particularly useful as the parameter n becomes large and, in fact, leads to relatively simple approximations for $\bar{f}_{ij}(u, n)$ and cov $[\tilde{f}_{\alpha\beta}, \tilde{f}_{\gamma\delta}]$ when n is sufficiently large, as is shown in the following corollary.

Corollary 6.1.4. If the $N \times N$ random matrix $\mathbf{F}$ has the Whittle distribution with parameter $(u, n, \mathbf{P})$, where $\mathbf{P}$ is ergodic and has distinct eigenvalues, then, for large n, the expected value of $\tilde{f}_{ij}$ and the covariance between $\tilde{f}_{\alpha\beta}$ and $\tilde{f}_{\gamma\delta}$ are given by the following asymptotic expressions:

$$\bar{f}_{ij}(u, n) \approx p_{ij}\left[n\pi_i + \sum_{m=2}^{N} \frac{a_{ui}^{(m)}}{1 - \lambda_m}\right], \qquad i, j = 1, \ldots, N, \quad (6.1.34)$$

$$\text{cov}\,[\tilde{f}_{\alpha\beta}, \tilde{f}_{\gamma\delta}] \approx n\left[\pi_\alpha p_{\alpha\beta}\delta_{\alpha\gamma}\delta_{\beta\delta} - \pi_\alpha p_{\alpha\beta}\pi_\gamma p_{\gamma\delta} + p_{\alpha\beta}p_{\gamma\delta}\sum_{m=2}^{N}\frac{\pi_\alpha a_{\beta\gamma}^{(m)} + \pi_\gamma a_{\delta\alpha}^{(m)}}{1 - \lambda_m}\right]$$

$$+ p_{\alpha\beta}\delta_{\alpha\gamma}\delta_{\beta\delta}\sum_{m=2}^{N}\frac{a_{u\alpha}^{(m)}}{1 - \lambda_m} - p_{\alpha\beta}p_{\gamma\delta}\sum_{m=2}^{N}\frac{\pi_\alpha(a_{u\gamma}^{(m)} + a_{\beta\gamma}^{(m)}) + \pi_\gamma(a_{u\alpha}^{(m)} + a_{\delta\alpha}^{(m)})}{(1 - \lambda_m)^2}$$

$$+ p_{\alpha\beta}p_{\gamma\delta}\sum_{\substack{m=2\\j=2}}^{N}\frac{a_{u\alpha}^{(m)}a_{\beta\gamma}^{(j)} + a_{u\gamma}^{(m)}a_{\delta\alpha}^{(j)} - a_{u\alpha}^{(m)}a_{u\gamma}^{(j)}}{(1 - \lambda_j)(1 - \lambda_m)},$$

$$\alpha, \beta, \gamma, \delta = 1, \ldots, N. \quad (6.1.35)$$

Proof. Equations 6.1.34 and 6.1.35 are obtained by letting n become large in Eqs. 6.1.15 and 6.1.23, dropping terms of order $\lambda_m^n (m = 2, \ldots, N)$, and noting that

$$\lim_{n \to \infty} n\lambda_m^n = 0, \qquad m = 2, \ldots, N. \tag{6.1.36}$$

Q.E.D.

The Whittle-1 Distribution

Let $\tilde{u}$ be a random integer with range set $\{1, \ldots, N\}$ and, given $\tilde{u} = u$, let $\tilde{\mathbf{F}} = [\tilde{f}_{ij}]$ be an $N \times N$ random matrix with range set $\phi_N(u, n, \mathbf{P})$. The ordered pair $(\tilde{u}, \tilde{\mathbf{F}})$ is said to have the Whittle-1 distribution with parameter $(\boldsymbol{p}, n, \mathbf{P})$ if $(\tilde{u}, \tilde{\mathbf{F}})$ has the joint probability mass function

$$\begin{aligned} f_{W1}^{(N)}(u, \mathbf{F} \mid \boldsymbol{p}, n, \mathbf{P}) &= p_u f_W^{(N)}(\mathbf{F} \mid u, n, \mathbf{P}), \\ &\qquad u = 1, \ldots, N, \quad \mathbf{F} \in \phi_N(u, n, \mathbf{P}) \\ &= 0, \qquad \text{otherwise,} \end{aligned} \tag{6.1.37}$$

where $\boldsymbol{p} = (p_1, \ldots, p_N)$ is a stochastic row vector, $n = 1, 2, 3, \ldots$, and $\mathbf{P} \in \mathcal{S}_N$.

Since $p_u \geqslant 0$ and $\sum_{u=1}^{N} p_u = 1$, it is clear that

$$f_{W1}^{(N)}(u, \mathbf{F} \mid \boldsymbol{p}, n, \mathbf{P}) \geqslant 0$$

and, using Eq. 6.1.9,

$$\sum_{u=1}^{N} \sum_{\mathbf{F} \in \phi_N(u,n,P)} f_{W1}^{(N)}(u, \mathbf{F} \mid \boldsymbol{p}, n, \mathrm{P}) = 1. \tag{6.1.38}$$

It is readily seen that, if $(\tilde{u}, \tilde{\mathbf{F}})$ has the Whittle-1 distribution with parameter $(\boldsymbol{p}, n, \mathbf{P})$, the marginal distribution of $\tilde{u}$ is

$$\begin{aligned} P[u \mid \boldsymbol{p}] &= p_u, \qquad u = 1, \ldots, N, \\ &= 0 \qquad \text{otherwise.} \end{aligned} \tag{6.1.39}$$

The marginal distribution of $\tilde{\mathbf{F}}$ is considered in the remaining paragraphs of this section.

The Whittle-2 Distribution

Let $\tilde{\mathbf{F}}$ be an $N \times N$ random matrix with range set

$$\phi_N^*(n, \mathbf{P}) = \bigcup_{u=1}^{N} \phi_N(u, n, \mathbf{P}), \qquad n = 1, 2, 3, \ldots, \quad \mathbf{P} \in \mathcal{S}_N. \tag{6.1.40}$$

The Whittle-2 distribution with parameter $(\boldsymbol{p}, n, \mathbf{P})$ is defined as the marginal distribution of $\tilde{\mathbf{F}}$ when $(\tilde{u}, \tilde{\mathbf{F}})$ has the Whittle-1 distribution with parameter $(\boldsymbol{p}, n, \mathbf{P})$:

$$\begin{aligned} f_{W2}^{(N)}(\mathbf{F} \mid \boldsymbol{p}, n, \mathbf{P}) &= \sum_{u=1}^{N} f_{W1}^{(N)}(u, \mathbf{F} \mid \boldsymbol{p}, n, \mathbf{P}) \qquad \mathbf{F} \in \phi_N^*(n, \mathbf{P}), \\ &= 0 \qquad \text{otherwise,} \end{aligned} \tag{6.1.41}$$

where p is an N-dimensional stochastic row vector, $n = 1, 2, \ldots,$ and $\mathbf{P} \in \mathcal{S}_N$.

It is clear from the definition of Eq. 6.1.41 and the fact that

$$f_{W1}^{(N)}(u, \mathbf{F} \mid p, u, \mathbf{P})$$

is a probability mass function that

$$f_{W2}^{(N)}(\mathbf{F} \mid p, n, \mathbf{P}) \geqslant 0$$

and

$$\sum_{\mathbf{F} \in \phi_N^*(n, \mathbf{P})} f_{W2}^{(N)}(\mathbf{F} \mid p, n, \mathbf{P}) = 1.$$

Before deriving an explicit formula for $f_{W2}^{(N)}(\mathbf{F} \mid p, n, \mathbf{P})$, a preliminary lemma is required. To this end let $\phi_N^*(n, \mathbf{P})$ be partitioned into two sets, $\phi_{N1}^*(n, \mathbf{P})$ and $\phi_{N2}^*(n, \mathbf{P})$, defined as

$$\phi_{N1}^*(n, \mathbf{P}) = \{\mathbf{F} \mid \mathbf{F} \in \phi_N^*(n, \mathbf{P}), f_{i.} = f_{.i}\ (i = 1, \ldots, N)\}, \quad (6.1.42)$$

$$\phi_{N2}^*(n, \mathbf{P}) = \phi_N^*(n, \mathbf{P}) - \phi_{N1}^*(n, \mathbf{P}). \quad (6.1.43)$$

$\phi_{N1}^*(n, \mathbf{P})$ is the set of all transition counts which start and end in the same state and $\phi_{N2}^*(n, \mathbf{P})$ is the set of all other transition counts in $\phi_N^*(n, \mathbf{P})$. Both sets are nonempty.

Lemma 6.1.5. Let the sets $\phi_{N1}^*(n, \mathbf{P})$ and $\phi_{N2}^*(n, \mathbf{P})$ be defined by Eqs. 6.1.42 and 6.1.43. If $\mathbf{F} \in \phi_{N1}^*(n, \mathbf{P})$, there are exactly N pairs of integers $(x, y) = (u, u)$, $u = 1, \ldots, N$, which satisfy the equations

$$f_{i.} - f_{.i} = \delta_{ix} - \delta_{iy}, \qquad i = 1, \ldots, N. \quad (6.1.44)$$

If, on the other hand, $\mathbf{F} \in \phi_{N2}^*(n, \mathbf{P})$, there is a unique solution $(x, y) = (u, v)$, where $u \neq v$, to Eq. 6.1.44.

Proof. If $F \in \phi_{N1}^*(n, \mathbf{P})$, then

$$f_{i.} - f_{.i} = 0, \qquad i = 1, \ldots, N,$$

and Eq. 6.1.44 becomes

$$\delta_{ix} = \delta_{iy}, \qquad i = 1, \ldots, N.$$

These equations are satisfied by $x = y = u$ $(u = 1, \ldots, N)$ and are not satisfied by any pair (x, y) such that $x \neq y$.

If $\mathbf{F} \in \phi_{N2}^*(n, \mathbf{P})$, there is, by the definition of $\phi_{N2}^*(n, \mathbf{P})$, at least one solution (u, v) to Eq. 6.1.44 with $u \neq v$. Assume (u^*, v^*) also satisfies Eq. 6.1.44. If $u^* = u$, Lemma 6.1.1 implies $v^* = v$. Assume $u^* \neq u$. Then, if $v^* \neq v$, substitution of (u, v) in Eq. 6.1.44 yields, for $i = v$,

$$f_{v.} - f_{.v} = -1,$$

while (u^*, v^*) substituted into Eq. 6.1.44 gives

$$f_{v.} - f_{.v} = \delta_{vu^*},$$

a contradiction. If $v^* = v$, then (u, v) substituted into Eq. 6.1.44 with $i = u$ implies

$$f_{u.} - f_{.u} = 1$$

and, since $v^* = v \neq u$, (u^*, v^*) substituted into Eq. 6.1.44 yields

$$f_{u.} - f_{.u} = \delta_{uu^*},$$

which contradicts the assumption $u^* \neq u$. Thus, $(u^*, v^*) = (u, v)$.

Q.E.D.

Theorem 6.1.6. Let $\tilde{\mathbf{F}}$ be an $N \times N$ random matrix with range set $\phi_N^*(n, \mathbf{P})$ which has the Whittle-2 distribution with parameter $(\boldsymbol{p}, n, \mathbf{P})$. Then the probability mass function of $\tilde{\mathbf{F}}$ is given by

$$\begin{aligned} f_{W2}^{(N)}(\mathbf{F} \mid \boldsymbol{p}, n, \mathbf{P}) &= \left(\sum_{i=1}^{N} p_i F_{ii}^*\right) \frac{\prod_{i=1}^{N} f_{i.}!}{\prod_{\substack{i=1\\j=1}}^{N} f_{ij}!} \prod_{\substack{i=1\\j=1}}^{N} p_{ij}^{f_{ij}}, \qquad \mathbf{F} \in \phi_{N1}(n, \mathbf{P}), \\ &= p_u F_{vu}^* \frac{\prod_{i=1}^{N} f_{i.}!}{\prod_{\substack{i=1\\j=1}}^{N} f_{ij}!} \prod_{\substack{i=1\\j=1}}^{N} p_{ij}^{f_{ij}}, \qquad \mathbf{F} \in \phi_{N2}(n, \mathbf{P}), \\ &= 0 \qquad \text{otherwise,} \end{aligned} \tag{6.1.45}$$

where F_{xy}^* is the (x, y)th cofactor of the matrix $\mathbf{F}^*$ defined by Eq. 6.1.8 and, when $\mathbf{F} \in \phi_{N2}^*(n, \mathbf{P})$, (u, v) is the unique solution to Eq. 6.1.44.

Proof. By definition, $\phi_{N1}^*(n, \mathbf{P})$ and $\phi_{N2}^*(n, \mathbf{P})$ are mutually exclusive sets and together exhaust the range set $\phi_N^*(n, \mathbf{P})$. If $\mathbf{F} \in \phi_{N1}^*(n, \mathbf{P})$, then, by Lemma 6.1.5, $\mathbf{F} \in \phi_N(i, n, \mathbf{P})$, $i = 1, \ldots, N$, and

$$f_W^{(N)}(\mathbf{F} \mid i, n, \mathrm{P}) > 0, \qquad i = 1, \ldots, N,$$

which yields the first line of Eq. 6.1.45. If $\mathbf{F} \in \phi_{N2}^*(n, \mathbf{P})$, Lemma 6.1.5 implies there is exactly one value of u in the range $\{1, \ldots, N\}$ such that

$$f_W^{(N)}(\mathbf{F} \mid u, n, \mathrm{P}) > 0,$$

which yields the second line of Eq. 6.1.45. Q.E.D.

Moments of the Whittle-2 Distribution

In this paragraph we derive formulas for the expected value of $\tilde{f}_{ij}$ and for the covariance between $\tilde{f}_{\alpha\beta}$ and $\tilde{f}_{\gamma\delta}$ when $\tilde{\mathbf{F}}$ has the Whittle-2 distribution with parameter $(\boldsymbol{p}, n, \mathbf{P})$. When $\mathbf{P}$ is ergodic and $\boldsymbol{p} = \boldsymbol{\pi}$, the steady-state distribution corresponding to $\mathbf{P}$, particularly simple formulas result. Related moments have been derived by other authors. Anderson and Goodman [1], assuming that many Markov chains which are governed by the same transition matrix are simultaneously observed, find expressions for the means, variances, and covariances of $\tilde{n}_{ij}(t)$, the number of systems making a transition from state i to state j on the tth transition $(i, j = 1, \ldots, N)$. Good [20] has derived formulas for the mean vector and variance-covariance matrix of the *frequency count*, $\tilde{f} = (\tilde{f}_{1.}, \ldots, \tilde{f}_{N.})$, where

$$\tilde{f}_{i.} = \sum_{j=1}^{N} \tilde{f}_{ij}, \qquad i = 1, \ldots, N,$$

is the number of times the system is observed to be in state i (including the initial state, but not the final state) in a sample of n consecutive transitions, assuming that the distribution of the initial state is $\boldsymbol{\pi}$, the steady-state distribution corresponding to $\mathbf{P}$. Equations 6.1.53 and 6.1.54, when summed over j and over β and δ respectively, reduce to Good's formulas.

Theorem 6.1.7. Let the $N \times N$ random matrix $\tilde{\mathbf{F}}$ have the Whittle-2 distribution with parameter $(\boldsymbol{p}, n, \mathbf{P})$. Then the expected value of $\tilde{f}_{ij}$ is

$$E[\tilde{f}_{ij}] = p_{ij} \sum_{k=0}^{n-1} \sum_{u=1}^{N} p_u p_{ui}^{(k)}, \qquad i, j = 1, \ldots, N. \tag{6.1.46}$$

If $\mathbf{P}$ is ergodic and has distinct eigenvalues, $\lambda_1, \ldots, \lambda_N$, then $E[\tilde{f}_{ij}]$ has the spectral representation

$$E[\tilde{f}_{ij}] = p_{ij}\left[n\pi_i + \sum_{m=2}^{N} \frac{1 - \lambda_m^n}{1 - \lambda_m} \sum_{u=1}^{N} p_u a_{ui}^{(m)}\right], \qquad i, j = 1, \ldots, N, \tag{6.1.47}$$

where the $N \times N$ matrices $\mathbf{A}^{(m)} = [a_{ij}^{(m)}]$ are defined by Eq. 6.1.11.

Proof. Since

$$E[\tilde{f}_{ij}] = \sum_{u=1}^{N} p_u f_{ij}(u, n), \tag{6.1.48}$$

Eq. 6.1.46 follows immediately from Eq. 6.1.14. When $\mathbf{P}$ is ergodic with distinct eigenvalues, Eq. 6.1.47 follows from Eq. 6.1.15. Q.E.D.

Theorem 6.1.8. Let the $N \times N$ random matrix $\tilde{\mathbf{F}}$ have the Whittle-2 distribution with parameter $(\boldsymbol{p}, n, \mathbf{P})$. Then, for $\alpha, \beta, \gamma, \delta = 1, \ldots, N$, the covariance between $\tilde{f}_{\alpha\beta}$ and $\tilde{f}_{\gamma\delta}$ is

$$\operatorname{cov}[\tilde{f}_{\alpha\beta}, \tilde{f}_{\gamma\delta}] = E[\tilde{f}_{\alpha\beta}](\delta_{\alpha\gamma}\delta_{\beta\delta} - E[\tilde{f}_{\gamma\delta}]) + \sum_{k=1}^{n-1}\left[p_{\alpha\beta}\tilde{f}_{\gamma\delta}(\beta, k)\sum_{u=1}^{N} p_u p_{u\alpha}^{(n-1-k)} + p_{\gamma\delta}\tilde{f}_{\alpha\beta}(\delta, k)\sum_{u=1}^{N} p_u p_{u\gamma}^{(n-1-k)}\right], \qquad n = 2, 3, \ldots, \tag{6.1.49a}$$

$$= E[\tilde{f}_{\alpha\beta}](\delta_{\alpha\gamma}\delta_{\beta\delta} - E[\tilde{f}_{\gamma\delta}]), \qquad n = 1. \tag{6.1.49b}$$

If $\mathbf{P}$ is ergodic with distinct eigenvalues, $\lambda_1, \ldots, \lambda_N$, and if

$$\boldsymbol{b}^{(m)} = \boldsymbol{p}\mathbf{A}^{(m)} = (b_1^{(m)}, \ldots, b_N^{(m)}), \qquad m = 2, \ldots, N, \tag{6.1.50}$$

where $\mathbf{A}^{(m)}$ is defined by Eq. 6.1.11, then Eq. 6.1.49a has the spectral representation

$$\begin{aligned}
\operatorname{cov}[\tilde{f}_{\alpha\beta}, \tilde{f}_{\gamma\delta}] = {} & p_{\alpha\beta}\delta_{\alpha\gamma}\delta_{\beta\delta}\left[n\pi_\alpha + \sum_{m=2}^{N}\frac{1-\lambda_m^n}{1-\lambda_m} b_\alpha^{(m)}\right] \\
& - p_{\alpha\beta}p_{\gamma\delta}\left\{n\sum_{m=2}^{N}\left[\frac{1-\lambda_m^n}{1-\lambda_m}(\pi_\alpha b_\gamma^{(m)} + \pi_\gamma b_\alpha^{(m)})\right]\right. \\
& \left. + \sum_{\substack{m=2\\ j=2}}^{N}\left(\frac{1-\lambda_m^n}{1-\lambda_m}\right)\left(\frac{1-\lambda_j^n}{1-\lambda_j}\right) b_\alpha^{(m)} b_\gamma^{(j)}\right\} \\
& + p_{\alpha\beta}p_{\gamma\delta}\left\{-n\pi_\alpha\pi_\gamma + \sum_{m=2}^{N}\frac{n-1-n\lambda_m+\lambda_m^n}{(1-\lambda_m)^2}\right. \\
& \times [\pi_\alpha(b_\gamma^{(m)} + a_{\beta\gamma}^{(m)}) + \pi_\gamma(b_\alpha^{(m)} + a_{\delta\alpha}^{(m)})] \\
& + \sum_{m=2}^{N}\frac{1-n\lambda_m^{n-1}+(n-1)\lambda_m^n}{(1-\lambda_m)^2}(b_\alpha^{(m)}a_{\beta\gamma}^{(m)} + b_\gamma^{(m)}a_{\delta\alpha}^{(m)}) \\
& \left. + \sum_{m=2}^{N}\sum_{\substack{j\neq 1\\ j\neq m}}\frac{b_\alpha^{(m)}a_{\beta\gamma}^{(j)} + b_\gamma^{(m)}a_{\delta\alpha}^{(j)}}{1-\lambda_j}\left[\frac{1-\lambda_m^{n-1}}{1-\lambda_m} - \frac{\lambda_j(\lambda_m^{n-1}-\lambda_j^{n-1})}{\lambda_m-\lambda_j}\right]\right\}.
\end{aligned} \tag{6.1.51}$$

Proof. Since

$$E[\tilde{f}_{\alpha\beta}\tilde{f}_{\gamma\delta}] = \sum_{u=1}^{N} p_u\sigma_{\alpha\beta\gamma\delta}(u, n), \tag{6.1.52}$$

Eq. 6.1.49 follows immediately from Eq. 6.1.27. By using Eq. 6.1.52 together with Eq. 6.1.50 and the spectral representation 6.1.29, Eq. 6.1.51 is obtained. Q.E.D.

Corollary 6.1.9. Let $\tilde{\mathbf{F}}$ be an $N \times N$ random matrix which has the Whittle-2 distribution with parameter $(\boldsymbol{\pi}, n, \mathbf{P})$, where $\mathbf{P}$ is ergodic and $\boldsymbol{\pi}$ is the steady-state distribution corresponding to $\mathbf{P}$. Then

$$E[\tilde{f}_{ij}] = n\pi_i p_{ij}, \qquad i, j = 1, \ldots, N, \tag{6.1.53}$$

and, for $\alpha, \beta, \gamma, \delta = 1, \ldots, N$,

$$\begin{aligned} \text{cov}\,[\tilde{f}_{\alpha\beta}, \tilde{f}_{\gamma\delta}] &= n\pi_\alpha p_{\alpha\beta}(\delta_{\alpha\gamma}\delta_{\beta\delta} - n\pi_\gamma p_{\gamma\delta}) \\ &\quad + \sum_{k=0}^{n-1} [(n - 1 - k)p_{\alpha\beta}p_{\gamma\delta}(\pi_\alpha p_{\beta\gamma}^{(k)} + \pi_\gamma p_{\delta\alpha}^{(k)})], \\ &\qquad\qquad n = 2, 3, \ldots, \qquad (6.1.54a) \\ &= \pi_\alpha p_{\alpha\beta}(\delta_{\alpha\gamma}\delta_{\beta\delta} - \pi_\gamma p_{\gamma\delta}), \qquad n = 1. \qquad (6.1.54b) \end{aligned}$$

If $\mathbf{P}$ has distinct eigenvalues, Eq. 6.1.54*a* has the spectral representation,

$$\begin{aligned} \text{cov}\,[\tilde{f}_{\alpha\beta}, \tilde{f}_{\gamma\delta}] &= n\pi_\alpha p_{\alpha\beta}(\delta_{\alpha\gamma}\delta_{\beta\delta} - \pi_\gamma p_{\gamma\delta}) \\ &\quad + p_{\alpha\beta}p_{\gamma\delta} \sum_{m=2}^{N} \frac{n - 1 - n\lambda_m + \lambda_m^n}{(1 - \lambda_m)^2} [\pi_\alpha a_{\beta\gamma}^{(m)} + \pi_\gamma a_{\delta\alpha}^{(m)}], \\ &\qquad\qquad n = 2, 3, \ldots. \qquad (6.1.55) \end{aligned}$$

Proof. Since

$$\sum_{u=1}^{N} \pi_u p_{ui}^{(k)} = \pi_i, \qquad k = 0, 1, 2, \ldots, \quad i = 1, \ldots, N, \tag{6.1.56}$$

Eq. 6.1.53 follows immediately from 6.1.46. Using Eq. 6.1.56 in Eq. 6.1.49*a*,

$$\begin{aligned} \text{cov}\,[\tilde{f}_{\alpha\beta}, \tilde{f}_{\gamma\delta}] &= n\pi_\alpha p_{\alpha\beta}(\delta_{\alpha\gamma}\delta_{\beta\delta} - n\pi_\gamma p_{\gamma\delta}) \\ &\quad + \sum_{k=1}^{n-1} [\pi_\alpha p_{\alpha\beta} \bar{f}_{\gamma\delta}(\beta, k) + \pi_\gamma p_{\gamma\delta} \bar{f}_{\alpha\beta}(\delta, k)], \\ &\qquad\qquad n = 2, 3, \ldots, \qquad (6.1.57a) \\ &= \pi_\alpha p_{\alpha\beta}(\delta_{\alpha\gamma}\delta_{\beta\delta} - \pi_\gamma p_{\gamma\delta}), \qquad n = 1. \qquad (6.1.57b) \end{aligned}$$

Noting that, if $n > 1$,

$$\begin{aligned} \sum_{k=1}^{n-1} \bar{f}_{ij}(u, k) &= \sum_{k=1}^{n-1} \sum_{m=0}^{k-1} p_{ui}^{(m)} p_{ij} \\ &= \sum_{m=0}^{n-1} \sum_{k=m+1}^{n-1} p_{ui}^{(m)} p_{ij} \\ &= p_{ij} \sum_{m=0}^{n-1} (n - 1 - m) p_{ui}^{(m)}, \end{aligned} \tag{6.1.58}$$

Eq. 6.1.54 follows from Eq. 6.1.57.

If **P** has distinct eigenvalues, then, by Eq. 6.1.12*a*,

$$b_j^{(m)} = \sum_{u=1}^{N} \pi_u a_{uj}^{(m)} = 0, \qquad m = 2, \ldots, N, \quad j = 1, \ldots, N, \quad (6.1.59)$$

and, in this case, Eq. 6.1.51 reduces to 6.1.55. Q.E.D.

6.2. THE MULTIVARIATE BETA DISTRIBUTION

In this section we consider the multivariate beta distribution, which is an extension of the beta distribution to N dimensions. There are several different generalizations of the beta distribution; this particular one is due to Mauldon [30]. The moments of this distribution have been derived by Mosimann [31], who also relates the multivariate beta distribution to the gamma distribution. Some of Mosimann's results are presented here for the sake of completeness; the proofs, for the most part, are original.

The Multivariate Beta Density Function

The random stochastic vector $\tilde{\boldsymbol{p}} = (\tilde{p}_1, \ldots, \tilde{p}_N)$ is said to have the multivariate beta distribution with parameter $\boldsymbol{m}$ if $\tilde{\boldsymbol{p}}$ has the joint density function

$$\begin{aligned} f_\beta^{(N)}(\boldsymbol{p} \mid \boldsymbol{m}) &= B_N(\boldsymbol{m}) \prod_{i=1}^{N-1} p_i^{m_i - 1} \left(1 - \sum_{k=1}^{N-1} p_k\right)^{m_N - 1}, \qquad \boldsymbol{p} \in \mathcal{S}_{1N}, \\ &= 0 \qquad \text{elsewhere}, \end{aligned} \quad (6.2.1)$$

where $\boldsymbol{m} = (m_1, \ldots, m_N)$ with

$$m_i > 0, \qquad i = 1, \ldots, N, \quad (6.2.2)$$

and, if $\Gamma(x)$ is the gamma function and

$$M = \sum_{i=1}^{N} m_i, \quad (6.2.3)$$

the normalizing constant is

$$B_N(\boldsymbol{m}) = \frac{\Gamma(M)}{\prod_{i=1}^{N} \Gamma(m_i)}. \quad (6.2.4)$$

It is to be noted that $f_\beta^{(N)}(\boldsymbol{p} \mid \boldsymbol{m})$ is the joint distribution of $N - 1$ of the elements of $\tilde{\boldsymbol{p}}$, the Nth element being determined by the constraint

$$\sum_{i=1}^{N} \tilde{p}_i = 1. \quad (6.2.5)$$

The following lemma provides an alternative representation of the normalizing constant $B_N(\boldsymbol{m})$.

Lemma 6.2.1. If $B_N(\boldsymbol{m})$ is defined by Eq. 6.2.4, then

$$B_N(\boldsymbol{m}) = \left[B\left(m_1, \sum_{i=2}^{N} m_i\right) B\left(m_2, \sum_{i=3}^{N} m_i\right) \cdots B(m_{N-1}, m_N)\right]^{-1}, \quad (6.2.6)$$

where $B(m, n)$ is the beta function.

Proof.

$$B_N(\boldsymbol{m}) = \frac{\Gamma(M)}{\prod_{i=1}^{N} \Gamma(m_i)}$$

$$= \frac{\Gamma\left(m_1 + \sum_{i=2}^{N} m_i\right)\Gamma\left(m_2 + \sum_{i=3}^{N} m_i\right) \cdots \Gamma(m_{N-1} + m_N)}{\Gamma(m_1)\Gamma\left(\sum_{i=2}^{N} m_i\right)\Gamma(m_2)\Gamma\left(\sum_{i=3}^{N} m_i\right) \cdots \Gamma(m_{N-1})\Gamma(m_N)}$$

$$= \left[B\left(m_1, \sum_{i=2}^{N} m_i\right) B\left(m_2, \sum_{i=3}^{N} m_i\right) \cdots B(m_{N-1}, m_N)\right]^{-1}.$$

Q.E.D. (6.2.7)

Since $B(m, n) > 0$, it is clear that

$$f_\beta^{(N)}(\boldsymbol{p} \mid \boldsymbol{m}) \geqslant 0, \qquad \boldsymbol{p} \in \mathcal{S}_{1N}.$$

In the next theorem it is established that

$$\int_{\mathcal{S}_{1N}} f_\beta^{(N)}(\boldsymbol{p} \mid \boldsymbol{m})\, d\boldsymbol{p} = 1.$$

It then follows that the multivariate beta density function, as defined by Eq. 6.2.1, is a proper density function.

Theorem 6.2.2. If $f_\beta^{(N)}(\boldsymbol{p} \mid \boldsymbol{m})$ is defined by Eq. 6.2.1, then

$$\int_{\mathcal{S}_{1N}} f_\beta^{(N)}(\boldsymbol{p} \mid \boldsymbol{m})\, d\boldsymbol{p} = 1, \quad (6.2.8)$$

where $d\boldsymbol{p} = dp_1 \cdots dp_{N-1}$.

Proof. The theorem is proved by induction on N. For $N = 2$, $f_\beta^{(N)}(\boldsymbol{p} \mid \boldsymbol{m})$ is the univariate beta density function and Eq. 6.2.8 holds. Assume that Eq. 6.2.8 is true for N. Then,

$$\int_{\mathcal{S}_{1,N+1}} f_\beta^{(N+1)}(\boldsymbol{p} \mid \boldsymbol{m})\, d\boldsymbol{p} = B_{N+1}(\boldsymbol{m}) \int_{\mathcal{S}_{1,N+1}} \prod_{i=1}^{N} p_i^{m_i-1}\left(1 - \sum_{i=1}^{N} p_i\right)^{m_{N+1}-1} \times dp_1 \cdots dp_N. \quad (6.2.9)$$

Let us make the integrand transformation

$$\boldsymbol{p}_1 = \left(p_1, \ldots, p_{N-1}, 1 - \sum_{i=1}^{N-1} p_i\right) \tag{6.2.10a}$$

$$\boldsymbol{u} = (u, 1 - u), \tag{6.2.10b}$$

where

$$u = \frac{p_N}{1 - \sum_{i=1}^{N-1} p_i}.$$

The Jacobian is

$$\frac{dp_N}{du} = 1 - \sum_{i=1}^{N-1} p_i. \tag{6.2.11}$$

Noting that $\boldsymbol{p}_1 \in \mathcal{S}_{1N}$ and $\boldsymbol{u} \in \mathcal{S}_{12}$, and letting

$$\boldsymbol{m}_1 = (m_1, \ldots, m_{N-1}, m_N + m_{N+1}),$$

$$\boldsymbol{m}_2 = (m_N, m_{N+1}),$$

Eq. 6.2.9 becomes

$$\begin{aligned} B_N(\boldsymbol{m}_1)\int_{\mathcal{S}_{1N}} \prod_{i=1}^{N-1} p_i^{m_i-1}\left(1 - \sum_{i=1}^{N-1} p_i\right)^{m_N+m_{N+1}-1} & dp_1 \cdots dp_{N-1} \\ \times \frac{1}{B(m_N, m_{N+1})} & \int_0^1 u^{m_N-1}(1-u)^{m_{N+1}-1}\, du \\ = \int_{\mathcal{S}_{1N}} f_\beta^{(N)}(\boldsymbol{p}_1 \mid \boldsymbol{m}_1)\, d\boldsymbol{p}_1 & \int_{\mathcal{S}_{12}} f_\beta^{(2)}(\boldsymbol{u} \mid \boldsymbol{m}_2)\, d\boldsymbol{u} \\ = 1. & \end{aligned} \tag{6.2.12}$$

Q.E.D.

The method by which Theorem 6.2.2 was proved can be generalized to provide an identity which will be useful in subsequent proofs.

Theorem 6.2.3. Let $\tilde{\boldsymbol{p}}$ be a random stochastic vector with the multivariate beta distribution, $f_\beta^{(N)}(\boldsymbol{p} \mid \boldsymbol{m})$. Let μ and ν be positive integers such that $\mu + \nu = N$ and make the transformation

$$\tilde{\boldsymbol{q}} = \left(\tilde{p}_1, \ldots, \tilde{p}_\mu, 1 - \sum_{k=1}^{\mu} \tilde{p}_k\right), \tag{6.2.13a}$$

$$\tilde{\boldsymbol{u}} = \left(\tilde{u}_1, \ldots, \tilde{u}_{\nu-1}, 1 - \sum_{i=1}^{\nu-1} \tilde{u}_i\right), \tag{6.2.13b}$$

where

$$\tilde{u}_i = \frac{\tilde{p}_{\mu+i}}{1 - \sum_{k=1}^{\mu} \tilde{p}_k}, \qquad i = 1, \ldots, \nu - 1.$$

Let

$$\boldsymbol{m}_1 = \left(m_1, \ldots, m_\mu, \sum_{k=1}^{\nu} m_{\mu+k}\right), \tag{6.2.14a}$$

$$\boldsymbol{m}_2 = (m_{\mu+1}, \ldots, m_N). \tag{6.2.14b}$$

Then the joint distribution of $(\tilde{\boldsymbol{q}}, \tilde{\boldsymbol{u}})$ is

$$D(\boldsymbol{q}, \boldsymbol{u} \mid \boldsymbol{m}_1, \boldsymbol{m}_2) = f_\beta^{(\mu+1)}(\boldsymbol{q} \mid \boldsymbol{m}_1) f_\beta^{(\nu)}(\boldsymbol{u} \mid \boldsymbol{m}_2). \tag{6.2.15}$$

Proof. Since $0 \leqslant \tilde{u} \leqslant 1$ $(i = 1, \ldots, \nu - 1)$, the range sets of $\tilde{\boldsymbol{q}}$ and $\tilde{\boldsymbol{u}}$ are respectively $\mathcal{S}_{1,\mu+1}$ and $\mathcal{S}_{1\nu}$. The Jacobian of the transformation 6.2.13 is

$$J\left(\frac{p_{\mu+1}, \ldots, p_{N-1}}{u_1, \ldots, u_{\nu-1}}\right) = \left|\frac{\partial p_{\mu+i}}{\partial u_j}\right| = \left(1 - \sum_{k=1}^{\mu} p_k\right)^{\nu-1}. \tag{6.2.16}$$

Making the transformation 6.2.13 in Eq. 6.2.1,

$$\begin{aligned} D(\boldsymbol{q}, \boldsymbol{u} \mid \boldsymbol{m}_1, \boldsymbol{m}_2) &= B_{\mu+1}(\boldsymbol{m}_1) B_\nu(\boldsymbol{m}_2) \prod_{i=1}^{\mu} p_i^{m_i - 1}\left(1 - \sum_{k=1}^{\mu} p_k\right)^{\sum_{k=1}^{\nu} m_{\mu+k} - 1} \\ &\quad \times \prod_{j=1}^{\nu-1} u_j^{m_{\mu+j}-1}\left(1 - \sum_{k=1}^{\nu-1} u_k\right)^{m_N - 1} \\ &= f_\beta^{(\mu+1)}(\boldsymbol{q} \mid \boldsymbol{m}_1) f_\beta^{(\nu)}(\boldsymbol{u} \mid \boldsymbol{m}_2). \end{aligned} \tag{6.2.17}$$

Q.E.D.

The Multivariate Beta Distribution Function

If the random stochastic vector $\tilde{\boldsymbol{p}}$ has the multivariate beta distribution with parameter $\boldsymbol{m}$, then the multivariate beta distribution function is denoted $F_\beta^{(N)}(\boldsymbol{p} \mid \boldsymbol{m})$, where, if $\boldsymbol{p} = (p_1, \ldots, p_N)$,

$$\begin{aligned} F_\beta^{(N)}(\boldsymbol{p} \mid \boldsymbol{m}) &= P[\tilde{p}_1 \leqslant p_1, \ldots, \tilde{p}_{N-1} \leqslant p_{N-1}] \\ &= \int_0^{p_1} \cdots \int_0^{p_{N-1}} f_\beta^{(N)}(\boldsymbol{q} \mid \boldsymbol{m})\, d\boldsymbol{q}. \end{aligned} \tag{6.2.18}$$

As is the case with the beta distribution function, there is no closed expression for Eq. 6.2.18. We can, however, express $F_\beta^{(N)}(\boldsymbol{p} \mid \boldsymbol{m})$ as an $(N - 1)$-fold infinite sum. The case $N = 3$ is illustrated here.

For notational simplicity, let the parameter vector be

$$\boldsymbol{m} = (\alpha, \beta, \gamma). \tag{6.2.19}$$

Then

$$F_\beta^{(3)}(\boldsymbol{p} \mid \boldsymbol{m}) = B_3(\boldsymbol{m}) \int_0^{p_1} \int_0^{p_2} q_1^{\alpha-1} q_2^{\beta-1} (1 - q_1 - q_2)^{\gamma-1}\, dq_1\, dq_2, \qquad \boldsymbol{p} \in \mathcal{S}_{13}. \tag{6.2.20}$$

If $0 < p_1 + p_2 < 1$, we have $0 < q_1 + q_2 < 1$ in the range of integration and

$$(1 - q_1 - q_2)^{\gamma-1} = \sum_{k=0}^{\infty} \binom{\gamma - 1}{k} (-1)^k (q_1 + q_2)^k, \tag{6.2.21}$$

the series converging uniformly in $q_1 + q_2$. Since k is a positive integer, we may expand $(q_1 + q_2)^k$ in a finite binomial series,

$$(q_1 + q_2)^k = \sum_{\nu=0}^{k} \binom{k}{\nu} q_1^{k-\nu} q_2^{\nu}. \tag{6.2.22}$$

Thus,

$$F_\beta^{(3)}(\boldsymbol{p} \mid \boldsymbol{m}) = B_3(\boldsymbol{m}) \sum_{k=0}^{\infty} \sum_{\nu=0}^{k} \binom{\gamma - 1}{k} \binom{k}{\nu} (-1)^k \int_0^{p_1} q_1^{k+\alpha-\nu-1}\, dq_1 \int_0^{p_2} q_2^{\beta+\nu-1}\, dq_2$$

$$= B_3(\boldsymbol{m}) \sum_{k=0}^{\infty} \sum_{\nu=0}^{k} \binom{\gamma - 1}{k} \binom{k}{\nu} (-1)^k \frac{p_1^{k+\alpha-\nu}}{k + \alpha - \nu} \frac{p_2^{\beta+\nu}}{\beta + \nu}. \tag{6.2.23}$$

Let $(x)_k$ denote the hypergeometric coefficient

$$\begin{aligned} (x)_k &= x(x + 1) \cdots (x + k - 1), \qquad & k &= 1, 2, \ldots, \\ &= 1, & k &= 0, \end{aligned} \tag{6.2.24}$$

where x is any real number. Then

$$(-1)^k \binom{\gamma - 1}{k} \binom{k}{\nu} = \frac{(1 - \gamma)_k}{(k - \nu)!\, \nu!}, \tag{6.2.25}$$

and Eq. 6.2.23 becomes

$$B_3(\boldsymbol{m}) p_1^{\alpha} p_2^{\beta} \sum_{k=0}^{\infty} \sum_{\nu=0}^{k} \frac{(1 - \gamma)_k}{(k + \alpha - \nu)(\beta + \nu)} \frac{p_1^{k-\nu}}{(k - \nu)!} \frac{p_2^{\nu}}{\nu!}. \tag{6.2.26}$$

Reversing the order of summation and noting that

$$\alpha + k = \frac{\alpha(\alpha + 1)_k}{(\alpha)_k},$$

$$\beta + \nu = \frac{\beta(\beta + 1)_\nu}{(\beta)_\nu},$$

we have

$$F^{(3)}(\boldsymbol{p} \mid \boldsymbol{m}) = B_3(\boldsymbol{m}) \frac{p_1^{\alpha} p_2^{\beta}}{\alpha\beta} \sum_{\nu=0}^{\infty} \sum_{k=0}^{\infty} \frac{(1 - \gamma)_{k+\nu} (\alpha)_k (\beta)_\nu}{(\alpha + 1)_k (\beta + 1)_\nu} \frac{p_1^{k}}{k!} \frac{p_2^{\nu}}{\nu!}. \tag{6.2.27}$$

The double infinite series of Eq. 6.2.27 is $F_2(1 - \gamma, \alpha, \beta, \alpha + 1, \beta + 1; p_1, p_2)$, Appell's second hypergeometric function of two variables [2].

Appell has shown that the double series of Eq. 6.2.27 converges absolutely whenever $p_1 + p_2 < 1$. Thus, we have

$$F_\beta^{(3)}(\boldsymbol{p} \mid \boldsymbol{m}) = B_3(\boldsymbol{m}) \frac{p_1^\alpha p_2^\beta}{\alpha\beta} F_2(1 - \gamma, \alpha, \beta, \alpha + 1, \beta + 1; p_1, p_2),$$

$$\boldsymbol{p} \in \mathcal{S}_{13}, \quad p_1 + p_2 < 1. \quad (6.2.28)$$

The question of convergence of Eq. 6.2.27 on the boundary of the region $p_1 + p_2 \leqslant 1$ has not yet been resolved. We note, however, that Eq. 6.2.23 remains valid when $p_1 + p_2 = 1$.

Nonstandard Multivariate Beta Distribution

Let $\tilde{\boldsymbol{q}} = (\tilde{q}_1, \ldots, \tilde{q}_N)$ be a random vector with range set

$$R_N(a) = \left\{\boldsymbol{q} \mid 0 \leqslant q_i \leqslant a \; (i = 1, \ldots, N), \; \sum_{i=1}^N q_i = a\right\}, \quad (6.2.29)$$

where $a > 0$. The vector $\tilde{\boldsymbol{q}}$ is said to have the nonstandard multivariate beta distribution with parameter $(a, \boldsymbol{m})$ if $\tilde{\boldsymbol{q}}$ has the density function

$$f_{\beta^*}^{(N)}(\boldsymbol{q} \mid a, \boldsymbol{m}) = \frac{B_N(\boldsymbol{m})}{a^{M-1}} \prod_{i=1}^{N-1} q_i^{m_i - 1} \left(a - \sum_{k=1}^{N-1} q_k\right)^{m_N - 1}, \qquad \boldsymbol{q} \in R_N(a),$$

$$= 0 \qquad \text{elsewhere}, \quad (6.2.30)$$

where $\boldsymbol{m} = (m_1, \ldots, m_N)$ and

$$a > 0, \quad (6.2.31a)$$

$$m_i > 0, \qquad i = 1, \ldots, N, \quad (6.2.31b)$$

$$M = \sum_{i=1}^N m_i. \quad (6.2.31c)$$

The nonstandard multivariate beta distribution is obtained from Eq. 6.2.1 by making the transformation

$$\tilde{\boldsymbol{q}} = a\tilde{\boldsymbol{p}}, \quad (6.2.32)$$

which has the Jacobian

$$J\left(\frac{p_1, \ldots, p_{N-1}}{q_1, \ldots, q_{N-1}}\right) = \frac{1}{a^{N-1}}. \quad (6.2.33)$$

It then follows that $f_{\beta^*}^{(N)}(\boldsymbol{q} \mid a, \boldsymbol{m}) \geqslant 0$ and

$$\int_{R_N(a)} f_{\beta^*}^{(N)}(\boldsymbol{q} \mid a, \boldsymbol{m}) \, dq_1 \cdots dq_{N-1} = 1.$$

Marginal and Conditional Distributions

Suppose that $\tilde{\boldsymbol{p}}$ is an N-dimensional random stochastic vector with the density function $f_\beta^{(N)}(\boldsymbol{p} \mid \boldsymbol{m})$. We now show that the marginal and conditional distributions of ν of the elements of $\tilde{\boldsymbol{p}}$ $(\nu = 1, 2, \ldots, N - 2)$ are, respectively, multivariate beta and nonstandard multivariate beta. It is assumed, without loss of generality, that the elements of interest are $\tilde{p}_1, \ldots, \tilde{p}_\nu$.

Let

$$\tilde{\boldsymbol{q}}(\nu) = \left(\tilde{p}_1, \ldots, \tilde{p}_\nu, 1 - \sum_{i=1}^{\nu} \tilde{p}_i\right), \tag{6.2.34}$$

and

$$\tilde{\boldsymbol{t}}(\nu) = \left(\tilde{p}_1, \ldots, \tilde{p}_\nu, 1 - \tilde{b}(\nu) - \sum_{i=1}^{\nu} \tilde{p}_i\right), \tag{6.2.35}$$

where

$$\tilde{b}(\nu) = \sum_{i=\nu+1}^{N-1} \tilde{p}_i. \tag{6.2.36}$$

Also, let

$$\tilde{\boldsymbol{t}}^*(\nu) = (\tilde{p}_{\nu+1}, \ldots, \tilde{p}_{N-1}). \tag{6.2.37}$$

Theorem 6.2.4. If the random N-dimensional stochastic vector $\tilde{\boldsymbol{p}}$ has the multivariate beta distribution with parameter $\boldsymbol{m}$, then, for $\nu = 1, \ldots, N-2$, the marginal distribution of $(\tilde{p}_1, \ldots, \tilde{p}_\nu)$ is multivariate beta,

$$D(p_1, \ldots, p_\nu \mid \boldsymbol{m}) = f_\beta^{(\nu+1)}(\boldsymbol{q}(\nu) \mid \boldsymbol{\mu}(\nu)), \tag{6.2.38}$$

and the conditional distribution of $(\tilde{p}_1, \ldots, \tilde{p}_\nu)$, given that

$$(\tilde{p}_{\nu+1}, \ldots, \tilde{p}_{N-1}) = (p_{\nu+1}, \ldots, p_{N-1}),$$

is nonstandard multivariate beta,

$$D(p_1, \ldots, p_\nu \mid \boldsymbol{m}, \boldsymbol{t}^*(\nu)) = f_{\beta^*}^{(\nu+1)}(\boldsymbol{t}(\nu) \mid 1 - b(\nu), \boldsymbol{\mu}^*(\nu)), \tag{6.2.39}$$

where

$$\boldsymbol{\mu}(\nu) = \left(m_1, \ldots, m_\nu, \sum_{i=\nu+1}^{N} m_i\right) \tag{6.2.40}$$

and

$$\boldsymbol{\mu}^*(\nu) = (m_1, \ldots, m_\nu, m_N). \tag{6.2.41}$$

Proof. Let

$$\tilde{\boldsymbol{u}} = \left(\tilde{u}_1, \ldots, \tilde{u}_{N-\nu-1}, 1 - \sum_{i=1}^{N-\nu-1} \tilde{u}_i\right),$$

where

$$\tilde{u}_i = \frac{\tilde{p}_{\nu+i}}{1 - \sum_{k=1}^{\nu} \tilde{p}_i}, \qquad i = 1, \ldots, N - \nu - 1$$

and let

$$\boldsymbol{m}_2 = (m_{\nu+1}, \ldots, m_N).$$

Then, by Theorem 6.2.3, the joint density function of $(\tilde{\boldsymbol{q}}(\nu), \tilde{\boldsymbol{u}})$ is

$$D(\boldsymbol{q}(\nu), \boldsymbol{u} \mid \boldsymbol{\mu}(\nu), \boldsymbol{m}_2) = f_\beta^{(\nu+1)}(\boldsymbol{q}(\nu) \mid \boldsymbol{\mu}(\nu)) f_\beta^{(N-\nu)}(\boldsymbol{u} \mid \boldsymbol{m}_2). \tag{6.2.42}$$

The marginal density function of $\tilde{q}(\nu)$ is, therefore,

$$\int_{S_{1,N-\nu}} D(q(\nu), u \mid \mu(\nu), m_2)\, du_1 \cdots du_{N-\nu-1} = f_\beta^{(\nu+1)}(q(\nu) \mid \mu(\nu)). \quad (6.2.43)$$

If $(\tilde{p}_{\nu+1}, \ldots, \tilde{p}_{N-1}) = (p_{\nu+1}, \ldots, p_{N-1})$, then the random variables $\tilde{p}_1, \ldots, \tilde{p}_\nu$ are constrained by

$$0 \leqslant \sum_{i=1}^{\nu} p_i \leqslant 1 - b(\nu), \qquad i = 1, \ldots, \nu, \quad (6.2.44)$$

and the conditional density function of $(\tilde{p}_1, \ldots, \tilde{p}_\nu)$ has the kernel

$$\prod_{i=1}^{\nu} p_i^{m_i-1}\left(1 - b(\nu) - \sum_{i=1}^{\nu} p_i\right)^{m_N-1}, \quad (6.2.45)$$

which is the kernel of the nonstandard multivariate beta density function,

$$f_{\beta^*}^{(\nu+1)}(t(\nu) \mid 1 - b(\nu), \mu^*(\nu)).$$

Q.E.D.

Moment Formulas

The moments of the multivariate beta distribution are most easily derived as a special case of the moments of the matrix beta distribution, and will be considered in Sec. 6.3. These results are merely stated here for the case of the multivariate beta distribution and proved in that section.

Let the random stochastic vector $\tilde{p} = (\tilde{p}_1, \ldots, \tilde{p}_N)$ have the multivariate beta distribution with parameter $m = (m_1, \ldots, m_N)$. Then, if $M = \sum_{i=1}^{N} m_1$,

$$E[\tilde{p}_i] = \bar{p}_i(m) = \frac{m_i}{M}, \qquad i = 1, \ldots, N, \quad (6.2.46)$$

$$\operatorname{var}[\tilde{p}_i] = \frac{m_i(M - m_i)}{M^2(M + 1)}, \qquad i = 1, \ldots, N, \quad (6.2.47)$$

and

$$\operatorname{cov}[\tilde{p}_i, \tilde{p}_j] = \frac{-m_i m_j}{M^2(M + 1)}, \qquad i, j = 1, \ldots, N, \quad i \neq j. \quad (6.2.48)$$

All higher moments can be computed from the recurrence relation

$$E\left[\prod_{i=1}^{N} \tilde{p}_i^{\nu_i} \mid m\right] = \bar{p}_\alpha(m) E\left[\tilde{p}_\alpha^{\nu_\alpha - 1} \prod_{i \neq \alpha} \tilde{p}_i^{\nu_i} \mid T_\alpha(m)\right], \quad (6.2.49)$$

where the ν_i are nonnegative integers, α is any index such that $\nu_\alpha > 0$, and $T_\alpha(m)$ is the vector m with the element m_α increased by unity.

In matrix form, Eqs. 6.2.46 through 6.2.48 can be summarized as the mean vector,

$$E[\tilde{p}] = \frac{1}{M}\,\boldsymbol{m}, \tag{6.2.50}$$

and the variance-covariance matrix,

$$V[\tilde{p}] = \frac{1}{M^2(M+1)}\,[M\boldsymbol{\lambda} - \boldsymbol{m}^t\boldsymbol{m}], \tag{6.2.51}$$

where $\boldsymbol{\lambda}$ is the $N \times N$ diagonal matrix $[m_i\delta_{ij}]$.

Using Eq. 6.2.32, it is easily seen that, if $\tilde{\boldsymbol{q}}$ has the nonstandard multivariate beta density function $f_{\beta^*}^{(N)}(\boldsymbol{q} \mid a, \boldsymbol{m})$, then

$$E[\tilde{\boldsymbol{q}}] = \frac{a}{M}\,\boldsymbol{m} \tag{6.2.52}$$

and

$$V[\tilde{\boldsymbol{q}}] = \frac{a^2}{M^2(M+1)}\,[M\boldsymbol{\lambda} - \boldsymbol{m}^t\boldsymbol{m}]. \tag{6.2.53}$$

6.3. THE MATRIX BETA DISTRIBUTION

The $K \times N$ random generalized stochastic matrix $\tilde{\mathscr{P}} = [\tilde{p}_{ij}^k]$ is said to have the matrix beta distribution with parameter $\mathcal{M} = [m_{ij}^k]$ if $\tilde{\mathscr{P}}$ has the joint density function

$$\begin{aligned} f_{M\beta}^{(K,N)}(\mathscr{P} \mid \mathcal{M}) &= \prod_{\substack{i=1\\j=1}}^{N} \prod_{k=1}^{K_i} B_N(\boldsymbol{m}_i^k)(p_{ij}^k)^{m_{ij}^k - 1}, \qquad \mathscr{P} \in \mathcal{S}_{KN}, \\ &= 0 \qquad\qquad \text{elsewhere}, \end{aligned} \tag{6.3.1}$$

where $\mathcal{M}$ is a $K \times N$ matrix such that

$$m_{ij}^k > 0, \qquad k = 1, \ldots, K_i, \quad i, j = 1, \ldots, N, \tag{6.3.2}$$

and $B_N(\boldsymbol{m}_i^k)$ is defined by Eq. 6.2.4. The generic row of $\mathcal{M}$ is denoted $\boldsymbol{m}_i^k$, an N-dimensional vector. The total number of rows of both $\tilde{\mathscr{P}}$ and $\mathcal{M}$ is $K = \sum_{i=1}^{N} K_i$. To be quite general, we admit the possibility that $K_i = 0$ for some i.

The matrix beta distribution is the joint distribution of $K(N-1)$ random variables $\tilde{p}_{ij}^k$. The remaining K elements of $\mathscr{P}$ are determined by the relations

$$\sum_{j=1}^{N} \tilde{p}_{ij}^k = 1, \qquad k = 1, \ldots, K_i, \quad i = 1, \ldots, N. \tag{6.3.3}$$

Inspection of Eq. 6.3.1 shows that the matrix beta density function is the product of K multivariate beta density functions,

$$f_{M\beta}^{(K,N)}(\mathscr{P} \mid \mathcal{M}) = \prod_{i=1}^{N} \prod_{k=1}^{K_i} f_\beta^{(N)}(\boldsymbol{p}_i^k \mid \boldsymbol{m}_i^k). \tag{6.3.4}$$

It follows that $f_{M\beta}^{(K,N)}(\mathscr{P} \mid \mathcal{M}) \geqslant 0$ and

$$\int_{S_{KN}} f_{M\beta}^{(K,N)}(\mathscr{P} \mid \mathcal{M})\, d\mathscr{P} = 1, \tag{6.3.5}$$

where

$$d\mathscr{P} = \prod_{i=1}^{N} \prod_{k=1}^{Ki} \prod_{j=1}^{N-1} dp_{ij}^{k}.$$

The family of matrix beta distributions is a family indexed by the parameter $\mathcal{M} \in \Psi_{KN}$, where the admissible parameter set is

$$\Psi_{KN} = \{\mathcal{M} \mid \mathcal{M} \text{ is } K \times N,\ m_{ij}^{k} > 0\ (k = 1, \ldots, K_i;\ i, j = 1, \ldots, N)\}, \tag{6.3.6}$$

the positive orthant of E_{KN}. Since $f_{M\beta}^{(K,N)}(\mathscr{P} \mid \mathcal{M})$ is a continuous function of $\mathcal{M}$ for all $\mathscr{P} \in S_{KN}$, Corollary 2.4.5 implies that the family of matrix beta distributions is continuous in $\mathcal{M}$. In Theorem 2.2.1 it was shown that the matrix beta distribution is the natural conjugate distribution for a Markov chain which is observed under the consecutive sampling rule. It then follows that the family of matrix beta distributions is closed under consecutive sampling. This property is used in the following theorem to derive the moments of the matrix beta distribution.

Theorem 6.3.1. Let $\tilde{\mathscr{P}} = [\tilde{p}_{ij}^{k}]$ be a random generalized stochastic matrix which has the matrix beta distribution with parameter $\mathcal{M} = [m_{ij}^{k}]$. Then,

$$E[\tilde{p}_{ij}^{k}] = \bar{p}_{ij}^{k}(\mathcal{M}) = \frac{m_{ij}^{k}}{M_i^{k}},$$

$$k = 1, \ldots, K_i, \quad i, j = 1, \ldots, N, \tag{6.3.7}$$

$$\operatorname{var}[\tilde{p}_{ij}^{k}] = \frac{m_{ij}^{k}(M_i^{k} - m_{ij}^{k})}{(M_i^{k})^2(M_i^{k} + 1)},$$

$$k = 1, \ldots, K_i, \quad i, j = 1, \ldots, N, \tag{6.3.8}$$

$$\operatorname{cov}[\tilde{p}_{\alpha\beta}^{k}, \tilde{p}_{\gamma\delta}^{j}] = \frac{-m_{\alpha\beta}^{k} m_{\alpha\delta}^{k}}{(M_\alpha^{k})^2(M_\alpha^{k} + 1)},$$

$$j = k = 1, \ldots, K_\alpha, \quad \alpha = \gamma = 1, \ldots, N,$$

$$\beta, \delta = 1, \ldots, N, \quad \beta \neq \delta \tag{6.3.9a}$$

$$= 0 \qquad j \neq k \text{ or } \alpha \neq \gamma, \tag{6.3.9b}$$

where

$$M_i^{k} = \sum_{j=1}^{N} m_{ij}^{k}, \qquad k = 1, \ldots, K_i, \quad i = 1, \ldots, N. \tag{6.3.10}$$

Proof. Let $T^k_{ij}(\mathcal{M})$ be the matrix $\mathcal{M}$ with the element m^k_{ij} increased by unity. Then

$$\begin{aligned} E[\tilde{p}^k_{ij}] &= \int_{S_{KN}} p^k_{ij} f^{(K,N)}_{M\beta}(\mathcal{P} \mid \mathcal{M})\, d\mathcal{P} \\ &= \frac{\Gamma(M^k_i)}{\Gamma(m^k_{ij})} \frac{\Gamma(m^k_{ij}+1)}{\Gamma(M^k_i+1)} \int_{S_{KN}} f^{(K,N)}_{M\beta}(\mathcal{P} \mid T^k_{ij}(\mathcal{M}))\, d\mathcal{P} \\ &= \frac{m^k_{ij}}{M^k_i}. \end{aligned} \tag{6.3.11}$$

For $j \neq k$ or $\alpha \neq \gamma$, $\tilde{p}^k_{\alpha\beta}$ and $\tilde{p}^j_{\gamma\delta}$ are independent random variables and $\mathrm{cov}\,[\tilde{p}^k_{\alpha\beta}, \tilde{p}^j_{\gamma\delta}] = 0$. If $j = k$ and $\alpha = \gamma$, Lemma 2.3.2 yields

$$\begin{aligned} E[\tilde{p}^k_{\alpha\beta}\tilde{p}^k_{\alpha\delta}] &= \int_{S_{KN}} p^k_{\alpha\beta} p^k_{\alpha\delta} f^{(K,N)}_{M\beta}(\mathcal{P} \mid \mathcal{M})\, d\mathcal{P} \\ &= \bar{p}^k_{\alpha\beta}(\mathcal{M})\bar{p}^k_{\alpha\delta}(T^k_{\alpha\beta}(\mathcal{M})) \\ &= \frac{m^k_{\alpha\beta} m^k_{\alpha\delta}}{M^k_\alpha(M^k_\alpha + 1)}, \qquad \beta \neq \delta, && (6.3.12a) \\ &= \frac{m^k_{\alpha\beta}(m^k_{\alpha\beta} + 1)}{M^k_\alpha(M^k_\alpha + 1)}, \qquad \beta = \delta, && (6.3.12b) \end{aligned}$$

from which Eqs. 6.3.8 and 6.3.9*a* follow. Q.E.D.

By writing Eq. 6.3.8 as

$$\mathrm{var}\,[\tilde{p}^k_{ij}] = \frac{\bar{p}^k_{ij}(1 - \bar{p}^k_{ij})}{M^k_i + 1}, \tag{6.3.13}$$

where $\bar{p}^k_{ij} = \bar{p}^k_{ij}(\mathcal{M})$, it is seen that

$$0 \leqslant \mathrm{var}\,[\tilde{p}^k_{ij}] < \tfrac{1}{4}, \qquad k = 1, \ldots, K_i, \quad i, j = 1, \ldots, N. \tag{6.3.14}$$

Similarly, Eq. 6.3.9*a* can be written as

$$\mathrm{cov}\,[\tilde{p}^k_{\alpha\beta}, \tilde{p}^k_{\alpha\delta}] = -\frac{\bar{p}^k_{\alpha\beta}\bar{p}^k_{\alpha\delta}}{M^k_\alpha + 1} \tag{6.3.15}$$

and, since $\bar{p}^k_{\alpha\delta} \leqslant 1 - \bar{p}^k_{\alpha\beta}$, we have the bounds

$$-\mathrm{var}\,[\tilde{p}^k_{\alpha\beta}] \leqslant \mathrm{cov}\,[\tilde{p}^k_{\alpha\beta}, \tilde{p}^k_{\alpha\delta}] \leqslant 0, \tag{6.3.16a}$$

$$-\mathrm{var}\,[\tilde{p}^k_{\alpha\delta}] \leqslant \mathrm{cov}\,[\tilde{p}^k_{\alpha\beta}, \tilde{p}^k_{\alpha\delta}] \leqslant 0, \tag{6.3.16b}$$

for $k = 1, \ldots, K_\alpha$; $\alpha, \beta, \delta = 1, \ldots, N$.

When $\tilde{\mathcal{P}}$ has the matrix beta distribution, the rows of $\tilde{\mathcal{P}}$ are mutually independent; thus, the general joint moment is

$$E\left[\prod_{\substack{i=1\\j=1}}^{N} \prod_{k=1}^{K_i} (\tilde{p}^k_{ij})^{\nu^k_{ij}}\right] = \prod_{i=1}^{N} \prod_{k=1}^{K_i} E\left[\prod_{j=1}^{N} (\tilde{p}^k_{ij})^{\nu^k_{ij}}\right], \tag{6.3.17}$$

where the ν_{ij}^k are nonnegative integers. Let

$$E\left[\prod_{j=1}^{N} (\tilde{p}_{ij}^k)^{\nu_{ij}^k} \mid \mathcal{M}\right] = \int_{S_{KN}} \prod_{j=1}^{N} (p_{ij}^k)^{\nu_{ij}^k} f_{M\beta}^{(K,N)}(\mathcal{P} \mid \mathcal{M})\, d\mathcal{P}. \quad (6.3.18)$$

The following theorem provides a recursive formula for computing this expectation.

Theorem 6.3.2. If the $K \times N$ random matrix $\tilde{\mathcal{P}}$ has the matrix beta distribution with parameter $\mathcal{M}$ then

$$E\left[\prod_{j=1}^{N} (\tilde{p}_{ij}^k)^{\nu_{ij}^k} \mid \mathcal{M}\right] = \bar{p}_{i\alpha}^k(\mathcal{M}) E\left[(\tilde{p}_{i\alpha}^k)^{\nu_{i\alpha}^k - 1} \prod_{j \neq \alpha} (\tilde{p}_{ij}^k)^{\nu_{ij}^k} \mid T_{i\alpha}^k(\mathcal{M})\right],$$

$$k = 1, \ldots, K_i, \quad i = 1, \ldots, N, \quad (6.3.19)$$

where the ν_{ij}^k are nonnegative integers and α is any index such that $\nu_{i\alpha}^k > 0$.

Proof. The theorem follows immediately by applying Lemma 2.3.2 to Eq. 6.3.18. Q.E.D.

Since the multivariate beta distribution is a special case of the matrix beta distribution in which $K = 1$, we immediately have the following corollary.

Corollary 6.3.3. Let the random stochastic vector $\boldsymbol{p} = (\tilde{p}_1, \ldots, \tilde{p}_N)$ have the multivariate beta distribution with parameter $\boldsymbol{m} = (m_1, \ldots, m_N)$. Then, if $M = \sum_{i=1}^{N} m_i$,

$$E[\tilde{p}_i] = \bar{p}_i(\boldsymbol{m}) = \frac{m_i}{M}, \qquad i = 1, \ldots, N, \quad (6.3.20)$$

$$\operatorname{var}[\tilde{p}_i] = \frac{m_i(M - m_i)}{M^2(M + 1)}, \qquad i = 1, \ldots, N, \quad (6.3.21)$$

$$\operatorname{cov}[\tilde{p}_i, \tilde{p}_j] = \frac{-m_i m_j}{M^2(M + 1)}, \qquad i \neq j, \quad (6.3.22)$$

and

$$E\left[\prod_{i=1}^{N} \tilde{p}_i^{\nu_i} \mid \boldsymbol{m}\right] = \bar{p}_\alpha(\boldsymbol{m}) E\left[\tilde{p}_\alpha^{\nu_\alpha - 1} \prod_{i \neq \alpha} \tilde{p}_i^{\nu_i} \mid T_\alpha(\boldsymbol{m})\right], \quad (6.3.23)$$

where the ν_i are nonnegative integers, α is any index such that $\nu_\alpha > 0$, and $T_\alpha(\boldsymbol{m})$ is the vector $\boldsymbol{m}$ with the element m_α increased by unity.

Before considering the marginal and conditional distributions of submatrices of $\tilde{\mathcal{P}}$, it is necessary to define the nonstandard matrix beta distribution. Let

$$\boldsymbol{a} = (a_1^1, \ldots, a_1^{K_1}, a_2^1, \ldots, a_N^{K_N}) \quad (6.3.24)$$

be a K-dimensional vector, where

$$a_i^k > 0, \qquad k = 1, \ldots, K_i, \quad i = 1, \ldots, N. \tag{6.3.25}$$

Let $\tilde{\mathscr{P}} = [\tilde{p}_{ij}^k]$ be a $K \times N$ random matrix with range set

$$R_{KN}(a) = \left\{ \mathscr{P} \mid \mathscr{P} \text{ is } K \times N,\ p_{ij}^k \geqslant 0,\ \sum_{j=1}^{N} p_{ij}^k = a_i^k, \right.$$
$$\left. (k = 1, \ldots, K_i;\ i, j = 1, \ldots, N) \right\}. \tag{6.3.26}$$

Let $\mathcal{M} = [m_{ij}^k]$ be a $K \times N$ matrix of positive elements. Then $\tilde{\mathscr{P}}$ is said to have the nonstandard matrix beta distribution with parameter $(\boldsymbol{a}, \mathcal{M})$ if $\tilde{\mathscr{P}}$ has the joint density function

$$f_{M\beta^*}^{(K,N)}(\mathscr{P} \mid \boldsymbol{a}, \mathcal{M}) = \prod_{i=1}^{N} \prod_{k=1}^{K_i} f_{\beta^*}^{(N)}(\boldsymbol{p}_i^k \mid a_i^k, \boldsymbol{m}_i^k), \tag{6.3.27}$$

where $\boldsymbol{p}_i^k$ and $\boldsymbol{m}_i^k$ are generic rows of $\mathscr{P}$ and $\mathcal{M}$ respectively, and

$$f_{\beta^*}^{(N)}(p_i^k \mid a_i^k, \boldsymbol{m}_i^k)$$

is the nonstandard multivariate beta distribution defined by Eq. 6.2.30.

We now consider the marginal and conditional distributions of any $\rho \times \nu$ submatrix of $\tilde{\mathscr{P}}$ when $\tilde{\mathscr{P}}$ has the matrix beta distribution. To simplify the notation, assume that the elements of $\tilde{\mathscr{P}}$ and $\mathcal{M}$ have been relabeled so that $\tilde{\mathscr{P}} = [\tilde{p}_{ij}]$ and $\mathcal{M} = [m_{ij}]$ $(i = 1, \ldots, K; j = 1, \ldots, N)$, and that the submatrix of $\tilde{\mathscr{P}}$ which is of interest consists of the elements $\tilde{p}_{ij}$ $(i = 1, \ldots, \rho; j = 1, \ldots, \nu)$, where $\rho \in \{1, \ldots, K\}$ and $\nu \in \{1, \ldots, N - 1\}$. Define the $\rho \times (\nu + 1)$ matrix

$$\tilde{\mathbf{Q}}_{\rho\nu} = \begin{bmatrix} \tilde{p}_{11} & \cdots & \tilde{p}_{1\nu} & 1 - \sum_{j=1}^{\nu} \tilde{p}_{1j} \\ \cdot & & & \\ \cdot & & & \\ \cdot & & & \\ \tilde{p}_{\rho 1} & \cdots & \tilde{p}_{\rho\nu} & 1 - \sum_{j=1}^{\nu} \tilde{p}_{\rho j} \end{bmatrix}, \tag{6.3.28}$$

and the $\rho \times (\nu + 1)$ matrix

$$\tilde{\mathbf{T}}_{\rho\nu} = \begin{bmatrix} \tilde{p}_{11} & \cdots & \tilde{p}_{1\nu} & 1 - \tilde{b}_1(\nu) - \sum_{j=1}^{\nu} \tilde{p}_{1j} \\ \cdot & & & \\ \cdot & & & \\ \cdot & & & \\ \tilde{p}_{\rho 1} & \cdots & \tilde{p}_{\rho\nu} & 1 - \tilde{b}_\rho(\nu) - \sum_{j=1}^{\nu} \tilde{p}_{\rho j} \end{bmatrix}, \tag{6.3.29}$$

where

$$\tilde{b}_i(\nu) = \sum_{j=\nu+1}^{N-1} \tilde{p}_{ij}, \qquad i = 1, \ldots, \rho. \tag{6.3.30}$$

Correspondingly, we define the $\rho \times (\nu + 1)$ parameter matrices,

$$\mathbf{M}_{\rho\nu} = \begin{bmatrix} m_{11} & \cdots & m_{1\nu} & \sum_{j=\nu+1}^{N} m_{1j} \\ \cdot & & & \\ \cdot & & & \\ \cdot & & & \\ m_{\rho 1} & \cdots & m_{\rho\nu} & \sum_{j=\nu-1}^{N} m_{\rho j} \end{bmatrix}, \tag{6.3.31}$$

$$\mathbf{M}^*_{\rho\nu} = \begin{bmatrix} m_{11} & \cdots & m_{1\nu} & m_{1N} \\ \cdot & & & \\ \cdot & & & \\ \cdot & & & \\ m_{\rho 1} & \cdots & m_{\rho\nu} & m_{\rho N} \end{bmatrix}. \tag{6.3.32}$$

Theorem 6.3.4. Let the $K \times N$ random generalized stochastic matrix $\tilde{\mathscr{P}}$ have the matrix beta distribution with parameter $\mathcal{M}$. Then, for $\rho = 1, \ldots, K$ and $\nu = 1, \ldots, N - 1$, the marginal joint distribution of $(\tilde{p}_{11}, \ldots, \tilde{p}_{1\nu}, \tilde{p}_{21}, \ldots, \tilde{p}_{\rho\nu})$ is matrix beta,

$$D(p_{11}, \ldots, p_{\rho\nu} \mid \mathcal{M}) = f^{(\rho,\nu+1)}_{M\beta}(\mathbf{Q}_{\rho\nu} \mid M_{\rho\nu}), \tag{6.3.33}$$

and the conditional joint distribution of $(\tilde{p}_{11}, \ldots, \tilde{p}_{\rho\nu})$, given that

$$(\tilde{p}_{1\nu,+1}, \ldots, \tilde{p}_{1,N-1}, \tilde{p}_{2,\nu+1}, \ldots, \tilde{p}_{K,N-1}) = (p_{1,\nu+1}, \ldots, p_{1,N-1}, p_{2\nu+1}, \ldots, p_{K,N-1}),$$

is nonstandard matrix beta,

$$D(p_{11}, \ldots, p_{\rho\nu} \mid \mathcal{M}, p_{1,\nu+1}, \ldots, p_{K,N-1}) = f^{(\rho,\nu+1)}_{M\beta*}(\mathbf{T}_{\rho\nu} \mid \boldsymbol{b}^*(\nu), \mathbf{M}^*_{\rho\nu}), \tag{6.3.34}$$

where

$$\boldsymbol{b}^*(\nu) = (1 - b_1(\nu), \ldots, 1 - b_\rho(\nu)). \tag{6.3.35}$$

Proof. The theorem follows immediately from Theorem 6.2.4, upon noting that the matrix beta density function if the product of K multivariate beta density functions.

6.4. EXTENDED NATURAL CONJUGATE DISTRIBUTIONS

If $\tilde{\mathscr{P}}$ has the matrix beta distribution, the rows of $\tilde{\mathscr{P}}$ are mutually independent random vectors. The decision maker may, however, wish to use a prior distribution which admits nonzero correlation between the rows of $\tilde{\mathcal{P}}$. Such a distribution may be constructed with the aid of Eq. 2.3.3, but at the expense of complicating the formulas for the moments. We illustrate this construction for a 2×2 random matrix,

$$\tilde{\mathbf{P}} = \begin{bmatrix} \tilde{p} & 1 - \tilde{p} \\ \tilde{q} & 1 - \tilde{q} \end{bmatrix}. \tag{6.4.1}$$

A theorem relating to the general $K \times N$ case is first given.

Theorem 6.4.1. Let $h(\mathcal{P} \mid \mathcal{M}, \omega)$ be the probability density function defined by Eq. 2.3.3, and let $\mathcal{H}_g$ be the corresponding extended natural conjugate family of distributions. Let $C(\mathcal{M}, \omega)$ be the normalizing constant defined by Eq. 2.3.2 and let $T_{ij}^k(\mathcal{M})$ be the matrix with the element m_{ij}^k increased by unity. Then the means, variances, and covariances of $h(\mathcal{P} \mid \mathcal{M}, \omega)$ are given by

$$E[\tilde{p}_{ij}^k \mid \mathcal{M}, \omega] = \bar{p}_{ij}^k(\mathcal{M}, \omega) = \frac{C(\mathcal{M}, \omega)}{C(T_{ij}^k(\mathcal{M}), \omega)},$$
$$k = 1, \ldots, K_i, \quad i, j = 1, \ldots, N, \tag{6.4.2}$$

$$\text{cov}\,[\tilde{p}_{ij}^\alpha, \tilde{p}_{kn}^\beta \mid \mathcal{M}, \omega] = \bar{p}_{ij}^\alpha(\mathcal{M}, \omega)[\bar{p}_{kn}^\beta(T_{ij}^\alpha(\mathcal{M}), \omega) - \bar{p}_{kn}^\beta(\mathcal{M}, \omega)],$$
$$\alpha = 1, \ldots, K_i, \quad \beta = 1, \ldots, K_i, \quad i, j, k, n = 1, \ldots, N. \tag{6.4.3}$$

Proof. Using Eqs. 2.3.3 and 2.3.2,

$$\bar{p}_{ij}^k(\mathcal{M}, \omega) = C(\mathcal{M}, \omega) \int_{S_{KN}} p_{ij}^k g(\mathcal{P} \mid \omega) \prod_{\substack{\alpha=1 \\ \beta=1}}^{N} \prod_{\gamma=1}^{K_\alpha} (p_{\alpha\beta}^\gamma)^{m_{\alpha\beta}^\gamma - 1} d\mathcal{P}$$
$$= \frac{C(\mathcal{M}, \omega)}{C(T_{ij}^k(\mathcal{M}), \omega)}, \tag{6.4.4}$$

which is Eq. 6.4.2. Theorem 2.3.1 shows that $\mathcal{H}_g$ is closed under consecutive sampling. Hence, Lemma 2.3.2 is applicable and yields

$$E[\tilde{p}_{ij}^\alpha \tilde{p}_{kn}^\beta \mid \mathcal{M}, \omega] = \int_{S_{KN}} p_{ij}^\alpha p_{kn}^\beta h(\mathcal{P} \mid \mathcal{M}, \omega)\, d\mathcal{P}$$
$$= \bar{p}_{ij}^\alpha(\mathcal{M}, \omega) \bar{p}_{kn}^\beta(T_{ij}^\alpha(\mathcal{M}), \omega), \tag{6.4.5}$$

from which Eq. 6.4.3 follows. Q.E.D.

Let $\tilde{\mathbf{P}}$ be given by Eq. 6.4.1 and let

$$\mathbf{M} = \begin{bmatrix} m_1 & m_2 \\ m_3 & m_4 \end{bmatrix}, \tag{6.4.6}$$

where $m_i > 0$ ($i = 1, \ldots, 4$). Let

$$g(\mathbf{P}) = (p - q)^2. \tag{6.4.7}$$

Then Eq. 2.3.3 becomes

$$h(\mathbf{P} \mid \mathbf{M}) = C(\mathbf{M})(p - q)^2 p^{m_1-1} q^{m_3-1}(1 - p)^{m_2-1}(1 - q)^{m_4-1}, \qquad \mathbf{P} \in \mathcal{S}_2. \tag{6.4.8}$$

Evaluating the normalizing constant by means of Eq. 2.3.2, we find that

$$C(\mathbf{M}) = [B(m_1 + 2, m_2)B(m_3, m_4) - 2B(m_1 + 1, m_2)B(m_3 + 1, m_4) + B(m_1, m_2)B(m_3 + 2, m_4)]^{-1}. \tag{6.4.9}$$

Equation 6.4.2 then yields the means,

$$\bar{p}(\mathbf{M}) = \frac{B(m_1 + 3, m_2)B(m_3, m_4) - 2B(m_1 + 2, m_2)B(m_3 + 1, m_4) + B(m_1 + 1, m_2)B(m_3 + 2, m_4)}{B(m_1 + 2, m_2)B(m_3, m_4) - 2B(m_1 + 1, m_2)B(m_3 + 1, m_4) + B(m_1, m_2)B(m_3 + 2, m_4)} \tag{6.4.10}$$

$$\bar{q}(\mathbf{M}) = \frac{B(m_1 + 2, m_2)B(m_3 + 1, m_4) - 2B(m_1 + 1, m_2)B(m_3 + 2, m_4) + B(m_1, m_2)B(m_3 + 3, m_4)}{B(m_1 + 2, m_2)B(m_3, m_4) - 2B(m_1 + 1, m_2)B(m_3 + 1, m_4) + B(m_1, m_2)B(m_3 + 2, m_4)}. \tag{6.4.11}$$

From Eq. 6.4.3 we obtain the covariance

$$\operatorname{cov}[\tilde{p}, \tilde{q} \mid \mathbf{M}] = \bar{p}(\mathbf{M})\left[\frac{B(m_1 + 3, m_2)B(m_3 + 1, m_4) - 2B(m_1 + 2, m_2) \times B(m_3 + 2, m_4) + B(m_1 + 1, m_2)B(m_3 + 3, m_4)}{B(m_1 + 3, m_2)B(m_3, m_4) - 2B(m_1 + 2, m_2) \times B(m_3 + 1, m_4) + B(m_1 + 1, m_2)B(m_3 + 2, m_4)} - \bar{q}(\mathbf{M})\right], \tag{6.4.12}$$

and it is seen that there is nonzero correlation between the rows of $\tilde{\mathbf{P}}$.

Let $\boldsymbol{\pi}(\mathbf{P}) = (\pi_1(\mathbf{P}), \ldots, \pi_N(\mathbf{P}))$ be the steady-state probability vector corresponding to the $N \times N$ stochastic matrix $\mathbf{P}$ and let $\boldsymbol{\nu} = (\nu_1, \ldots, \nu_N)$ be a vector of nonnegative integers. An extended natural conjugate distribution for $\tilde{\mathbf{P}}$ which is required for the analysis to be carried out in Chap. 7 is formed by letting

$$g(\mathbf{P} \mid \boldsymbol{\nu}) = \prod_{i=1}^{N} (\pi_i(\mathbf{P}))^{\nu_i}, \qquad \mathbf{P} \in \mathcal{S}_N^*,$$
$$= 0 \qquad \text{otherwise}. \tag{6.4.13}$$

Let $\mathbf{M} = [m_{ij}]$ be an $N \times N$ matrix of positive elements, and let $\boldsymbol{m}_i$ denote the ith row of $\mathbf{M}$ ($i = 1, \ldots, N$). Then the $N \times N$ random stochastic matrix $\tilde{\mathbf{P}}$ is said to have the matrix beta-1 distribution with parameter $(\mathbf{M}, \boldsymbol{\nu})$ if $\tilde{\mathbf{P}}$ has the joint probability density function

$$f_{M\beta 1}^{(N)}(\mathbf{P} \mid \mathbf{M}, \boldsymbol{\nu}) = W(\mathbf{M}, \nu) \prod_{\substack{i=1\\j=1}}^{N} B_N(\boldsymbol{m}_i)(\pi_i(\mathbf{P}))^{\nu_i} p_{ij}^{m_{ij}-1}, \qquad \mathbf{P} \in \mathcal{S}_N^*$$

$$= 0 \qquad \text{otherwise,} \quad (6.4.14)$$

where $B_N(\boldsymbol{m}_1)$ is defined by Eq. 6.2.4. The normalizing constant $W(\mathbf{M}, \boldsymbol{\nu})$ is the reciprocal of $E[\prod_{i=1}^{N} (\tilde{\pi}_i(\mathbf{P}))^{\nu_i}]$ when $\tilde{\mathbf{P}}$ has the matrix beta distribution with parameter $\mathbf{M}$,

$$\frac{1}{W(\mathbf{M}, \boldsymbol{\nu})} = \int_{\mathcal{S}_N} \prod_{i=1}^{N} (\pi_i(\mathbf{P}))^{\nu_i} f_{M\beta}^{(N,N)}(\mathbf{P} \mid \mathbf{M})\, d\mathbf{P}. \qquad (6.4.15)$$

$W(\mathbf{M}, \boldsymbol{\nu})$ can be computed with the methods of Sec. 4.2, but this may require lengthy calculations.

Using Lemma 4.2.1, it is easily seen that

$$\int_{\mathcal{S}_N} f_{M\beta 1}^{(N)}(\mathbf{P} \mid \mathbf{M}, \boldsymbol{\nu})\, d\mathbf{P} = 1. \qquad (6.4.16)$$

The first two moments of the distribution are obtained from Eqs. 6.4.2 and 6.4.5,

$$E[\tilde{p}_{ij} \mid \mathbf{M}, \boldsymbol{\nu}] = \frac{m_{ij}}{M_i} \frac{W(\mathbf{M}, \boldsymbol{\nu})}{W(T_{ij}(\mathbf{M}), \boldsymbol{\nu})}, \qquad i, j = 1, \ldots, N, \quad (6.4.17)$$

and for $\alpha, \beta, \gamma, \delta = 1 \ldots, N$,

$$E[\tilde{p}_{\alpha\beta}\tilde{p}_{\gamma\delta} \mid \mathbf{M}, \boldsymbol{\nu}] = \frac{m_{\alpha\beta}m_{\gamma\delta}}{M_\alpha M_\gamma} \frac{W(\mathbf{M}, \boldsymbol{\nu})}{W(T_{\gamma\delta}(T_{\alpha\beta}(\mathbf{M})), \boldsymbol{\nu})}, \qquad \alpha \neq \gamma, \quad (6.4.18a)$$

$$= \frac{m_{\alpha\beta}m_{\alpha\delta}}{M_\alpha(M_\alpha + 1)} \frac{W(\mathbf{M}, \boldsymbol{\nu})}{W(T_{\alpha\delta}(T_{\alpha\beta}(\mathbf{M})), \boldsymbol{\nu})}, \qquad \alpha = \gamma, \quad \beta \neq \delta, \quad (6.4.18b)$$

$$= \frac{m_{\alpha\beta}(m_{\alpha\beta} + 1)}{M_\alpha(M_\alpha + 1)} \frac{W(\mathbf{M}, \boldsymbol{\nu})}{W(T_{\alpha\beta}(T_{\alpha\beta}(\mathbf{M})), \boldsymbol{\nu})}, \qquad \alpha = \gamma, \quad \beta = \delta, \quad (6.4.18c)$$

where $M_i = \sum_{j=1}^{N} m_{ij}$ and $T_{ij}(\mathbf{M})$ is the matrix $\mathbf{M}$ with its (i, j)th element increased by unity.

Due to the lengthy calculations required to obtain the normalizing constant $W(\mathbf{M}, \boldsymbol{\nu})$, the matrix beta-1 distribution is presently of limited usefulness. This distribution is, however, of some importance since it is the natural conjugate distribution for one of the data-generating processes to be considered in Chap. 7.

6.5. THE BETA-WHITTLE DISTRIBUTION

The beta-Whittle distribution is defined to be the unconditional distribution of the transition count $\tilde{\mathbf{F}}$ of a Markov chain with transition probability matrix $\mathbf{P}$ which is drawn from a matrix beta distribution. The beta-Whittle-2 distribution is defined in an analogous fashion. In this section explicit probability mass functions are derived for these distributions and their moments are discussed.

The Beta-Whittle Distribution

For fixed u and v ($u, v = 1, \ldots, N$) and fixed n ($n = 1, 2, 3, \ldots$), let

$$\phi_N(u, v, n) = \left\{\mathbf{F} \mid f_{ij} \in I;\ \sum_{\substack{i=1\\j=1}}^{N} f_{ij} = n;\ f_{i.} - f_{.i} = \delta_{iu} - \delta_{iv} \quad (i = 1, \ldots, N)\right\}, \quad (6.5.1)$$

and let

$$\phi_N(u, n) = \bigcup_{v=1}^{N} \phi_N(u, v, n), \qquad u = 1, \ldots, N, \quad n = 1, 2, 3, \ldots. \quad (6.5.2)$$

$\phi_N(u, n)$ is the set of all possible transition counts $\mathbf{F}$ which can arise from a sample of n consecutive transitions in a Markov chain with initial state u and a positive transition probability matrix.

The beta-Whittle probability mass function with parameter $(u, n, \mathbf{M})$ is defined as

$$\begin{aligned} f_{\beta W}^{(N)}(\mathbf{F} \mid u, n, \mathbf{M}) &= \int_{S_N} f_W^{(N)}(\mathbf{F} \mid u, n, \mathbf{P}) f_{M\beta}^{(N,N)}(\mathbf{P} \mid \mathbf{M})\, d\mathbf{P}, \qquad \mathbf{F} \in \phi_N(u, n), \\ &= 0 \qquad \text{elsewhere,} \quad (6.5.3) \end{aligned}$$

where $u = 1, \ldots, N$, $n = 1, 2, 3, \ldots$, and $\mathbf{M} = [m_{ij}]$ is an $N \times N$ matrix such that $m_{ij} > 0$ ($i, j = 1, \ldots, N$).

When $\tilde{\mathbf{F}}$ has the beta-Whittle distribution with parameter $(u, n, \mathbf{M})$, it is clear that $\tilde{\mathbf{F}}$ must have the range set $\phi_N(u, n)$, since the set of stochastic matrices which have one or more elements equal to zero is a set of measure zero relative to the matrix beta distribution.

It is seen from Eq. 6.5.3 that $f_{\beta W}^{(N)}(\mathbf{F} \mid u, n, \mathbf{M}) \geqslant 0$. By comparing Eq. 6.5.1 with Eq. 6.1.6, it is seen that $\phi_N(u, n) = \phi_N(u, n, \mathbf{P})$, provided $\mathbf{P}$ is a positive matrix. Since the set of nonpositive matrices **P** is a set of measure zero and since $\phi_N(u, n)$ is a finite set, we have

$$\sum_{\mathbf{F}\in\phi_N(u,n)} f_{\beta W}^{(N)}(\mathbf{F} \mid u, n, \mathbf{M}) = \int_{S_N} \sum_{\mathbf{F}\in\phi_N(u,n,\mathbf{P})} f_W^{(N)}(\mathbf{F} \mid u, n, \mathbf{P}) f_{M\beta}^{(N,N)}(\mathbf{P} \mid \mathbf{M})\, d\mathbf{P}$$
$$= 1. \tag{6.5.4}$$

Thus, the beta-Whittle mass function is a proper probability mass function.

Theorem 6.5.1. The beta-Whittle mass function with parameter $(u, n, \mathbf{M})$ is given by

$$f_{\beta W}^{(N)}(\mathbf{F} \mid u, n, \mathbf{M}) = F_{vu}^* \frac{\prod_{i=1}^{N} f_{i.} B(f_{i.}, m_{i.})}{\prod_{\substack{i=1\\j=1}}^{N} f_{ij} B(f_{ij}, m_{ij})}, \qquad \mathbf{F} \in \phi_N(u, n),$$
$$= 0 \qquad \text{elsewhere}, \tag{6.5.5}$$

where $m_{i.} = \sum_{j=1}^{N} m_{ij}$, $B(x, y)$ is the beta function, and v is the unique solution of the equations

$$f_{i.} - f_{.i} = \delta_{iu} - \delta_{iv}, \qquad i = 1, \ldots, N.$$

Proof. Letting $\boldsymbol{m}_i$ denote the ith row of **M**,

$$f_{\beta W}^{(N)}(\mathbf{F} \mid u, n, \mathbf{M}) = F_{vu}^* \frac{\prod_{i=1}^{N} f_{i.}!}{\prod_{\substack{i=1\\j=1}}^{N} f_{ij}!} \prod_{i=1}^{N} B_N(\boldsymbol{m}_i) \int_{S_N} \prod_{\substack{i=1\\j=1}}^{N} p_{ij}^{f_{ij}+m_{ij}-1}\, d\mathbf{P}. \tag{6.5.6}$$

The integrand is the kernel of a matrix beta density function with parameter $\mathbf{M} + \mathbf{F}$; hence, using Eq. 6.2.4,

$$f_{\beta W}^{(N)}(\mathbf{F} \mid u, n, \mathbf{M}) = F_{vu}^* \prod_{i=1}^{N} \left[\frac{f_{i.}\Gamma(f_{i.})\Gamma(m_{i.})}{\Gamma(f_{i.} + m_{i.})}\right] \prod_{\substack{i=1\\j=1}}^{N} \left[\frac{\Gamma(f_{ij} + m_{ij})}{f_{ij}\Gamma(f_{ij})\Gamma(m_{ij})}\right]$$
$$= F_{vu}^* \frac{\prod_{i=1}^{N} f_{i.} B(f_{i.}, m_{i.})}{\prod_{\substack{i=1\\j=1}}^{N} f_{ij} B(f_{ij}, m_{ij})}. \qquad \text{Q.E.D.} \tag{6.5.7}$$

The moments of the beta-Whittle distribution are somewhat complicated to compute. Referring to Eqs. 6.1.14 and 6.1.27, if $\tilde{\mathbf{F}} = [\tilde{f}_{ij}]$ has the beta-Whittle distribution with parameter $(u, n, \mathbf{M})$, then

$$E[\tilde{f}_{ij}] = E_{\mathbf{P}}E_{\mathbf{F}\mid\mathbf{P}}[\tilde{f}_{ij}] = \sum_{k=0}^{n-1} E_{\mathbf{P}}[\tilde{p}_{ui}^{(k)}\tilde{p}_{ij}], \qquad i, j = 1, \ldots, N, \quad (6.5.8)$$

and, similarly,

$$E[\tilde{f}_{\alpha\beta}\tilde{f}_{\gamma\delta}] = \delta_{\alpha\gamma}\delta_{\beta\delta}E[\tilde{f}_{\alpha\beta}]$$

$$+\sum_{k=1}^{n-1} E_{\mathbf{P}}[\tilde{p}_{n\alpha}^{(n-1-k)}\tilde{p}_{\alpha\beta}\sum_{\nu=0}^{k-1}\tilde{p}_{\beta\gamma}^{(\nu)}\tilde{p}_{\gamma\delta} + \tilde{p}_{u\gamma}^{(n-1-k)}\tilde{p}_{\gamma\delta}\sum_{\nu=0}^{k-1}\tilde{p}_{\delta\alpha}^{(\nu)}\tilde{p}_{\alpha\beta}],$$

$$\alpha, \beta, \gamma, \delta = 1, \ldots, N, \quad n = 2, 3, \ldots, \quad (6.5.9a)$$

$$= \delta_{\alpha\gamma}\delta_{\beta\delta}E[\tilde{f}_{\alpha\beta}], \qquad \alpha, \beta, \gamma, \delta = 1, \ldots, N, \quad n = 1. \quad (6.5.9b)$$

In both of these equations $E_{\mathbf{P}}[\cdot]$ denotes the expectation operator relative to the distribution $f_{M\beta}^{(N,N)}(\mathbf{P} \mid \mathbf{M})$. These expectations can be evaluated by repeated application of Lemma 2.3.2 in a manner which should, by now, be familiar, but the calculations, particularly in Eq. 6.5.9*a*, tend to become extensive. Approximations of the sort we have discussed in Chap. 4 can also be made. For small values of the parameter n, direct calculation of the moments is probably the most convenient way to approach the problem.

The Beta-Whittle-2 Distribution

The set of all possible transition counts $\mathbf{F}$ which can arise from a sample of n consecutive transitions in a Markov chain with arbitrary initial state and a positive transition probability matrix is

$$\phi_N^*(n) = \bigcup_{u=1}^{N} \phi_N(u, n), \qquad n = 1, 2, \ldots. \quad (6.5.10)$$

The $N \times N$ random matrix $\tilde{\mathbf{F}}$ with range set $\phi_N^*(n)$ is said to have the standard beta-Whittle-2 distribution with parameter $(\boldsymbol{p}, n, \mathbf{M})$ if $\tilde{\mathbf{F}}$ has the probability mass function

$$f_{\beta W2}^{(N)}(\mathbf{F} \mid \boldsymbol{p}, n, \mathbf{M}) = \int_{S_N} f_{W2}^{(N)}(\mathbf{F} \mid \boldsymbol{p}, n, \mathbf{P}) f_{M\beta}^{(N,N)}(\mathbf{P} \mid \mathbf{M})\, d\mathbf{P}, \quad (6.5.11)$$

where $\boldsymbol{p} = (p_1, \ldots, p_N)$ is a stochastic vector which is functionally independent of $\mathbf{P}$, $n = 1, 2, 3, \ldots$, and $\mathbf{M} = [m_{ij}]$ is an $N \times N$ matrix with $m_{ij} > 0$ $(i, j = 1, \ldots, N)$. It is readily established that $f_{\beta W2}^{(N)}(\mathbf{F} \mid \boldsymbol{p}, n, \mathbf{M}) \geqslant 0$ and that

$$\sum_{\mathbf{F}\in\phi_N^*(n)} f_{\beta W2}^{(N)}(\mathbf{F} \mid \boldsymbol{p}, n, \mathbf{M}) = 1.$$

Let

$$\phi_{N1}^*(n) = \{\mathbf{F} \mid \mathbf{F} \in \phi_N^*(n), f_{i.} = f_{.i} \ (i = 1, \ldots, N)\} \quad (6.5.12)$$

and

$$\phi_{N2}^*(n) = \phi_N^*(n) - \phi_{N1}^*(n). \quad (6.5.13)$$

Since

$$f_{W2}^{(N)}(\mathbf{F} \mid \boldsymbol{p}, n, \mathbf{P}) = \sum_{u=1}^{N} p_u f_W^{(N)}(\mathbf{F} \mid u, n, \mathbf{P}),$$

it follows from Lemma 6.1.5 and the fact that $\boldsymbol{p}$ is functionally independent of $\mathbf{P}$ that

$$\begin{aligned} f_{\beta W2}^{(N)}(\mathbf{F} \mid \boldsymbol{p}, n, \mathbf{M}) &= \sum_{u=1}^{N} p_u f_{\beta W}^{(N)}(\mathbf{F} \mid u, n, \mathbf{M}) \\ &= \left(\sum_{i=1}^{N} p_i F_{ii}^*\right) \frac{\prod_{i=1}^{N} f_{i\cdot} B(f_{i\cdot}, m_{i\cdot})}{\prod_{\substack{i=1\\j=1}}^{N} f_{ij} B(f_{ij}, m_{ij})}, \qquad \mathbf{F} \in \phi_{N1}^*(n), \\ &= p_u F_{vu}^* \frac{\prod_{i=1}^{N} f_{i\cdot} B(f_{i\cdot}, m_{i\cdot})}{\prod_{\substack{i=1\\j=1}}^{N} f_{ij} B(f_{ij}, m_{ij})}, \qquad \mathbf{F} \in \phi_{N2}^*(n), \\ &= 0, \qquad \text{elsewhere.} \end{aligned} \tag{6.5.14}$$

In Eq. 6.5.14, if $\mathbf{F} \in \phi_{N2}^*(n)$, (u, v) is the unique solution to the equations

$$f_{i\cdot} - f_{\cdot i} = \delta_{ix} - \delta_{iy}, \qquad i = 1, \ldots, N.$$

An important case in which $\boldsymbol{p}$ is not functionally independent of $\mathbf{P}$ occurs when $\boldsymbol{p} = \boldsymbol{\pi}(\mathbf{P})$, the steady-state probability vector corresponding to $\mathbf{P}$. In this instance we define the nonstandard beta-Whittle-2 distribution with parameter $(n, \mathbf{M})$ in terms of the following probability mass function:

$$f_{\beta W2^*}^{(N)}(\mathbf{F} \mid n, \mathbf{M}) = \int_{S_N} f_{W2}^{(N)}(\mathbf{F} \mid \boldsymbol{\pi}, n, \mathbf{P}) f_{M\beta}^{(N,N)}(\mathbf{P} \mid \mathbf{M})\, d\mathbf{P}, \tag{6.5.15}$$

where $n = 1, 2, 3, \ldots$ and $\mathbf{M} = [m_{ij}]$ is an $N \times N$ matrix such that $m_{ij} > 0$ $(i, j = 1, \ldots, N)$. The vector $\boldsymbol{\pi}$ in the integrand of Eq. 6.5.15 is the steady-state vector corresponding to $\mathbf{P}$ and is uniquely defined for all $\mathbf{P}$ except a set of measure zero. It is clear that the range set of $\tilde{\mathbf{F}}$ is $\phi_N^*(n)$ and that $f_{\beta W2^*}^{(N)}(\mathbf{F} \mid n, \mathbf{M})$ is a proper probability mass function.

Theorem 6.5.2. If

$$\bar{\pi}_u(\mathbf{M}) = \int_{S_N} \pi_u(\mathbf{P}) f_{M\beta}^{(N,N)}(\mathbf{P} \mid \mathbf{M})\, d\mathbf{P}, \qquad u = 1, \ldots, N, \tag{6.5.16}$$

is the expected value of $\pi_u(\tilde{\mathbf{P}})$, then the nonstandard beta-Whittle-2 probability mass function with parameter $(n, \mathbf{M})$ is given by

$$f^{(N)}_{\beta W2^*}(\mathbf{F} \mid n, \mathbf{M}) = \left(\sum_{i=1}^{N} \bar{\pi}_i(\mathbf{F} + \mathbf{M})F^*_{ii}\right) \frac{\prod_{i=1}^{N} f_{i.}B(f_{i.}, m_{i.})}{\prod_{\substack{i=1\\j=1}}^{N} f_{ij}B(f_{ij}, m_{ij})}, \qquad \mathbf{F} \in \phi^*_{N1}(n),$$

$$= \bar{\pi}_u(\mathbf{F} + \mathbf{M})F^*_{vu} \frac{\prod_{i=1}^{N} f_{i.}B(f_{i.}, m_{i.})}{\prod_{\substack{i=1\\j=1}}^{N} f_{ij}B(f_{ij}, m_{ij})}, \qquad \mathbf{F} \in \phi^*_{N2}(n),$$

$$= 0, \qquad \text{elsewhere.} \qquad (6.5.17)$$

In Eq. 6.5.17, if $\mathbf{F} \in \phi^*_{N2}(n)$, (u, v) is the unique solution to the equations

$$f_{i.} - f_{.i} = \delta_{ix} - \delta_{iy}, \qquad i = 1, \ldots, N.$$

Proof. Since

$$f^{(N)}_{W2}(\mathbf{F} \mid \boldsymbol{\pi}, n, \mathbf{P}) = \sum_{i=1}^{N} \pi_i(\mathbf{P}) f^{(N)}_{W}(\mathbf{F} \mid i, n, \mathbf{P}),$$

we have

$$f^{(N)}_{\beta W2^*}(\mathbf{F} \mid n, \mathbf{M}) = \sum_{i=1}^{N} \int_{S_N} \pi_i(\mathbf{P}) f^{(N)}_{W}(\mathbf{F} \mid i, n, \mathbf{P}) f^{(N,N)}_{M\beta}(\mathbf{P} \mid \mathbf{M})\, d\mathbf{P}. \qquad (6.5.18)$$

The kernel of the integrand of Eq. 6.5.18 is

$$\pi_i(\mathbf{P}) \prod_{\substack{j=1\\k=1}}^{N} p_{jk}^{f_{jk}+m_{jk}-1}.$$

Thus, proceeding as in the proof of Theorem 6.5.1,

$$f^{(N)}_{\beta W2^*}(\mathbf{F} \mid n, \mathbf{M}) = \sum_{i=1}^{N} f^{(N)}_{\beta W}(\mathbf{F} \mid i, n, \mathbf{M}) \int_{S_N} \pi_i(\mathbf{P}) f^{(N,N)}_{M\beta}(\mathbf{P} \mid \mathbf{F} + \mathbf{M})\, d\mathbf{P}. \qquad (6.5.19)$$

Equation 6.5.17 follows from Eq. 6.5.19 and Lemma 6.1.5. Q.E.D.

The moments of the standard beta-Whittle-2 distribution can be obtained from the moments of the beta-Whittle distribution by using the relation

$$f^{(N)}_{\beta W2}(\mathbf{F} \mid \boldsymbol{p}, n, \mathbf{P}) = \sum_{u=1}^{N} p_u f^{(N)}_{\beta W}(\mathbf{F} \mid u, n, \mathbf{M}). \qquad (6.5.20)$$

The moments of the nonstandard beta-Whittle-2 distribution are given by the following theorem.

Theorem 6.5.3. Let $E[\cdot]$ denote the expectation operator relative to the nonstandard beta-Whittle-2 distribution with parameter $(n, \mathbf{M})$ and $E_{\mathbf{P}}[\cdot]$ denote the expectation operator relative to the matrix beta distribution with parameter $\mathbf{M}$. Then

$$E[\tilde{f}_{ij}] = nE_{\mathbf{P}}[\tilde{\pi}_i \tilde{p}_{ij}], \qquad i, j = 1, \ldots, N, \tag{6.5.21}$$

and

$$E[\tilde{f}_{\alpha\beta}\tilde{f}_{\gamma\delta}] = \delta_{\alpha\gamma}\delta_{\beta\delta}E[\tilde{f}_{\alpha\beta}] + \sum_{k=0}^{n=1}(n - 1 - k)E_{\mathbf{P}}[\tilde{p}_{\alpha\beta}\tilde{p}_{\gamma\delta}(\tilde{\pi}_\alpha \tilde{p}_{\beta\gamma}^{(k)} + \tilde{\pi}_\gamma \tilde{p}_{\delta\alpha}^{(k)})],$$

$$\alpha, \beta, \gamma, \delta = 1, \ldots, N, \quad n = 2, 3, \ldots, \tag{6.5.22a}$$

$$= \delta_{\alpha\gamma}\delta_{\beta\delta}E[\tilde{f}_{\alpha\beta}], \qquad \alpha, \beta, \gamma, \delta = 1, \ldots, N, \quad n = 1. \tag{6.5.22b}$$

Proof. The theorem follows immediately from Eqs. 6.1.53 and 6.1.54, together with the relation

$$E[g(\tilde{\mathbf{F}})] = E_{\mathbf{P}}E_{\mathbf{F}\,|\,\mathbf{P}}[g(\tilde{\mathbf{F}})],$$

where $g(\mathbf{F})$ is any function of $\mathbf{F}$ for which the expectation exists and $E_{\mathbf{F}\,|\,\mathbf{P}}[\cdot]$ is the expectation operator relative to the Whittle-2 distribution with parameter $(\boldsymbol{\pi}, n, \mathbf{P})$. Q.E.D.

Chapter 7

FIXED SAMPLE SIZE ANALYSIS

In Chaps. 3 through 5 we examined some sequential sampling problems in a Markov chain with alternatives. We now consider the prior-posterior and preposterior analysis of a Markov chain governed by a fixed, but unknown, $N \times N$ matrix of transition probabilities $\tilde{\mathbf{P}}$ when a fixed number of consecutive observations is made. In Sec. 7.1 this analysis is carried out under the assumption that the initial state is known to the decision maker before the sample is observed. In Sec. 7.2 it is assumed that the initial state is unknown and has a distribution which is functionally independent of $\tilde{\mathbf{P}}$; in the final section it is assumed that the chain is operating in the steady state and that the initial state is unknown.

The results of this chapter follow readily from the definitions and properties of the distributions given in the preceding chapter; indeed, fixed sample size analysis provided the rationale for these distributions. The fixed sample size analysis is, however, presented separately from the distribution theory for convenient reference.

7.1. INITIAL STATE KNOWN

An N-state Markov chain can be considered to be a process which generates a sequence of random variables, $\tilde{x}_0, \tilde{x}_1, \ldots, \tilde{x}_i, \ldots$, where $\tilde{x}_i \in \{1, \ldots, N\}$ is the state of the system immediately after the ith transition ($i = 1, 2, \ldots$) and $\tilde{x}_0$ is the initial state observed before the first transition. This initial state $\tilde{x}_0 = \tilde{u}$ is subject to the distribution $\boldsymbol{p} = (p_1, \ldots, p_N)$, where $\boldsymbol{p}$ is a stochastic vector and $p_i = P[u = i]$ $(i = 1, \ldots, N)$. The transitions of the chain are governed by the $N \times N$ stochastic matrix $\mathbf{P} = [p_{ij}]$, where $p_{ij} = P[\tilde{x}_{n+1} = j \mid \tilde{x}_n = i]$ $(i, j = 1, \ldots, N; n = 0, 1, 2, \ldots)$. It is assumed in this section that the initial state u is known to the decision maker before observation of the chain commences. Thus, in this case,

$$p_i = \delta_{iu}, \qquad i = 1, \ldots, N. \tag{7.1.1}$$

Prior-Posterior Analysis

Let $\boldsymbol{x}_n = (x_0, \ldots, x_n)$ be a sample of n consecutive transitions in a Markov chain, where $x_0 = u$ is assumed known to the decision maker before the sample is obtained. Thus, $\boldsymbol{x}_n$ is obtained under the consecutive sampling rule. Let $\mathbf{F} = [f_{ij}]$ be the transition count of $\boldsymbol{x}_n$. Then the conditional probability, given $\tilde{\mathbf{P}} = \mathbf{P}$, of observing the sample $\boldsymbol{x}_n$ is

$$p_{x_0 x_1} p_{x_1 x_2} \cdots p_{x_{n-1} x_n} = \prod_{\substack{i=1 \\ j=1}}^{N} p_{ij}^{f_{ij}}. \tag{7.1.2}$$

If the stopping process is noninformative, then Eq. 7.1.2 is the kernel of the likelihood of the sample. It is clear that the statistic $\mathbf{F}$ conveys all the information of the sample and that, if stopping is noninformative, $\mathbf{F}$ is a sufficient statistic.

When the transition probability matrix is regarded as a random matrix $\tilde{\mathbf{P}}$, the natural conjugate of Eq. 7.1.2 is the matrix beta distribution defined by Eq. 6.3.1 with $K_i = 1$ $(i = 1, \ldots, N)$,

$$f_{M\beta}^{(N,N)}(\mathbf{P} \mid \mathbf{M}) \propto \prod_{\substack{i=1 \\ j=1}}^{N} p_{ij}^{m_{ij}-1}. \tag{7.1.3}$$

If $\tilde{\mathbf{P}}$ has the matrix beta distribution with parameter $\mathbf{M}' = [m'_{ij}]$ and if a sample from the process yields a sufficient statistic $\mathbf{F}$, Theorem 2.2.1 shows that the posterior distribution of $\tilde{\mathbf{P}}$ is matrix beta with parameter

$$\mathbf{M}'' = \mathbf{M}' + \mathbf{F}. \tag{7.1.4}$$

Sampling Distributions and Preposterior Analysis

It is assumed that $x_0 = u$ is known and that n, the number of transitions to be observed, is determined before the sample is obtained. Prior to sampling, the transition count $\tilde{\mathbf{F}}$ is a random matrix and the conditional probability, given $\tilde{\mathbf{P}} = \mathbf{P}$, that the Markov chain will generate a specific sample $\boldsymbol{x}_n$ which has the transition count $\mathbf{F}$ is given by Eq. 7.1.2. Whittle [41] has shown that the number of samples of size n with $x_0 = u$ which have the transition count $\mathbf{F}$ is given by

$$F^*_{vu} \frac{\prod_{i=1}^{N} f_{i.}!}{\prod_{\substack{i=1 \\ j=1}}^{N} f_{ij}!}, \tag{7.1.5}$$

where $f_{i.} = \sum_{j=1}^{N} f_{ij}$ $(i = 1, \ldots, N)$, v is the final state of the sample, and F^*_{vu} is the (v, u)th cofactor of the matrix $\mathbf{F}^*$ defined by Eq. 6.1.8. Thus, the conditional probability of $\tilde{\mathbf{F}}$ is given by the Whittle probability mass function defined by Eq. 6.1.7,

$$P[\mathbf{F} \mid u, n, \mathbf{P}] = f_W^{(N)}(\mathbf{F} \mid u, n, \mathbf{P}). \tag{7.1.6}$$

If a sample of n consecutive transitions is obtained from a Markov chain with known initial state u, and if the transition matrix $\tilde{\mathbf{P}}$ has the matrix beta distribution with parameter $\mathbf{M}'$, then the unconditional distribution of the transition count $\tilde{\mathbf{F}}$ is

$$D(\mathbf{F} \mid u, n, \mathbf{M}') = \int_{S_N} f_W^{(N)}(\mathbf{F} \mid u, n, \mathbf{P}) f_{M\beta}^{(N,N)}(\mathbf{P} \mid \mathbf{M}')\, d\mathbf{P}. \tag{7.1.7}$$

It is seen from Eq. 6.5.3 that the unconditional distribution of $\tilde{\mathbf{F}}$ is the beta-Whittle mass function given by Eq. 6.5.5,

$$D(\mathbf{F} \mid u, n, \mathbf{M}') = f_{\beta W}^{(N)}(\mathbf{F} \mid u, n, \mathbf{M}'). \tag{7.1.8}$$

For many common types of utility function preposterior analysis can be easily carried out by using the prior distribution of some of the moments of the porterior distribution. The distribution theory is illustrated here for the mean of the posterior distribution. If the prior distribution of $\tilde{\mathbf{P}}$ is matrix beta with parameter $\mathbf{M}'$ and if a sample of size n yields a sufficient statistic $\mathbf{F}$, then Eqs. 7.1.4 and 6.3.7 show that the mean of the posterior distribution is

$$\bar{\mathbf{P}}'' = [\bar{p}''_{ij}], \tag{7.1.9}$$

where, if $m'_{i\cdot} = \sum_{j=1}^{N} m'_{ij}$,

$$\bar{p}''_{ij} = \frac{m'_{ij} + f_{ij}}{m'_{i\cdot} + f_{i\cdot}}, \qquad i, j = 1, \ldots, N. \tag{7.1.10}$$

Before observing the sample, $\tilde{\bar{\mathbf{P}}}''$ is a random matrix which can take one of a finite set of values in the range set $R(u, n, \mathbf{M}')$. Let

$$S(\mathbf{P}) = \{\mathbf{F} \mid \mathbf{F} \in \phi_N(u, n), \bar{\mathbf{P}}'' = \mathbf{P}\}, \qquad \mathbf{P} \in R(u, n, \mathbf{M}'), \tag{7.1.11}$$

be the set of possible transition counts which result in a posterior mean with the value $\mathbf{P} \in R(u, n, \mathbf{M}')$. Then, by Eq. 7.1.8, the distribution of the posterior mean is given by the following probability mass function,

$$\begin{aligned} P[\tilde{\bar{\mathbf{P}}}'' = \mathbf{P} \mid u, n, \mathbf{M}'] &= \sum_{\mathbf{F} \in S(\mathbf{P})} f_{\beta W}^{(N)}(\mathbf{F} \mid u, n, \mathbf{M}'), \qquad \mathbf{P} \in R(u, n, \mathbf{M}'), \\ &= 0 \qquad \text{elsewhere.} \end{aligned} \tag{7.1.12}$$

7.2. INITIAL STATE UNKNOWN

We now assume that the initial state, $\tilde{x}_0 = \tilde{u}$, is known to the decision maker before the sample is observed, but that $\tilde{u}$ has a probability distribution $p = (p_1, \ldots, p_N)$ which is functionally independent of $\tilde{\mathbf{P}}$ and which may or may not be known to the decision maker. If $\tilde{p}$ is unknown, it is also assumed that the utility of any terminal decision made after $\boldsymbol{x}_n$ is observed depends only on $\tilde{\mathbf{P}}$ and not on $\tilde{p}$.

Prior-Posterior Analysis

Let $\boldsymbol{x}_n = (x_0, \ldots, x_n)$ be a sample of n consecutive transitions in a Markov chain. Let $u = x_0$ be the initial state observed and let $\mathbf{F} = [f_{ij}]$ be the transition count of the sample. Then the conditional probability, given $\tilde{\mathbf{P}} = \mathbf{P}$ and $\tilde{p} = p$, of observing the sample $\boldsymbol{x}_n$ is

$$p_{x_0} p_{x_0 x_1} \cdots p_{x_{n-1} x_n} = p_u \prod_{\substack{i=1 \\ j=1}}^{N} p_{ij}^{f_{ij}}. \tag{7.2.1}$$

If the stopping process is noninformative, then, since terminal utilities depend only on $\tilde{\mathbf{P}}$ and not on $\tilde{p}$, the kernel of the likelihood of the sample is

$$\prod_{\substack{i=1 \\ j=1}}^{N} p_{ij}^{f_{ij}}, \tag{7.2.2}$$

and $\mathbf{F}$ is a marginally sufficient statistic.

When the matrix of transition probabilities is treated as a random matrix $\tilde{\mathbf{P}}$, the natural conjugate of Eq. 7.2.2 is the matrix beta distribution defined by Eq. 6.3.1 with $K_i = 1$ $(i = 1, \ldots, N)$. If $\tilde{\mathbf{P}}$ has the matrix beta distribution with parameter $\mathbf{M}' = [m'_{ij}]$ and if a sample from the process yields a marginally sufficient statistic $\mathbf{F}$, then the posterior distribution of $\tilde{\mathbf{P}}$ is matrix beta with parameter

$$\mathbf{M}'' = \mathbf{M}' + \mathbf{F}. \tag{7.2.3}$$

Sampling Distributions and Preposterior Analysis

It is assumed that n, the number of transitions to be observed, is determined before the sample is obtained. Prior to sampling, the pair $(\tilde{u}, \tilde{\mathbf{F}})$ is a random quantity and the conditional probability, given $\tilde{\mathbf{P}} = \mathbf{P}$ and $\tilde{p} = p$, that the Markov chain will generate a specific sample $\boldsymbol{x}_n$ with the statistic $(u, \mathbf{F})$ is given by Eq. 7.2.1. The number of samples of size n with initial state u which have the transition count $\mathbf{F}$ is given by Eq. 7.1.5. Therefore, the conditional probability of $(\tilde{u}, \tilde{\mathbf{F}})$ is given by the Whittle-1 probability mass function defined by Eq. 6.1.37,

$$P[u, \mathbf{F} \mid p, n, \mathbf{P}] = f_{W1}^{(N)}(u, \mathbf{F} \mid p, n, \mathbf{P}). \tag{7.2.4}$$

The conditional distribution of the marginally sufficient statistic $\tilde{\mathbf{F}}$ is the Whittle-2 probability mass function given by Eq. 6.1.45,

$$P[\mathbf{F} \mid p, n, \mathbf{P}] = f_{W2}^{(N)}(\mathbf{F} \mid p, n, \mathbf{P}). \tag{7.2.5}$$

If a sample of n consecutive transitions is obtained from a Markov chain where the distribution of the initial state is known to be $\boldsymbol{p}$ and where the transition probability matrix $\tilde{\mathbf{P}}$ has the matrix beta distribution with parameter $\mathbf{M}'$, then, provided $\boldsymbol{p}$ is functionally independent of $\tilde{\mathbf{P}}$, the unconditional distribution of the transition count $\tilde{\mathbf{F}}$ is

$$D(\mathbf{F} \mid \boldsymbol{p}, n, \mathbf{M}') = \int_{S_N} f_{W2}^{(N)}(\mathbf{F} \mid \boldsymbol{p}, n, \mathbf{P}) f_{M\beta}^{(N,N)}(\mathbf{P} \mid \mathbf{M}')\, d\mathbf{P}. \quad (7.2.6)$$

Thus, by Eq. 6.5.11, the unconditional distribution of $\tilde{\mathbf{F}}$ is the beta-Whittle-2 probability mass function given by Eq. 6.5.14,

$$D(\mathbf{F} \mid \boldsymbol{p}, n, \mathbf{M}') = f_{\beta W2}^{(N)}(\mathbf{F} \mid \boldsymbol{p}, n, \mathbf{M}'). \quad (7.2.7)$$

If $\boldsymbol{p}$ is unknown and has the prior distribution function $H(\boldsymbol{p} \mid \psi)$, with mean $\bar{\boldsymbol{p}}(\psi)$, then Eqs. 7.2.7 and 6.5.14 show that the unconditional distribution of $\tilde{\mathbf{F}}$ is also beta-Whittle-2,

$$\begin{aligned} D(\mathbf{F} \mid \psi, n, \mathbf{M}') &= \int_{S_{1N}} f_{\beta W2}^{(N)}(\mathbf{F} \mid \boldsymbol{p}, n, \mathbf{M}')\, dH(\boldsymbol{p} \mid \psi) \\ &= f_{\beta W2}^{(N)}(\mathbf{F} \mid \bar{\boldsymbol{p}}(\psi), n, \mathbf{M}'). \end{aligned} \quad (7.2.8)$$

If $\tilde{\mathbf{P}}$ has the matrix beta distribution with prior parameter $\mathbf{M}'$ and if a sample yields the marginally sufficient statistic $\mathbf{F}$, the mean of the posterior distribution of $\tilde{\mathbf{P}}$ is given by Eqs. 7.1.9 and 7.1.10. Prior to observing the sample, the posterior mean $\tilde{\bar{\mathbf{P}}}''$ is a random matrix with the finite range set $R^*(n, \mathbf{M}')$. Let

$$S^*(\mathbf{P}) = \{\mathbf{F} \mid \mathbf{F} \in \phi_N^*(n), \bar{\mathbf{P}}'' = P\}, \qquad \mathbf{P} \in R^*(n, \mathbf{M}'), \quad (7.2.9)$$

be the set of possible transition counts which result in the posterior mean $\bar{\mathbf{P}}'' = \mathbf{P} \in R^*(n, \mathbf{M}')$. Then, from Eq. 7.2.7, we find that, if $\boldsymbol{p}$ is known, the distribution of the posterior mean is given by the following probability mass function,

$$\begin{aligned} P[\tilde{\bar{\mathbf{P}}}'' = \mathbf{P} \mid \boldsymbol{p}, n, \mathbf{M}'] &= \sum_{\mathbf{F} \in S^*(\mathbf{P})} f_{\beta W2}^{(N)}(\mathbf{F} \mid \boldsymbol{p}, n, \mathbf{M}'), \qquad \mathbf{P} \in R^*(n, \mathbf{M}'), \\ &= 0, \qquad \text{elsewhere.} \end{aligned} \quad (7.2.10)$$

Similarly, if $\tilde{\boldsymbol{p}}$ is unknown and has the prior distribution function $H(\boldsymbol{p} \mid \psi)$, the distribution of the posterior mean is

$$\begin{aligned} P[\tilde{\bar{\mathbf{P}}}'' = \mathbf{P} \mid \psi, n, \mathbf{M}'] &= \sum_{F \in S^*(\mathbf{P})} f_{\beta W2}^{(N)}(\mathbf{F} \mid \bar{\boldsymbol{p}}(\psi), n, \mathbf{M}'), \qquad \mathbf{P} \in R^*(n, \mathbf{M}') \\ &= 0, \qquad \text{elsewhere.} \end{aligned} \quad (7.2.11)$$

7.3. SYSTEM OPERATING IN THE STEADY STATE

When the Markov chain is operating in the steady state and the initial state $\tilde{u}$ is unknown, the distribution of $\tilde{u}$ is $\boldsymbol{\pi}(\tilde{\mathbf{P}}) = (\pi_1(\tilde{\mathbf{P}}), \ldots, \pi_N(\tilde{\mathbf{P}}))$, the steady-state probability vector associated with the transition matrix $\tilde{\mathbf{P}}$. In this case, observation of $\tilde{u}$ provides information about $\tilde{\mathbf{P}}$.

Prior-Posterior Analysis

Let $\boldsymbol{x}_n = (x_0, \ldots, x_n)$ be a sample of n consecutive transitions in a Markov chain which is operating in the steady state. If $u = x_0$ is the initial state and $\mathbf{F} = [f_{ij}]$ is the transition count of the sample, the conditional probability, given that $\tilde{\mathbf{P}} = \mathbf{P}$, of observing the sample $\boldsymbol{x}_n$ is

$$\pi_{x_0}(\mathbf{P}) p_{x_0 x_1} \cdots p_{x_{n-1} x_n} = \pi_u(\mathbf{P}) \prod_{\substack{i=1 \\ j=1}}^{N} p_{ij}^{f_{ij}}. \tag{7.3.1}$$

When stopping is noninformative, Eq. 7.3.1 is the kernel of the likelihood of the sample and the ordered pair $(u, \mathbf{F})$ is a sufficient statistic.

When $\tilde{\mathbf{P}}$, the matrix of transition probabilities, is regarded as a random matrix, the natural conjugate of Eq. 7.3.1 is the matrix beta-1 distribution defined by Eq. 6.4.14, $f_{M\beta 1}^{(N)}(\mathbf{P} \mid \mathbf{M}, \boldsymbol{\nu})$. It is easily seen that, if $\tilde{\mathbf{P}}$ has the matrix beta-1 distribution with parameter $(\mathbf{M}', \boldsymbol{\nu}')$ and if a sample from the process yields a sufficient statistic $(u, \mathbf{F})$, the posterior distribution of $\tilde{\mathbf{P}}$ is matrix beta-1 with parameter $(\mathbf{M}'', \boldsymbol{\nu}'')$, where, if $\boldsymbol{e}_u$ is an N-dimensional row vector with uth component equal to one and all other components equal to zero,

$$\mathbf{M}'' = \mathbf{M}' + \mathbf{F}, \tag{7.3.2a}$$

$$\boldsymbol{\nu}'' = \boldsymbol{\nu}' + \boldsymbol{e}_u. \tag{7.3.2b}$$

As was noted in Sec. 6.4, the normalizing constant and the moments of the matrix beta-1 distribution are difficult to compute. This difficulty complicates the task of assigning a specific matrix beta-1 prior distribution to $\tilde{\mathbf{P}}$. Since the matrix beta distribution is also a matrix beta-1 distribution with the parameter $\boldsymbol{\nu} = (0, \ldots, 0) = \boldsymbol{\nu}_0$,

$$f_{M\beta}^{(N,N)}(\mathbf{P} \mid \mathbf{M}) = f_{M\beta 1}^{(N)}(\mathbf{P} \mid \mathbf{M}, \boldsymbol{\nu}_0), \tag{7.3.3}$$

it may be convenient for the decision maker to use a matrix beta prior distribution for $\tilde{\mathbf{P}}$, and we shall assume this to be the case in discussing the preposterior analysis of a Markov chain operating in the steady state.

Sampling Distributions and Preposterior Analysis

We assume that n, the number of transitions to be observed, is fixed in advance of sampling and that the prior distribution of $\tilde{\mathbf{P}}$ is matrix beta. Prior to sampling, the conditional probability, given $\tilde{\mathbf{P}} = \mathbf{P}$, of obtaining a specific sample $\boldsymbol{x}_n$ with the statistic $(u, \mathbf{F})$ is given by Eq. 7.3.1. The number of samples of size n with initial state u which have the transition count $\mathbf{F}$ is given by Eq. 7.1.5 and, therefore, the conditional probability of the statistic $(\tilde{u}, \tilde{\mathbf{F}})$ is given by the Whittle-1 probability mass function as defined by Eq. 6.1.37,

$$P[u, \mathbf{F} \mid n, \mathbf{P}] = f_{W1}^{(N)}(u, \mathbf{F} \mid \boldsymbol{\pi}(\mathbf{P}), n, \mathbf{P}). \tag{7.3.4}$$

The marginal conditional distribution of $\tilde{u}$ is $\boldsymbol{\pi}(\mathbf{P})$ and the marginal conditional distribution of $\tilde{\mathbf{F}}$ is the Whittle-2 distribution,

$$f_{W2}^{(N)}(\mathbf{F} \mid \boldsymbol{\pi}(\mathbf{P}), n, \mathbf{P}).$$

When a sample $\boldsymbol{x}_n$ is obtained from a Markov chain operating in the steady state, where the initial state is unknown and the transition probability matrix $\tilde{\mathbf{P}}$ has the matrix beta distribution with parameter $\mathbf{M}'$, the unconditional distribution of the transition count $\tilde{\mathbf{F}}$ is

$$D(\mathbf{F} \mid n, \mathbf{M}') = \int_{S_N} f_{W2}^{(N)}(\mathbf{F} \mid \boldsymbol{\pi}(\mathbf{P}), n, \mathbf{P}) f_{M\beta}^{(N,N)}(\mathbf{P} \mid \mathbf{M}')\, d\mathbf{P}. \tag{7.3.5}$$

Therefore, using Eq. 6.5.15, the unconditional distribution of $\tilde{\mathbf{F}}$ is nonstandard beta-Whittle-2, as given by Eq. 6.5.17,

$$D(\mathbf{F} \mid n, \mathbf{M}') = f_{\beta W2^*}^{(N)}(\mathbf{F} \mid n, \mathbf{M}'). \tag{7.3.6}$$

It is then easily seen that, if the set $S^*(\mathbf{P})$ is defined by Eq. 7.2.9, the prior distribution of the posterior mean is given by the following probability mass function:

$$\begin{aligned} P[\tilde{\bar{\mathbf{P}}}'' = \mathbf{P} \mid n, \mathbf{M}'] &= \sum_{\mathbf{F} \in S^*(\mathbf{P})} f_{\beta W2^*}^{(N)}(\mathbf{F} \mid n, \mathbf{M}'), \qquad && \mathbf{P} \in R^*(n, \mathbf{M}') \\ &= 0, && \text{elsewhere.} \end{aligned} \tag{7.3.7}$$

Chapter 8

SPECIFIC RESULTS FOR A TWO-STATE MARKOV CHAIN

Many of the matters considered in preceding chapters are specialized to the case of a two-state Markov chain in this chapter. The 2×2 transition probability matrix $\tilde{\mathbf{P}}$ is assumed to have the matrix beta distribution, and explicit formulas are found for the means and product moments of the n-step transition probabilities, the steady-state probabilities, the process gain, and the expected total discounted rewards. The chapter concludes with a result concerning the selection of an optimal terminal policy for a two-state process with a special type of reward structure. Most of the formulas derived here are double-infinite series; it appears doubtful that similar expressions can be obtained for chains with more than two states.

8.1. PRELIMINARIES

Let

$$\mathbf{P} = \begin{bmatrix} 1 - x & x \\ y & 1 - y \end{bmatrix}, \qquad 0 \leqslant x, y \leqslant 1, \tag{8.1.1}$$

be the transition probability matrix for a two-state Markov chain. The eigenvalues of $\mathbf{P}$ are the roots of the equation

$$|\lambda \mathbf{I} - \mathbf{P}| = \lambda^2 - (2 - x - y)\lambda + (1 - x - y) = 0, \tag{8.1.2}$$

and are found to be

$$\lambda_1 = 1, \qquad 0 \leqslant x, y \leqslant 1, \tag{8.1.3a}$$

$$\lambda_2 = 1 - x - y, \qquad 0 \leqslant x, y \leqslant 1. \tag{8.1.3b}$$

The eigenvalues of $\mathbf{P}$ are distinct provided x and y are not both equal to zero. When $\lambda_1 \neq \lambda_2$, Sylvester's theorem leads to the spectral decomposition

$$\mathbf{P} = \begin{bmatrix} \dfrac{y}{x+y} & \dfrac{x}{x+y} \\ \dfrac{y}{x+y} & \dfrac{x}{x+y} \end{bmatrix} + (1-x-y) \begin{bmatrix} \dfrac{x}{x+y} & \dfrac{-x}{x+y} \\ \dfrac{-y}{x+y} & \dfrac{y}{x+y} \end{bmatrix}, \quad x \neq 0 \text{ or } y \neq 0. \tag{8.1.4}$$

Equation 8.1.4 immediately gives the following expressions for the steady-state vector,

$$\boldsymbol{\pi}(\mathbf{P}) = \left[\frac{y}{x+y}, \frac{x}{x+y}\right], \qquad x \neq 0 \text{ or } y \neq 0, \tag{8.1.5}$$

and the n-step probability matrix,

$$\mathbf{P}^{\mu} = \begin{bmatrix} p_{11}^{(\mu)} & p_{12}^{(\mu)} \\ p_{21}^{(\mu)} & p_{22}^{(\mu)} \end{bmatrix} = \begin{bmatrix} \dfrac{y}{x+y} & \dfrac{x}{x+y} \\ \dfrac{y}{x+y} & \dfrac{x}{x+y} \end{bmatrix} + (1-x-y)^{\mu} \begin{bmatrix} \dfrac{x}{x+y} & \dfrac{-x}{x+y} \\ \dfrac{-y}{x+y} & \dfrac{y}{x+y} \end{bmatrix},$$

$$\mu = 0, 1, 2, \ldots, \quad x \neq 0 \text{ or } y \neq 0. \tag{8.1.6}$$

In particular,

$$p_{12}^{(\mu)} = \frac{x}{x+y}[1-(1-x-y)^{\mu}] = x\frac{1-(1-x-y)^{\mu}}{1-(1-x-y)}$$

$$= x\sum_{k=0}^{\mu-1}(1-x-y)^k, \qquad \mu = 1, 2, 3, \ldots, \quad x \neq 0 \text{ or } y \neq 0, \tag{8.1.7}$$

and, similarly,

$$p_{21}^{(\mu)} = y\sum_{k=0}^{\mu-1}(1-x-y)^k, \qquad \mu = 1, 2, 3, \ldots, \quad x \neq 0 \text{ or } y \neq 0. \tag{8.1.8}$$

Let the process have the reward matrix

$$\mathbf{R} = [r_{ij}] = \begin{bmatrix} a & b \\ c & d \end{bmatrix}, \tag{8.1.9}$$

where r_{ij} is the reward earned when the process makes a transition from state i to state j $(-\infty < r_{ij} < \infty)$.

Let

$$\mathbf{M} = \begin{bmatrix} m & n \\ p & q \end{bmatrix}, \tag{8.1.10}$$

and assume that $\tilde{\mathbf{P}}$ has the matrix beta distribution with parameter $\mathbf{M}$,

$$f_{M\beta}^{(2,2)}(\mathbf{P} \mid \mathbf{M}) = \frac{1}{B(m, n)B(p, q)} x^{n-1}(1 - x)^{m-1}y^{p-1}(1 - y)^{q-1}. \quad (8.1.11)$$

Thus, $\tilde{x}$ and $\tilde{y}$ are independent random variables, each having the univariate beta distribution. It is to be noted that Eqs. 8.1.7 and 8.1.8 are valid for all $\mathbf{P} \in \mathcal{S}_2$ except a set of measure zero relative to the matrix beta distribution.

8.2. HYPERGEOMETRIC COEFFICIENTS

It will be convenient to use the hypergeometric coefficient $(x)_k$ in the equations of subsequent sections. This coefficient is defined here and some of its properties are derived.

Let x be any real number and k any nonnegative integer. The hypergeometric coefficient is defined by

$$(x)_k = x(x + 1) \cdots (x + k - 1), \qquad k = 1, 2, \ldots, \qquad (8.2.1a)$$

$$= 1, \qquad k = 0. \qquad (8.2.1b)$$

If $x > 0$ it is clear that

$$(x)_k = \frac{\Gamma(x + k)}{\Gamma(x)}, \qquad (8.2.2)$$

and in the case $x = 1$,

$$(1)_k = k!. \qquad (8.2.3)$$

Lemma 8.2.1. If $(x)_k$ is the hypergeometric coefficient defined by Eq. 8.2.1, then the following relations hold,

$$x(x + 1)_k = (x)_k(x + k), \qquad (8.2.4)$$

$$x(x + 1)_k = (x)_{k+1}, \qquad (8.2.5)$$

$$(x)_{k+1} = (x)_k(x + k), \qquad (8.2.6)$$

$$x(x + 1)_{k+1} = (x)_k(x + k)(x + k + 1), \qquad (8.2.7)$$

$$(x)_k(x + k)_v = (x)_{k+v}. \qquad (8.2.8)$$

Proof. Equations 8.2.4 and 8.2.5 follow by writing

$$x(x + 1)_k = x(x + 1) \cdots (x + k) = (x)_k(x + k) = (x)_{k+1}. \quad (8.2.9)$$

Equation 8.2.6 follows directly from Eqs. 8.2.4 and 8.2.5. To obtain Eq. 8.2.7 we use Eq. 8.2.6 and 8.2.4 to obtain

$$\begin{aligned} x(x + 1)_{k+1} &= x(x + 1)_k(x + k + 1) \\ &= (x)_k(x + k)(x + k + 1). \end{aligned} \qquad (8.2.10)$$

Equation 8.2.8 follows by direct expansion,

$$(x)_k(x+k)_\nu = x(x+1)\cdots(x+k-1)(x+k)\cdots(x+k+\nu-1)$$
$$= (x)_{k+\nu}. \tag{8.2.11}$$

Q.E.D.

8.3. EXPECTED *n*-STEP TRANSITION PROBABILITIES

We first consider the expected value of $\tilde{p}_{12}^{(\mu)}$. Using the binomial theorem to expand the factor $(1-x-y)^k$ of Eq. 8.1.7,

$$(1-x-y)^k = \sum_{\nu=0}^{k} \binom{k}{\nu}(-1)^\nu y^\nu (1-x)^{k-\nu},$$
$$k = 0, 1, 2, \ldots, \quad 0 \leqslant x, y \leqslant 1, \tag{8.3.1}$$

we can write

$$E[\tilde{p}_{12}^{(\mu)}] = \int_{S_2} x \sum_{k=0}^{\mu-1} (1-x-y)^k f_{M\beta}^{(2,2)}(\mathbf{P} \mid \mathbf{M})\, d\mathbf{P}$$
$$= \sum_{k=0}^{\mu-1} \sum_{\nu=0}^{k} \binom{k}{\nu}(-1)^\nu E_y[\tilde{y}^\nu] E_x[\tilde{x}(1-\tilde{x})^{k-\nu}]. \tag{8.3.2}$$

For $\alpha = 0, 1, 2, \ldots,$

$$E_x[\tilde{x}(1-\tilde{x})^\alpha] = \frac{1}{B(m, n)} \int_0^1 x^{(n+1)-1}(1-x)^{m+\alpha-1}\, dx$$
$$= \frac{B(m+\alpha, n+1)}{B(m, n)} = \frac{n}{m+n} \frac{(m)_\alpha}{(m+n+1)_\alpha} \tag{8.3.3}$$

and

$$E_y[\tilde{y}^\alpha] = \frac{1}{B(p, q)} \int_0^1 y^{(p+\alpha)-1}(1-y)^{q-1}\, dy$$
$$= \frac{B(p+\alpha, q)}{B(p, q)} = \frac{(p)_\alpha}{(p+q)_\alpha}. \tag{8.3.4}$$

Thus we have

$$E[\tilde{p}_{12}^{(\mu)}] = \frac{n}{m+n} \sum_{k=0}^{\mu-1} \sum_{\nu=0}^{k} \binom{k}{\nu}(-1)^\nu \frac{(m)_{k-\nu}(p)_\nu}{(m+n+1)_{k-\nu}(p+q)_\nu},$$
$$\mu = 1, 2, 3, \ldots. \tag{8.3.5}$$

The following recurrence relation, which follows immediately from Eq. 8.3.5, is of use for computing successive values of $E[\tilde{p}_{12}^{(\mu)}]$,

$$E[\tilde{p}_{12}^{(\mu+1)}] = E[p_{12}^{(\mu)}] + \frac{n}{m+n} \sum_{\nu=0}^{\mu} \binom{\mu}{\nu}(-1)^\nu \frac{(m)_{\mu-\nu}(p)_\nu}{(m+n+1)_{\mu-\nu}(p+q)_\nu},$$
$$\mu = 1, 2, 3, \ldots. \tag{8.3.6}$$

In a similar fashion an expression for $E[\tilde{p}_{21}^{(\mu)}]$ is easily derived, using Eq. 8.1.8.

$$E[\tilde{p}_{21}^{(\mu)}] = \sum_{k=0}^{\mu-1} \sum_{\nu=0}^{k} \binom{k}{\nu} (-1)^{\nu} E_y[\tilde{y}^{\nu+1}] E_x[(1-\tilde{x})^{k-\nu}]$$

$$= \sum_{k=0}^{\mu-1} \sum_{\nu=0}^{k} \binom{k}{\nu} (-1)^{\nu} \frac{(m)_{k-\nu}(p)_{\nu+1}}{(m+n)_{k-\nu}(p+q)_{\nu+1}}, \quad \mu = 1, 2, \ldots. \qquad (8.3.7)$$

For purposes of computation, we have the recurrence relation

$$E[\tilde{p}_{21}^{(\mu+1)}] = E[\tilde{p}_{21}^{(\mu)}] + \sum_{\nu=0}^{\mu} \binom{\mu}{\nu} (-1)^{\nu} \frac{(m)_{\mu-\nu}(p)_{\nu+1}}{(m+n)_{\mu-\nu}(p+q)_{\nu+1}}, \quad \mu = 1, 2, \ldots. \qquad (8.3.8)$$

The derivation of Eqs. 8.3.5 and 8.3.7 depended upon the form of Eqs. 8.1.7 and 8.1.8. Similar expressions cannot be obtained for $p_{11}^{(\mu)}$ and $p_{22}^{(\mu)}$. Thus, the diagonal elements of the mean n-step transition probability matrix must be computed from the relations

$$E[\tilde{p}_{11}^{(\mu)}] = 1 - E[\tilde{p}_{12}^{(\mu)}], \qquad (8.3.9a)$$

and

$$E[\tilde{p}_{22}^{(\mu)}] = 1 - E[\tilde{p}_{21}^{(\mu)}]. \qquad (8.3.9b)$$

We now verify that $E[\tilde{p}_{12}^{(\mu)}]$ satisfies the recursive Eq. 4.1.2. That is, we shall show that $\bar{p}_{12}^{(\mu)}(\mathbf{M}) = E[\tilde{p}_{12}^{(\mu)}]$ satisfies

$$\bar{p}_{12}^{(\mu+1)}(\mathbf{M}) = \sum_{k=1}^{2} \bar{p}_{1k}^{(\mu)}(T_{k2}(\mathbf{M}))\bar{p}_{k2}(\mathbf{M}), \qquad (8.3.10)$$

where $\bar{p}_{ij}(\mathbf{M})$ is the expected value of $\tilde{p}_{ij}$ when $\tilde{\mathbf{P}}$ has the distribution $f_{M\beta}^{(2,2)}(\mathbf{P} \mid \mathbf{M})$ and where $T_{ij}(\mathbf{M})$ is the parameter matrix $\mathbf{M}$ with its (i, j)th element increased by unity.

Since

$$\bar{p}_{12}(\mathbf{M}) = \frac{n}{m+n}, \qquad (8.3.11a)$$

$$\bar{p}_{22}(\mathbf{M}) = \frac{q}{p+q}, \qquad (8.3.11b)$$

the right side of Eq. 8.3.10 is

$$\frac{n}{m+n}\left[1 - \frac{n+1}{m+n+1} \sum_{k=0}^{\mu-1} \sum_{\nu=0}^{k} \binom{k}{\nu} (-1)^{\nu} \frac{(m)_{k-\nu}(p)_{\nu}}{(m+n+2)_{k-\nu}(p+q)_{\nu}}\right]$$

$$+ \frac{q}{p+q} \frac{n}{m+n} \sum_{k=0}^{\mu-1} \sum_{\nu=0}^{k} \binom{k}{\nu} (-1)^{\nu} \frac{(m)_{k-\nu}(p)_{\nu}}{(m+n+1)_{k-\nu}(p+q+1)_{\nu}}. \qquad (8.3.12)$$

Using Eq. 8.2.4, Eq. 8.3.12 can be written as

$$\frac{n}{m+n}\left[1+\sum_{k=0}^{\mu-1}\sum_{\nu=0}^{k}\binom{k}{\nu}(-1)^{\nu}\frac{(m)_{k-\nu}(p)_{\nu}}{(m+n+1)_{k-\nu}(p+q)_{\nu}}\right.$$
$$\left.\times\left[\frac{q}{p+q+\nu}-\frac{n+1}{m+n+1+k-\nu}\right]\right]. \quad (8.3.13)$$

Since

$$\frac{q}{p+q+\nu}-\frac{n+1}{m+n+1+k-\nu}=\frac{m+k-\nu}{m+n+1+k-\nu}-\frac{p+\nu}{p+q+\nu}, \quad (8.3.14)$$

Eq. 8.3.13 becomes, upon applying Eq. 8.2.6,

$$\frac{n}{m+n}\left[1+\sum_{k=0}^{\mu-1}\sum_{\nu=0}^{k}\binom{k}{\nu}(-1)^{\nu+1}\frac{(m)_{k-\nu}(p)_{\nu+1}}{(m+n+1)_{k-\nu}(p+q)_{\nu+1}}\right.$$
$$\left.+\sum_{k=0}^{\mu-1}\sum_{\nu=0}^{k}\binom{k}{\nu}(-1)^{\nu}\frac{(m)_{k+1-\nu}(p)_{\nu}}{(m+n+1)_{k+1-\nu}(p+q)_{\nu}}\right]. \quad (8.3.15)$$

Letting $j = \nu + 1$ in the first sum and noting that $\binom{k}{\nu-1}+\binom{k}{\nu}=\binom{k+1}{\nu}$, we obtain

$$\frac{n}{m+n}\left[1+\sum_{k=0}^{\mu-1}\left[\frac{(m)_{k+1}}{(m+n+1)_{k+1}}+\sum_{\nu=1}^{k}\binom{k+1}{\nu}(-1)^{\nu}\right.\right.$$
$$\left.\left.\times\frac{(m)_{k+1-\nu}(p)_{\nu}}{(m+n+1)_{k+1-\nu}(p+q)_{\nu}}+(-1)^{k+1}\frac{(p)_{k+1}}{(p+q)_{k+1}}\right]\right], \quad (8.3.16)$$

which, upon letting $j = k + 1$ and collecting terms, is $\bar{p}_{12}^{(\mu+1)}(\mathbf{M})$, as required. A similar derivation shows that $\bar{p}_{21}^{(\mu)}(\mathbf{M})$, as given by Eq. 8.3.7, satisfies Eq. 4.1.2.

8.4. EXPECTED VALUE OF $\tilde{p}_{\alpha\beta}^{(\mu)}\tilde{p}_{\gamma\delta}^{(\nu)}$

Using Eq. 8.1.7, we have, for fixed $\mathbf{P}$,

$$(p_{12}^{(\mu)})^2 = x^2\sum_{\substack{j=0\\k=0}}^{\mu-1}(1-x-y)^{j+k}, \quad (8.4.1)$$

and, therefore,

$$E[(\tilde{p}_{12}^{(\mu)})^2]=\sum_{\substack{j=0\\k=0}}^{\mu-1}\sum_{\nu=0}^{j+k}\binom{j+k}{\nu}(-1)^{\nu}E_y[\tilde{y}^{\nu}]E_x[\tilde{x}^2(1-\tilde{x})^{j+k-\nu}]. \quad (8.4.2)$$

Since

$$E_x[\tilde{x}^2(1-\tilde{x})^{\alpha}]=\frac{B(m+\alpha, n+2)}{B(m,n)}=\frac{(n)_2}{(m+n)_2}\frac{(m)_{\alpha}}{(m+n+2)_{\alpha}},$$
$$\alpha = 0, 1, 2, \ldots, \quad (8.4.3)$$

we have

$$E[(\tilde{p}_{12}^{(\mu)})^2] = \frac{(n)_2}{(m+n)_2} \sum_{\substack{j=0\\k=0}}^{\mu-1} \sum_{\nu=0}^{j+k} \binom{j+k}{\nu} (-1)^\nu \frac{(m)_{j+k-\nu}(p)_\nu}{(m+n+2)_{j+k-\nu}(p+q)_\nu},$$

$$\mu = 1, 2, \ldots . \quad (8.4.4)$$

Similarly, by Eq. 8.1.8,

$$(p_{21}^{(\mu)})^2 = y^2 \sum_{\substack{j=0\\k=0}}^{\mu-1} (1-x-y)^{j+k}, \quad (8.4.5)$$

and

$$E[(\tilde{p}_{21}^{(\mu)})^2] = \sum_{\substack{j=0\\k=0}}^{\mu-1} \sum_{\nu=0}^{j+k} \binom{j+k}{\nu} (-1)^\nu \frac{(m)_{j+k-\nu}(p)_{\nu+2}}{(m+n)_{j+k-\nu}(p+q)_{\nu+2}},$$

$$\mu = 1, 2, \ldots . \quad (8.4.6)$$

Finally, since

$$p_{12}^{(\mu)} p_{21}^{(\mu)} = xy \sum_{\substack{j=0\\k=0}}^{\mu-1} (1-x-y)^{j+k}, \quad (8.4.7)$$

we have

$$E[\tilde{p}_{12}^{(\mu)} \tilde{p}_{21}^{(\mu)}] = \frac{n}{m+n} \sum_{\substack{j=0\\k=0}}^{\mu-1} \sum_{\nu=0}^{j+k} \binom{j+k}{\nu} (-1)^\nu \frac{(m)_{j+k-\nu}(p)_{\nu+1}}{(m+n+1)_{j+k-\nu}(p+q)_{\nu+1}},$$

$$\mu = 1, 2, \ldots . \quad (8.4.8)$$

The same method can be used to derive more general product moments of the form $E[\tilde{p}_{\alpha\beta}^{(\mu)} \tilde{p}_{\gamma\delta}^{(\nu)}]$.

8.5. STEADY-STATE PROBABILITIES

We now obtain expressions for the means and product moments of $\boldsymbol{\pi}(\tilde{\mathbf{P}}) = (\tilde{\pi}_1, \tilde{\pi}_2)$. Silver [38], treating the special case where y is known and $\tilde{x}$ has the beta distribution, has shown that $E[\tilde{\pi}_1]$ is a Gaussian hypergeometric function.†

By Theorem 4.2.5, $\lim_{\mu\to\infty} E[\tilde{p}_{ij}^{(\mu)}] = E[\tilde{\pi}_j]$ and using Eqs. 8.3.7 and 8.3.5, we immediately have

$$E[\tilde{\pi}_1] = \sum_{k=0}^{\infty} \sum_{\nu=0}^{k} \binom{k}{\nu} (-1)^\nu \frac{(m)_{k-\nu}(p)_{\nu+1}}{(m+n)_{k-\nu}(p+q)_{\nu+1}}, \quad (8.5.1)$$

$$E[\tilde{\pi}_2] = \frac{n}{m+n} \sum_{k=0}^{\infty} \sum_{\nu=0}^{k} \binom{k}{\nu} (-1)^\nu \frac{(m)_{k-\nu}(p)_\nu}{(m+n+1)_{k-\nu}(p+q)_\nu}. \quad (8.5.2)$$

Theorem 4.2.5 implies that the series 8.5.1 and 8.5.2 both converge. We shall show that they converge conditionally. Neglecting the constant

† Erdélyi [17], Chap. 2.

multiplier $n/(m+n)$ and noting that $\binom{k}{\nu} = \binom{k}{k-\nu}$, the series of absolute values corresponding to Eq. 8.5.2 is

$$\sum_{k=0}^{\infty}\sum_{\nu=0}^{k}\binom{k}{\nu}\frac{(m)_{k-\nu}(p)_\nu}{(m+n+1)_{k-\nu}(p+q)_\nu} = \sum_{\substack{\nu=0\\k=0}}^{\infty}\binom{\nu+k}{k}\frac{(m)_k(p)_\nu}{(m+n+1)_k(p+q)_\nu}$$
$$= \sum_{\substack{\nu=0\\k=0}}^{\infty}\frac{(1)_{\nu+k}(m)_k(p)_\nu}{(m+n+1)_k(p+q)_\nu}\frac{1}{k!}\frac{1}{\nu!}$$
$$= F_2(1, m, p, m+n+1, p+q;\ 1, 1), \tag{8.5.3}$$

where $F_2(\alpha, \beta, \beta', \gamma, \gamma';\ x, y)$ is Appell's second hypergeometric function of two arguments [2]. Since $F_2(\alpha, \beta, \beta', \gamma, \gamma';\ x, y)$ diverges whenever $|x| + |y| > 1$, the series 8.5.3 diverges and, therefore, the series 8.5.2 converges conditionally. A similar proof establishes the conditional convergence of Eq. 8.5.1.

It is easily verified that $E[\tilde{\pi}_1]$ and $E[\tilde{\pi}_2]$ satisfy Eq. 4.2.40*a*. Let $\bar{\pi}_j(\mathbf{M}) = E[\tilde{\pi}_j]$ $(j = 1, 2)$. Then it must be shown that $\bar{\pi}_j(\mathbf{M})$ satisfies

$$\bar{\pi}_j(\mathbf{M}) = \sum_{k=1}^{2}\bar{\pi}_k(T_{kj}(\mathbf{M}))\bar{p}_{kj}(\mathbf{M}), \qquad j = 1, 2. \tag{8.5.4}$$

We shall consider the case $j = 2$; the proof for $j = 1$ is similar.

For $j = 2$, the right side of Eq. 8.5.4 is

$$\sum_{k=0}^{\infty}\sum_{\nu=0}^{k}\binom{k}{\nu}(-1)^\nu\left[\frac{n}{m+n}\frac{(m)_{k-\nu}(p)_{\nu+1}}{(m+n+1)_{k-\nu}(p+q)_{\nu+1}}\right.$$
$$\left.+\frac{n}{m+n}\frac{q}{p+q}\frac{(m)_{k-\nu}(p)_\nu}{(m+n+1)_{k-\nu}(p+q+1)_\nu}\right]$$
$$= \frac{n}{m+n}\sum_{k=0}^{\infty}\sum_{\nu=0}^{k}\binom{k}{\nu}(-1)^\nu\frac{(m)_{k-\nu}}{(m+n+1)_{k-\nu}}\left[\frac{(p)_{\nu+1}}{(p+q)_{\nu+1}} + \frac{q(p)_\nu}{(p+q)_{\nu+1}}\right]. \tag{8.5.5}$$

By using Eq. 8.2.6 we see that

$$\frac{(p)_{\nu+1} + q(p)_\nu}{(p+q)_{\nu+1}} = \frac{(p)_\nu(p+q+\nu)}{(p+q)_\nu(p+q+\nu)} = \frac{(p)_\nu}{(p+q)_\nu}, \tag{8.5.6}$$

and, therefore, that Eq. 8.5.5 is equal to $\bar{\pi}_2(\mathbf{M})$.

By Theorem 4.2.8, $\lim_{\mu\to\infty} E[\tilde{p}_{\alpha\beta}^{(\mu)}\tilde{p}_{\gamma\delta}^{(\mu)}] = E[\tilde{\pi}_\beta\tilde{\pi}_\delta]$, and we obtain the following equations from Eqs. 8.4.6, 8.4.4, and 8.4.8,

$$E[\tilde{\pi}_1^2] = \sum_{\substack{j=0\\k=0}}^{\infty} \sum_{\nu=0}^{j+k} \binom{j+k}{\nu}(-1)^\nu \frac{(m)_{j+k-\nu}(p)_{\nu+2}}{(m+n)_{j+k-\nu}(p+q)_{\nu+2}}, \tag{8.5.7}$$

$$E[\tilde{\pi}_2^2] = \frac{(n)_2}{(m+n)_2} \sum_{\substack{j=0\\k=0}}^{\infty} \sum_{\nu=0}^{j+k} \binom{j+k}{\nu}(-1)^\nu \frac{(m)_{j+k-\nu}(p)_{\nu}}{(m+n+2)_{j+k-\nu}(p+q)_{\nu}}, \tag{8.5.8}$$

$$E[\tilde{\pi}_2\tilde{\pi}_1] = \frac{n}{m+n} \sum_{\substack{j=0\\k=0}}^{\infty} \sum_{\nu=0}^{j+k} \binom{j+k}{\nu}(-1)^\nu \frac{(m)_{j+k-\nu}(p)_{\nu+1}}{(m+n+1)_{j+k-\nu}(p+q)_{\nu+1}}. \tag{8.5.9}$$

The series 8.5.7 through 8.5.9 are conditionally convergent. We illustrate the proof for Eq. 8.5.8. By Theorem 4.2.8, the double-infinite series 8.5.8 converges. Neglecting the constant multiplier $(n)_2/(m+n)_2$, the corresponding series of absolute values is

$$\sum_{\substack{j=0\\k=0}}^{\infty} \sum_{\nu=0}^{j+k} \binom{j+k}{\nu} \frac{(m)_{j+k-\nu}(p)_{\nu}}{(m+n+2)_{j+k-\nu}(p+q)_{\nu}}. \tag{8.5.10}$$

Using Eq. 8.5.3, we can write Eq. 8.5.10 as

$$F_2(1, m, p, m+n+2, p+q; 1, 1) + \sum_{\substack{j=1\\k=0}}^{\infty} \sum_{\nu=0}^{j+k} \binom{j+k}{\nu} \frac{(m)_{j+k-\nu}(p)_{\nu}}{(m+n+2)_{j+k-\nu}(p+q)_{\nu}}, \tag{8.5.11}$$

which diverges. Thus Eq. 8.5.8 is conditionally convergent. Similar proofs show that Eqs. 8.5.7 and 8.5.9 also converge conditionally.

It can be verified that $E[\tilde{\pi}_i\tilde{\pi}_j]$ satisfies Eq. 4.2.55*a*. The algebra is straightforward but tedious and will not be reproduced here.

8.6. PROCESS GAIN

The expected gain of the two-state Markov chain considered in this chapter is, by Eq. 4.4.3,

$$\bar{g}(\mathbf{M}) = \sum_{\substack{i=1\\j=1}}^{2} \bar{\pi}_i(T_{ij}(\mathbf{M}))\bar{p}_{ij}(\mathbf{M})r_{ij}. \tag{8.6.1}$$

If the reward matrix **R** is given by Eq. 8.1.9, the expected gain is

$$\bar{g}(\mathbf{M}) = \sum_{k=0}^{\infty}\sum_{\nu=0}^{k}\binom{k}{\nu}(-1)^{\nu}\left[a\frac{m}{m+n}\frac{(m+1)_{k-\nu}(p)_{\nu+1}}{(m+n+1)_{k-\nu}(p+q)_{\nu+1}}\right.$$
$$+ b\frac{n}{m+n}\frac{(m)_{k-\nu}(p)_{\nu+1}}{(m+n+1)_{k-\nu}(p+q)_{\nu+1}}$$
$$+ c\frac{n}{m+n}\frac{p}{p+q}\frac{(m)_{k-\nu}(p+1)_{\nu}}{(m+n+1)_{k-\nu}(p+q+1)_{\nu}}$$
$$\left.+ d\frac{n}{m+n}\frac{q}{p+q}\frac{(m)_{k-\nu}(p)_{\nu}}{(m+n+1)_{k-\nu}(p+q+1)_{\nu}}\right]. \tag{8.6.2}$$

Applying Eqs. 8.2.4, 8.2.5, and 8.2.6, we have

$$\bar{g}(\mathbf{M}) = \frac{n}{m+n}\sum_{k=0}^{\infty}\sum_{\nu=0}^{k}\binom{k}{\nu}(-1)^{\nu}\frac{(m)_{k-\nu}(p)_{\nu+1}}{(m+n+1)_{k-\nu}(p+q)_{\nu+1}}$$
$$\times\left[\frac{a}{n}(m+k-\nu) + b + c + \frac{dq}{p+\nu}\right]. \tag{8.6.3}$$

It is clear that Eq. 8.6.3 must converge conditionally.

8.7. TOTAL DISCOUNTED REWARD VECTOR

The expected discounted reward over an infinite period when the system starts in state i is given by Eq. 4.3.7 as

$$\bar{V}_i(\mathbf{M}) = \sum_{\mu=0}^{\infty}\beta^{\mu}\sum_{\substack{j=1\\k=1}}^{2}\bar{p}_{ij}^{(\mu)}(T_{jk}(\mathbf{M}))\bar{p}_{jk}(\mathbf{M})r_{jk},$$
$$i = 1, 2, \quad 0 \leqslant \beta < 1. \tag{8.7.1}$$

Let

$$S_{ij}(\mathbf{M}) = \sum_{\mu=1}^{\infty}\beta^{\mu}\bar{p}_{ij}^{(\mu)}(\mathbf{M}), \qquad i, j = 1, 2. \tag{8.7.2}$$

For $(i, j) = (1, 2)$, we have, by Eq. 8.3.5,

$$S_{12}(\mathbf{M}) = \sum_{\mu=1}^{\infty}\beta^{\mu}\frac{n}{m+n}\sum_{k=0}^{\mu-1}\sum_{\nu=0}^{k}\binom{k}{\nu}(-1)^{\nu}\frac{(m)_{k-\nu}(p)_{\nu}}{(m+n+1)_{k-\nu}(p+q)_{\nu}}$$
$$= \frac{\beta n}{m+n}\sum_{\mu=0}^{\infty}\sum_{k=0}^{\mu}\beta^{\mu}\sum_{\nu=0}^{k}\binom{k}{\nu}(-1)^{\nu}\frac{(m)_{k-\nu}(p)_{\nu}}{(m+n+1)_{k-\nu}(p+q)_{\nu}}. \tag{8.7.3}$$

Since

$$\frac{n}{m+n}\left|\sum_{\nu=0}^{k}\binom{k}{\nu}(-1)^{\nu}\frac{(m)_{k-\nu}(p)_{\nu}}{(m+n+1)_{k-\nu}(p+q)_{\nu}}\right|$$
$$= |E[\tilde{x}(1-\tilde{x}-\tilde{y})^k]| \leqslant 1, \tag{8.7.4}$$

we have

$$\frac{\beta n}{m+n}\sum_{\mu=0}^{\infty}\sum_{k=0}^{\mu}\beta^{\mu}\left|\sum_{\nu=0}^{k}\binom{k}{\nu}(-1)^{\nu}\frac{(m)_{k-\nu}(p)_{\nu}}{(m+n+1)_{k-\nu}(p+q)_{\nu}}\right| \leqslant \beta\sum_{\mu=0}^{\infty}\sum_{k=0}^{\mu}\beta^{\mu} = \beta\sum_{\mu=0}^{\infty}(\mu+1)\beta^{\mu}. \quad (8.7.5)$$

The ratio test shows that $\sum_{\mu=0}^{\infty}(\mu+1)\beta^{\mu}$ converges, hence, we may interchange the first two summation operators in Eq. 8.7.3 to obtain

$$S_{12}(\mathbf{M}) = \frac{\beta n}{(1-\beta)(m+n)}\sum_{k=0}^{\infty}\sum_{\nu=0}^{k}\binom{k}{\nu}\beta^{k}(-1)^{\nu}\frac{(m)_{k-\nu}(p)_{\nu}}{(m+n+1)_{k-\nu}(p+q)_{\nu}}. \quad (8.7.6)$$

Neglecting the constant multiplier, the series of absolute values corresponding to Eq. 8.7.6 is, upon interchanging the order of summation,

$$\sum_{\substack{\nu=0\\k=0}}^{\infty}\frac{(k+\nu)!\,(m)_{k}(p)_{\nu}}{k!\,\nu!\,(m+n+1)_{k}(p+q)_{\nu}}\beta^{k}\beta^{\nu} = F_2(1, m, p, m+n+1, p+q; \beta, \beta), \quad (8.7.7)$$

where $F_2(\alpha, \beta, \beta', \gamma, \gamma'; x, y)$ is Appell's second hypergeometric function of two variables [2]. Appell has shown that the series 8.7.7 converges if $0 \leqslant \beta < \frac{1}{2}$ and diverges if $\frac{1}{2} < \beta < 1$. The case $\beta = \frac{1}{2}$ has not yet been investigated. We conclude, therefore, that Eq. 8.7.6 converges absolutely for $0 \leqslant \beta < \frac{1}{2}$ and, since Theorem 4.3.2 implies the convergence of Eq. 8.7.6, that the series converges conditionally for $\frac{1}{2} < \beta < 1$.

For $(i, j) = (2, 1)$ we use Eq. 8.3.7 to obtain

$$S_{21}(\mathbf{M}) = \frac{\beta}{1-\beta}\sum_{k=0}^{\infty}\sum_{\nu=0}^{k}\binom{k}{\nu}\beta^{k}(-1)^{\nu}\frac{(m)_{k-\nu}(p)_{\nu+1}}{(m+n)_{k-\nu}(p+q)_{\nu+1}}, \quad (8.7.8)$$

the series converging absolutely for $0 \leqslant \beta < \frac{1}{2}$ and conditionally for $\frac{1}{2} < \beta < 1$.

The remaining cases are

$$S_{11}(\mathbf{M}) = \sum_{\mu=1}^{\infty}\beta^{\mu}[1 - \bar{p}_{12}^{(\mu)}(\mathbf{M})] = \frac{\beta}{1-\beta} - S_{12}(\mathbf{M}) \quad (8.7.9)$$

and

$$S_{22}(\mathbf{M}) = \frac{\beta}{1-\beta} - S_{21}(\mathbf{M}). \quad (8.7.10)$$

The expected discounted reward starting from state 1 is

$$\bar{V}_1(\mathbf{M}) = \sum_{k=1}^{2}\bar{p}_{1k}(\mathbf{M})r_{1k} + \sum_{\substack{j=1\\k=1}}^{2}S_{1j}(T_{jk}(\mathbf{M}))\bar{p}_{jk}(\mathbf{M})r_{jk}. \quad (8.7.11)$$

Using the reward matrix of Eq. 8.1.9 and Eqs. 8.7.6 and 8.7.9, we obtain, upon collecting terms,

$$\bar{V}_1(\mathbf{M}) = \frac{ma + nb}{(1-\beta)(m+n)} + \frac{n\beta}{(1-\beta)(m+n)} \times \sum_{k=0}^{\infty} \sum_{\nu=0}^{k} \binom{k}{\nu} \beta^k (-1)^\nu \frac{(m)_{k-\nu}(p)_\nu}{(m+n+1)_{k-\nu}(p+q)_\nu} \times \left[\frac{c(p+\nu)+dq}{p+q+\nu} - \frac{a(m+k-\nu)+b(n+1)}{m+n+1+k-\nu} \right]. \quad (8.7.12)$$

In a similar manner we find

$$\bar{V}_2(\mathbf{M}) = \frac{cp + dq}{(1-\beta)(p+q)} + \frac{\beta}{1-\beta} \times \sum_{k=0}^{\infty} \sum_{\nu=0}^{k} \binom{k}{\nu} \beta^k (-1)^\nu \frac{(m)_{k-\nu}(p)_{\nu+1}}{(m+n)_{k-\nu}(p+q)_{\nu+1}} \times \left[\frac{a(m+k-\nu)+bn}{m+n+k-\nu} - \frac{c(p+\nu+1)+dq}{p+q+\nu+1} \right]. \quad (8.7.13)$$

It can be shown that $\bar{V}_1(\mathbf{M})$ and $\bar{V}_2(\mathbf{M})$ satisfy Eq. 4.3.9.

8.8. A GENERALIZATION OF A RESULT OF SHOR

Shor [37] has considered a game-theoretic model of a two-state Markov chain with alternatives and rewards. He shows that under certain circumstances each player should act so as to maximize his expected one-step transition reward. This result is generalized here.

Consider a two-state Markov chain with K_i alternatives in state i $(i = 1, 2)$. Assume that the rewards depend only on the initial and final states i and j and not on the alternative used in making a transition from i to j. Assume further that the reward matrix is

$$\mathfrak{R} = [r_{ij}^k], \quad (8.8.1)$$

where, if r is any real number,

$$r_{11}^k = r, \qquad k = 1, \ldots, K_1, \quad (8.8.2a)$$

$$r_{12}^k = r + \Delta_1, \qquad k = 1, \ldots, K_1, \quad (8.8.2b)$$

$$r_{21}^k = r + \rho, \qquad k = 1, \ldots, K_2, \quad (8.8.2c)$$

$$r_{22}^k = r + \rho + \Delta_2, \qquad k = 1, \ldots, K_2. \quad (8.8.2d)$$

We require that $\rho \geqslant 0$ and $\Delta_2 \geqslant \Delta_1 \geqslant 0$.

Let $\tilde{\mathscr{P}} = [\tilde{p}_{ij}^k]$ be the matrix of alternative transition probabilities and let $\tilde{\mathscr{P}}$ have the prior distribution function $H(\mathscr{P} \mid \psi)$. If $F_{\boldsymbol{\sigma}}(\mathscr{P} \mid \psi)$ is the marginal distribution function of $\tilde{\mathbf{P}}(\boldsymbol{\sigma})$, it is assumed that, for all $\boldsymbol{\sigma} \in \Sigma$, $F_{\boldsymbol{\sigma}}(\mathbf{P} \mid \psi)$ is continuous on the boundary of $\mathcal{S}_2$.

The expected gain of the system under the policy $\boldsymbol{\sigma}$ is $\bar{g}(\boldsymbol{\sigma}, \psi)$. Suppose it is desired to choose a policy $\boldsymbol{\sigma}^*$ which maximizes the expected gain,

$$\bar{g}(\boldsymbol{\sigma}^*, \psi) = \max_{\boldsymbol{\sigma} \in \Sigma} \{\bar{g}(\boldsymbol{\sigma}, \psi)\}. \tag{8.8.3}$$

We shall show that, with the reward structure of Eq. 8.8.2, it is sufficient to solve the corresponding deterministic problem for $\bar{\mathscr{P}}(\psi) = E[\tilde{\mathscr{P}} \mid \psi]$, and that the optimal policy $\boldsymbol{\sigma}^* = (\sigma_1^*, \sigma_2^*)$ is determined by the equations

$$\bar{p}_{i2}^{\sigma_i^*}(\psi) = \max_{k=1,\ldots,K_i} \{\bar{p}_{i2}^k(\psi)\}, \qquad i = 1, 2. \tag{8.8.4}$$

Let $G_i^{(n)}(\boldsymbol{\sigma}, \mathbf{P})$ be the conditional total expected reward in n transitions under the policy $\boldsymbol{\sigma}$ when the system starts from state i ($i = 1, 2$) and $\tilde{\mathbf{P}}(\boldsymbol{\sigma}) = \mathbf{P}$. Let $\bar{G}_i^{(n)}(\boldsymbol{\sigma}, \psi)$ be the corresponding unconditional expected reward,

$$\bar{G}_i^{(n)}(\boldsymbol{\sigma}, \psi) = \int_{\mathcal{S}_2} G_i^{(n)}(\boldsymbol{\sigma}, \mathbf{P})\, dF_{\boldsymbol{\sigma}}(\mathbf{P} \mid \psi),$$
$$i = 1, 2, \quad n = 1, 2, \ldots, \quad \boldsymbol{\sigma} \in \Sigma. \tag{8.8.5}$$

Lemma 8.8.1. For $n = 1, 2, \ldots$ and all $\boldsymbol{\sigma} \in \Sigma$,

$$\bar{G}_1^{(n)}(\boldsymbol{\sigma}, \psi) - \bar{G}_2^{(n)}(\boldsymbol{\sigma}, \leqslant \psi)\ \Delta_1. \tag{8.8.6}$$

Proof. We show that, for all $\mathbf{P} \in \mathcal{S}_2^*$,

$$G_1^{(n)}(\boldsymbol{\sigma}, \mathbf{P}) - G_2^{(n)}(\boldsymbol{\sigma}, \mathbf{P}) \leqslant \Delta_1, \qquad n = 1, 2, \ldots, \quad \boldsymbol{\sigma} \in \Sigma, \tag{8.8.7}$$

from which Eq. 8.8.6 follows, since $\mathcal{S}_2 - \mathcal{S}_2^*$ is a set of measure zero relative to $F_{\boldsymbol{\sigma}}(\mathbf{P} \mid \psi)$.

Let $\bar{f}_{ij}(u, n)$ be the expected number of transitions from state i to state j in n transitions when the system starts from state u. Then, for all $\mathbf{P} \in \mathcal{S}_2^*$,

$$G_i^{(n)}(\boldsymbol{\sigma}, \mathbf{P}) = nr + \rho[\bar{f}_{21}(i, n) + \bar{f}_{22}(i, n)] + \Delta_1 \bar{f}_{12}(i, n) + \Delta_2 \bar{f}_{22}(i, n),$$
$$i = 1, 2, \quad n = 1, 2, \ldots, \quad \boldsymbol{\sigma} \in \Sigma. \tag{8.8.8}$$

If $\mathbf{P}$ is represented as in Eq. 8.1.1 and the eigenvalues of $\mathbf{P}$ are $\lambda_1 = 1$ and $\lambda_2 = 1 - x - y$, we can use the spectral representation of $\mathbf{P}$ given by Eq. 8.1.4 together with the expression for $\bar{f}_{ij}(u, n)$ given by Eq. 6.1.15 to obtain

$$G_1^{(n)}(\boldsymbol{\sigma}, \mathbf{P}) - G_2^{(n)}(\boldsymbol{\sigma}, \mathbf{P}) = \frac{1 - \lambda_2^n}{1 - \lambda_2} [- \rho + x\Delta_1 - (1 - y)\Delta_2]. \tag{8.8.9}$$

Since $\rho \geqslant 0$ and $\Delta_2 \geqslant \Delta_1 \geqslant 0$,

$$G_1^{(n)}(\boldsymbol{\sigma}, \mathbf{P}) - G_2^{(n)}(\boldsymbol{\sigma}, \mathbf{P}) \leqslant \frac{1 - \lambda_2^n}{1 - \lambda_2}(x + y - 1)\Delta_1 = -\lambda_2 \frac{1 - \lambda_2^n}{1 - \lambda_2}\Delta_1. \tag{8.8.10}$$

If $0 \leqslant \lambda_2 < 1$, then

$$-\lambda_2 \frac{1 - \lambda_2^n}{1 - \lambda_2}\Delta_1 \leqslant 0 \leqslant \Delta_1, \tag{8.8.11}$$

whereas, if $-1 < \lambda_2 < 0$,

$$-\lambda_2 \frac{1 - \lambda_2^n}{1 - \lambda_2}\Delta_1 = -\lambda_2\Delta_1(1 + \lambda_2 + \lambda_2^2 + \cdots + \lambda_2^{n-1}) \leqslant -\lambda_2\Delta_1 < \Delta_1. \tag{8.8.12}$$

In either case, we obtain Eq. 8.8.7. Q.E.D.

Lemma 8.8.2. For $i = 1, 2$ and $\boldsymbol{\sigma} \in \Sigma$,

$$\lim_{n \to \infty} \frac{1}{n} \bar{G}_i^{(n)}(\boldsymbol{\sigma}, \psi) = \bar{g}(\boldsymbol{\sigma}, \psi). \tag{8.8.13}$$

Proof. Since

$$G_i^{(n)}(\boldsymbol{\sigma}, \mathbf{P}) = \sum_{\substack{\alpha=1\\ \beta=1}}^{2} \bar{f}_{\alpha\beta}(i, n) r_{\alpha\beta}, \tag{8.8.14}$$

Eq. 6.1.14 yields

$$\bar{G}_i^{(n)}(\boldsymbol{\sigma}, \psi) = \sum_{\substack{\alpha=1\\ \beta=1}}^{2} r_{\alpha\beta} \sum_{k=0}^{n-1} E_{\boldsymbol{\sigma}}[\tilde{p}_{\alpha\beta}\tilde{p}_{i\alpha}^{(k)}], \tag{8.8.15}$$

where

$$E_{\boldsymbol{\sigma}}[\tilde{p}_{\alpha\beta}\tilde{p}_{i\alpha}^{(k)}] = \int_{S_2} p_{\alpha\beta} p_{i\alpha}^{(k)}\, dF_{\boldsymbol{\sigma}}(\mathbf{P} \mid \psi). \tag{8.8.16}$$

Let $\epsilon > 0$ be given. By a trivial extension of Theorem 4.2.5, there exists an integer $\nu > 0$ such that, if $k > \nu$,

$$|E_{\boldsymbol{\sigma}}[\tilde{p}_{\alpha\beta}\tilde{p}_{i\alpha}^{(k)}] - E_{\boldsymbol{\sigma}}[\tilde{p}_{\alpha\beta}\tilde{\pi}_\alpha]| < \frac{\epsilon}{2}. \tag{8.8.17}$$

Then, for $n > \nu$,

$$\begin{aligned} &\left| E_{\boldsymbol{\sigma}}[\tilde{p}_{\alpha\beta}\tilde{\pi}_\alpha] - \frac{1}{n}\sum_{k=0}^{n-1} E_{\boldsymbol{\sigma}}[\tilde{p}_{\alpha\beta}\tilde{p}_{i\alpha}^{(k)}] \right| \\ &\qquad < \frac{1}{n}\sum_{k=0}^{\nu} |E_{\boldsymbol{\sigma}}[\tilde{p}_{\alpha\beta}\tilde{\pi}_\alpha] - E_{\boldsymbol{\sigma}}[\tilde{p}_{\alpha\beta}\tilde{p}_{i\alpha}^{(k)}]| + \frac{n - \nu}{n}\frac{\epsilon}{2} \\ &\qquad < \epsilon \end{aligned} \tag{8.8.18}$$

for n sufficiently large. Thus,

$$\lim_{n\to\infty} \frac{1}{n} \sum_{k=0}^{n-1} E_{\sigma}[\tilde{p}_{\alpha\beta}\tilde{p}_{i\alpha}^{(k)}] = E_{\sigma}[\tilde{p}_{\alpha\beta}\tilde{\pi}_{\alpha}], \tag{8.8.19}$$

and, by Eq. 4.4.4,

$$\lim_{n\to\infty} \frac{1}{n} \bar{G}_i^{(n)}(\boldsymbol{\sigma}, \psi) = \bar{g}(\boldsymbol{\sigma}, \psi). \qquad \text{Q.E.D.} \tag{8.8.20}$$

Theorem 8.8.3. Let $\boldsymbol{\sigma}^* = (\sigma_1^*, \sigma_2^*)$ be a policy such that

$$\bar{p}_{i2}^{\overset{*}{\sigma_i}}(\psi) = \max_{k=1,\ldots,K_i} \{\bar{p}_{i2}^k(\psi)\}, \qquad i = 1, 2. \tag{8.8.21}$$

Then

$$\bar{g}(\boldsymbol{\sigma}^*, \psi) \geqslant \bar{g}(\boldsymbol{\sigma}, \psi), \qquad \boldsymbol{\sigma} \in \Sigma. \tag{8.8.22}$$

Proof. We first establish by induction that

$$\bar{G}_i^{(n)}(\boldsymbol{\sigma}^*, \psi) \geqslant \bar{G}_i^{(n)}(\boldsymbol{\sigma}, \psi),$$
$$i = 1, 2, \quad n = 1, 2, \ldots, \quad \boldsymbol{\sigma} \in \Sigma. \tag{8.8.23}$$

For $n = 1$,

$$\bar{G}_1^{(1)}(\boldsymbol{\sigma}^*, \psi) = r + \bar{p}_{12}^{\overset{*}{\sigma_1}}(\psi)\Delta_1 \geqslant \bar{G}_1^{(1)}(\boldsymbol{\sigma}, \psi),$$
$$\bar{G}_2^{(1)}(\boldsymbol{\sigma}^*, \psi) = r + \rho + \bar{p}_{22}^{\overset{*}{\sigma_2}}(\psi)\Delta_2 \geqslant \bar{G}_2^{(1)}(\boldsymbol{\sigma}, \psi), \qquad \boldsymbol{\sigma} \in \Sigma. \tag{8.8.24}$$

Assume Eq. 8.8.23 holds for n. For $i = 1$,

$$\begin{aligned}\bar{G}_1^{(n+1)}(\boldsymbol{\sigma}^*, \psi) &= \bar{p}_{11}^{\overset{*}{\sigma_1}}(\psi)[r + \bar{G}_1^{(n)}(\boldsymbol{\sigma}^*, \psi)] + \bar{p}_{12}^{\overset{*}{\sigma_1}}(\psi)[r + \Delta_1 + \bar{G}_2^{(n)}(\boldsymbol{\sigma}^*, \psi)] \\ &= r + \bar{p}_{12}^{\overset{*}{\sigma_1}}(\psi)[\Delta_1 + \bar{G}_2^{(n)}(\boldsymbol{\sigma}^*, \psi) - \bar{G}_1^{(n)}(\boldsymbol{\sigma}^*, \psi)] + \bar{G}_1^{(n)}(\boldsymbol{\sigma}^*, \psi).\end{aligned} \tag{8.8.25}$$

Since $\boldsymbol{\sigma}^*$ is an optimal policy for a transition interval of length n, we have, for all $\boldsymbol{\sigma} \in \Sigma$,

$$\begin{aligned}\bar{G}_1^{(n+1)}(\boldsymbol{\sigma}, \psi) \leqslant r + \bar{p}_{12}^{\sigma_1}(\psi)[\Delta_1 &+ \bar{G}_2^{(n)}(\boldsymbol{\sigma}^*, \psi) \\ &- \bar{G}_1^{(n)}(\boldsymbol{\sigma}^*, \psi)] + \bar{G}_1^{(n)}(\boldsymbol{\sigma}^*, \psi),\end{aligned} \tag{8.8.26}$$

and, by Eq. 8.8.21 and Lemma 8.8.1,

$$\begin{aligned}&\bar{G}_1^{(n+1)}(\boldsymbol{\sigma}^*, \psi) - \bar{G}_1^{(n+1)}(\boldsymbol{\sigma}, \psi) \\ &\qquad \geqslant [\bar{p}_{12}^{\overset{*}{\sigma_1}}(\psi) - \bar{p}_{12}^{\sigma_1}(\psi)][\Delta_1 + \bar{G}_2^{(n)}(\boldsymbol{\sigma}^*, \psi) - \bar{G}_1^{(n)}(\boldsymbol{\sigma}^*, \psi)] \\ &\qquad \geqslant 0.\end{aligned} \tag{8.8.27}$$

Similarly,

$$\bar{G}_2^{(n+1)}(\boldsymbol{\sigma}^*, \psi) = r + \rho + \bar{p}_{22}^{\overset{*}{\sigma_2}}(\psi)[\Delta_2 + \bar{G}_2^{(n)}(\boldsymbol{\sigma}^*, \psi) - \bar{G}_1^{(n)}(\boldsymbol{\sigma}^*, \psi)] + \bar{G}_1^{(n)}(\boldsymbol{\sigma}^*, \psi), \quad (8.8.28)$$

and, since $\Delta_2 \geqslant \Delta_1$,

$$\begin{aligned} &\bar{G}_2^{(n+1)}(\boldsymbol{\sigma}^*, \psi) - \bar{G}_2^{(n+1)}(\boldsymbol{\sigma}, \psi) \\ &\qquad \geqslant [\bar{p}_{22}^{\overset{*}{\sigma_2}}(\psi) - \bar{p}_{22}^{\sigma_2}(\psi)][\Delta_2 + \bar{G}_2^{(n)}(\boldsymbol{\sigma}^*, \psi) - \bar{G}_1^{(n)}(\boldsymbol{\sigma}^*, \psi)] \\ &\qquad \geqslant 0, \qquad \boldsymbol{\sigma} \in \Sigma, \end{aligned} \quad (8.8.29)$$

proving the induction.

Equation 8.8.23 and Lemma 8.8.2 together imply that, for all $\boldsymbol{\sigma} \in \Sigma$,

$$\begin{aligned} \bar{g}(\boldsymbol{\sigma}^*, \psi) &= \lim_{n\to\infty} \frac{1}{n} \bar{G}_i^{(n)}(\boldsymbol{\sigma}^*, \psi) \\ &\geqslant \lim_{n\to\infty} \frac{1}{n} \bar{G}_i^{(n)}(\boldsymbol{\sigma}, \psi) \\ &= \bar{g}(\boldsymbol{\sigma}, \psi). \end{aligned} \quad (8.8.30)$$

Q.E.D.

Chapter 9

CONCLUDING REMARKS

In the foregoing chapters we have described a formal structure for certain broad classes of sequential sampling and fixed-sample-size decision problems in a Markov chain with unknown transition probabilities. Since there is very little theory in this area, most of our efforts have been directed toward answering questions of existence and convergence. For this reason the portions of this book that deal with numerical computation set forth the obvious, but not necessarily the most efficient, ways to approach problems of calculation. It does seem clear, however, that, for problems with a large number of states in which a high degree of accuracy is required, we must think in terms of hours, not minutes, of computer time. This is not to say that the Bayesian method of dealing with Markov chains with uncertain transition probabilities must be abandoned as impractical. But it must be recognized that, for the present state of the art, the Bayesian treatment is probably most practical for problems with two or three states, loose prior distributions, and large differences in the rewards associated with different actions. As problems tend to differ from these criteria, the decision maker must balance increasing computation time against the required accuracy of the solution and choose an appropriate approximation.

There are numerous questions of immediate interest which remain unanswered, some theoretical and some numerical. Many of these are listed in the following:

1. Certain error bounds were derived in Chaps. 3, 4, and 5 which depend on the discount factor β but not on ψ, the parameter of the prior distribution. These bounds should be made tighter for specific prior distributions by including factors which involve ψ.

2. The rate of convergence of the successive-approximation methods developed in Chaps. 3, 4, and 5 depend upon the choice of terminal functions. Classes of terminal functions which accelerate this convergence rate should be investigated.

3. The analysis of undiscounted adaptive control models by letting $\beta \to 1$ in the corresponding discounted problem may provide a workable approach to a difficult problem. The remarks of Sec. 3.7 are relevant in this connection.

4. The question of the uniqueness of solutions to Eqs. 4.2.40 and 4.2.55 is of considerable importance for the calculation of the means and product moments of the steady-state vector $\tilde{\boldsymbol{\pi}}$ when a method of successive approximations is used. The problem of the convergence of the approximant $\bar{\boldsymbol{\pi}}(n, \psi)$, as defined by Eq. 4.2.42 with the terminal function of Eq. 4.2.51, is also of importance.

5. In the terminal-control models of Chap. 5 it is necessary to evaluate expressions of the form

$$\bar{V}_i(\boldsymbol{\sigma}^*, \psi) = \max_{\boldsymbol{\sigma} \in \Sigma} \{\bar{V}_i(\boldsymbol{\sigma}, \psi)\},$$

and

$$\bar{g}(\boldsymbol{\sigma}^*, \psi) = \max_{\boldsymbol{\sigma} \in \Sigma} \{\bar{g}(\boldsymbol{\sigma}, \psi)\}.$$

At present, the only method of finding the maximizing policy $\boldsymbol{\sigma}^*$ is by direct search over the elements of Σ. More efficient methods of finding $\boldsymbol{\sigma}^*$ should be investigated; approximations to $\boldsymbol{\sigma}^*$ of the sort described in Sec. 5.4 should also be studied.

6. A formal analysis of the undiscounted terminal-control models III and IV, which were introduced in Sec. 5.5, should be carried out. This analysis would examine such questions as the existence and uniqueness of solutions, the convergence of successive-approximation methods, and whether a terminal-decision point is reached with probability one in an optimal sampling strategy. In this regard it is to be noted that Eqs. 5.5.2 and 5.5.3 can be made more precise by replacing the expression

$$\max_{\boldsymbol{\sigma} \in \Sigma} \{\nu \bar{g}(\boldsymbol{\sigma}, \psi)\}$$

by the expression

$$\max_{\boldsymbol{\sigma} \in \Sigma} \{\bar{w}_i(\boldsymbol{\sigma}, \psi) + \nu \bar{g}(\boldsymbol{\sigma}, \psi)\},$$

where $\bar{w}_i(\boldsymbol{\sigma}, \psi)$ is the expected *relative value*† of starting the system in state i and operating it indefinitely under the policy $\boldsymbol{\sigma}$ when the prior distribution function of $\tilde{\mathscr{P}}$ is $H(\mathscr{P} \mid \psi)$. Methods of computing $\bar{w}_i(\boldsymbol{\sigma}, \psi)$ have not yet been studied.

7. There are well-known difficulties in assigning a multivariate prior distribution to the elements of $\tilde{\mathscr{P}}$ in such a manner as to reflect accurately the decision maker's state of knowledge. It would be of considerable

† See Howard [22], Chap. 4.

interest, therefore, to investigate the sensitivity of some of the models in the foregoing chapters to relatively small changes in the prior distribution.

In addition to these and other immediate questions that arise in connection with the research reported here, there are several fairly obvious directions in which this research can be extended. For example, many of the results and techniques developed here can be extended to decision problems in a semi-Markov chain in which both the transition probabilities and the parameters of the holding-time distributions are uncertain.

More general stochastic processes are, in principle, amenable to Bayesian analysis, although different techniques than those utilized here may be required. The Weiner process, for example, can be analyzed with the existing Bayesian theory for normal processes.

APPENDIX A

GLOSSARY OF SYMBOLS

Symbol	Meaning	Defined on Page
$B(p, q)$	Beta function.	—
$B_N(\boldsymbol{m})$	Generalized beta function.	133
β	Discount factor.	35
c_i	Sampling cost when system is observed in state i.	95
$\bar{c}_i^k(\psi)$	Expected one-step sampling cost when process is in state i and alternative k is to be used.	96
C	Maximum sampling cost.	99
$\text{cov}\,[\cdot]$ or $\text{cov}\,[\cdot \mid \psi]$	Covariance operator.	—
$e_i(n, \psi)$	Error of nth successive approximant in adaptive and terminal control problems.	46, 102, 109
$e_i(\boldsymbol{\sigma}, \psi)$	Error of the terminal decision $\boldsymbol{\sigma}$.	110, 113
$E[\cdot]$ or $E[\cdot \mid \psi]$	Expectation operator.	—
$f_{i.}$	Sum of ith row of transition count.	119
$f_{.i}$	Sum of ith column of transition count.	119
$f_{ij}(u, n)$	Number of transitions from state i to state j in n transitions when process starts from state u.	122
$\bar{f}_{ij}(u, n)$	Expected value of $\tilde{f}_{ij}(u, n)$.	122
$f_\beta^{(N)}(\boldsymbol{p} \mid \boldsymbol{m})$	Multivariate beta probability density function.	133
$f_{\beta*}^{(N)}(\boldsymbol{p} \mid a, \boldsymbol{m})$	Nonstandard multivariate beta probability density function.	138
$f_{\beta W}^{(N)}(\mathbf{F} \mid u, n, \mathbf{M})$	Beta-Whittle probability mass function.	150, 151
$\bar{f}_{\beta W2}^{(N)}(\mathbf{F} \mid \boldsymbol{p}, n, \mathbf{M})$	Beta-Whittle-2 probability mass function.	152, 153
$f_{\beta W2*}^{(N)}(\mathbf{F} \mid n, \mathbf{M})$	Nonstandard beta-Whittle-2 mass function.	153, 154
$f_{M\beta}^{(K,N)}(\ \mid \mathscr{P}\,\mathcal{M})$	Matrix beta probability density function.	141
$f_{M\beta*}^{(K,N)}(\mathscr{P} \mid \boldsymbol{a}, \mathcal{M})$	Nonstandard matrix beta probability density function.	145

Symbol	Meaning	Defined on Page
$f_{M\beta 1}^{(N)}(\mathscr{P} \mid \mathcal{M}, \boldsymbol{\nu})$	Matrix beta-1 probability density function.	149
$f_{W}^{(N)}(\mathbf{F} \mid u, n, \mathbf{P})$	Whittle probability mass function.	120
$f_{W1}^{(N)}(u, \mathbf{F} \mid \boldsymbol{p}, n, \mathbf{P})$	Whittle-1 probability mass function.	127
$f_{W2}^{(N)}(\mathbf{F} \mid \boldsymbol{p}, n, \mathbf{P})$	Whittle-2 probability mass function.	127, 129
$\mathbf{F} = [f_{ij}]$	Transition count.	118
$F_{\beta}^{(N)}(\boldsymbol{p} \mid \boldsymbol{m})$	Multivariate beta probability distribution function.	136
$F_{\boldsymbol{\sigma}}(\mathbf{P} \mid \psi)$ or $F(\mathbf{P} \mid \psi)$	Marginal distribution function of the N rows of $\tilde{\mathscr{P}}$ specified by $\boldsymbol{\sigma}$.	13
$F_2(\alpha, \beta, \beta', \gamma, \gamma', x, y)$	Appell's second hypergeometric function of two arguments.	—
$\mathcal{F}$	Family of probability distribution functions, $F(\mathbf{P} \mid \psi)$.	32
$g(\mathbf{P})$	Conditional expected reward per transition in the steady state, or process gain, when $\tilde{\mathbf{P}} = \mathbf{P}$.	88
$\bar{g}(\psi)$ or $\bar{g}(\boldsymbol{\sigma}, \psi)$	Expected gain under the policy $\boldsymbol{\sigma}$.	88, 113
$\Gamma(x)$	Gamma function.	—
$H(\mathscr{P} \mid \psi)$	Probability distribution function for the generalized stochastic matrix $\tilde{\mathscr{P}}$.	12
$\mathcal{H}$	Family of probability distribution functions $H(\mathscr{P} \mid \psi)$.	15
$\ell(\boldsymbol{x}_n \mid \mathscr{P})$	Likelihood function for the sample $\boldsymbol{x}_n$.	10, 16
$\bar{p}_{ij}^{k}(\psi)$	Expected value of $\tilde{p}_{ij}^{k}$.	37
$p_{ij}^{(n)}$	n-step transition probability when $\tilde{\mathbf{P}} = \mathbf{P}$.	6
$\bar{p}_{ij}^{(n)}(\psi) = \bar{p}_{ij}^{(n)}(\boldsymbol{\sigma}, \psi)$	Expected n-step transition probability under the policy $\boldsymbol{\sigma}$.	59
$\mathbf{P}(\boldsymbol{\sigma}) = \mathbf{P} = [p_{ij}]$	An $N \times N$ stochastic matrix consisting of the N rows of $\mathscr{P}$ specified by $\boldsymbol{\sigma}$.	12
$\mathbf{P}^{t}$	Transpose of the matrix $\mathbf{P}$.	—
$\mathscr{P} = [p_{ij}^{k}]$	A $K \times N$ generalized stochastic matrix $(K \geqslant N)$.	12
$\boldsymbol{\pi} = (\pi_1, \ldots, \pi_N)$	Steady-state probability vector of an ergodic Markov chain when $\tilde{\mathbf{P}} = \mathbf{P}$.	7
$\bar{\boldsymbol{\pi}}(\psi) = (\bar{\pi}_1(\psi), \ldots, \bar{\pi}_N(\psi))$	Expected steady-state probability vector.	67
$\bar{\boldsymbol{\pi}}(n, \psi) = (\bar{\pi}_1(n, \psi), \ldots, \bar{\pi}_N(n, \psi))$	The nth successive approximation to $\bar{\boldsymbol{\pi}}(\bar{\psi})$.	73
$\bar{\pi}_{ij}(\psi)$	Expected value of $\tilde{\pi}_i\tilde{\pi}_j$.	77
$\phi_N(u, v, n, \mathbf{P})$	Set of all transition counts of size n which start in state u and end in state v when $\mathbf{P}$ is the matrix of transition probabilities.	120

Symbol	Meaning	Defined on Page
$\phi_N(u, n, \mathbf{P})$	Set of all transition counts of size n which start in state u when $\mathbf{P}$ is the matrix of transition probabilities.	120
$\phi_N^*(n, \mathbf{P})$	Set of all transition counts of size n when $\mathbf{P}$ is the matrix of transition probabilities.	127
$\phi_{N1}^*(n, \mathbf{P})$	Set of all transition counts of size n which start and end in the same state when $\mathbf{P}$ is the matrix of transition probabilities.	128
$\phi_{N2}^*(n, \mathbf{P})$	Set of all transition counts of size n which start and end in different states when $\mathbf{P}$ is the matrix of transition probabilities.	128
$\phi_N(u, v, n)$	Set of all transition counts of size n which start in state u and end in state v when the matrix of transition probabilities is positive.	150
$\phi_N(u, n)$	Set of all transition counts of size n which start in state u when the matrix of transition probabilities is positive.	150
$\phi_N^*(n)$	Set of all transition counts of size n when the matrix of transition probabilities is positive.	152
$\phi_{N1}^*(n)$	Set of all transition counts of size n which start and end in the same state when the matrix of transition probabilities is positive.	152
$\phi_{N2}^*(n)$	Set of all transition counts of size n which start and end in different states when the matrix of transition probabilities is positive.	152
ψ	Generic symbol for the parameters of a probability distribution function.	12
Ψ	Admissible parameter set.	16
$\mathfrak{Q} = [q_{ij}^k]$	True state of nature.	24
$\bar{q}_i^k(\psi)$	Expected one-step transition reward when the system is in state i and alternative k is to be used.	37
$q_{ij}^{(n)}(\boldsymbol{\sigma})$	The n-step transition probability under the policy $\boldsymbol{\sigma}$ when $\mathfrak{Q}$ is the true state of nature.	24
$\bar{q}_i^{(n)}(\boldsymbol{\sigma}, \beta, \psi)$ or $\bar{q}_i^{(n)}(\beta, \psi)$	Expected discounted reward in n transitions when the system starts in state i.	61
r	Minimum element of $\mathfrak{R}$.	45
r^*	The element of $\mathfrak{R}$ with the smallest absolute value.	40

Symbol	Meaning	Defined on Page
$\mathbf{R}(\boldsymbol{\sigma}) = \mathbf{R} = [r_{ij}]$	The $N \times N$ matrix of one-step transition rewards consisting of the N rows of $\mathfrak{R}$ specified by $\boldsymbol{\sigma}$.	12
R	Maximum element of $\mathfrak{R}$.	45
R^*	The element of $\mathfrak{R}$ with the largest absolute value.	40
$R_N(a)$	Range set of a random vector with the non-standard multivariate beta distribution.	138
$R_{KN}(\boldsymbol{a})$	Range set of a random matrix with the non-standard matrix beta distribution.	145
$\mathfrak{R} = [r_{ij}^k]$	The $K \times N$ matrix of one-step transition rewards.	12
$\mathcal{S}_N$	Set of all $N \times N$ stochastic matrices.	13
$\mathcal{S}_N^*$	Set of all $N \times N$ positive stochastic matrices.	62
$\mathcal{S}_N^\alpha$	Set of all $N \times N$ stochastic matrices with elements in the closed interval $[\alpha, 1 - \alpha]$.	62
$\mathcal{S}_{KN}$	Set of all $K \times N$ generalized stochastic matrices.	12
$\boldsymbol{\sigma} = (\sigma_1, \ldots, \sigma_N)$	Policy vector.	12
$\sigma_{\alpha\beta\gamma\delta}(u, n)$	Expected value of $\tilde{f}_{\alpha\beta}(u, n)\tilde{f}_{\gamma\delta}(u, n)$.	124
Σ	Set of all policy vectors $\boldsymbol{\sigma}$.	12
$T_{ij}^k(\psi)$	Parameter of the posterior distribution of $\tilde{\mathscr{P}}$ when the parameter of the prior distribution is ψ and a transition from state i to state j under alternative k is observed.	16
$T_{ij}(\psi)$	Parameter of the posterior distribution of $\tilde{\mathbf{P}}$ when the parameter of the prior distribution is ψ and a transition from state i to state j is observed.	16
$T_{ij}(n, \boldsymbol{\sigma}, \psi)$	Parameter of the posterior distribution of $\tilde{\mathscr{P}}$ when the parameter of the prior distribution is ψ, the system starts in state i and is observed in state j after n transitions under the policy $\boldsymbol{\sigma}$.	104
$v_i(\psi)$	Expected total discounted reward over an infinite period when the system starts in state i and an optimal sampling strategy is followed.	37, 95, 103
$v_i(n, \psi)$	The nth successive approximation to $v_i(\psi)$.	41, 99, 107

Symbol	Meaning	Defined on Page
$v_i(\psi; \nu)$	Expected total reward over a period with terminal operation phase of length ν when the system starts from state i and an optimal sampling strategy is followed.	115, 116
$v_i(\psi, \boldsymbol{\sigma})$	Expected total discounted reward over an infinite period when the system starts in state i with the policy $\boldsymbol{\sigma}$ in force and an optimal sampling strategy is followed (discounted process with setup cost).	117
v^*	Minimum of a set of constant terminal reward functions.	45
V^*	Maximum of a set of constant terminal reward functions.	45
$V_i(\psi)$	Terminal reward function.	41
V	Bound on the terminal reward functions.	41
$V_i(\mathbf{P})$	Conditional expected total discounted reward over an infinite period when $\tilde{\mathbf{P}} = \mathbf{P}$, the system starts from state i, and a fixed policy is used.	79
$\bar{V}_i(\boldsymbol{\sigma}, \psi)$ or $\bar{V}_i(\psi)$	Expected total discounted reward over an infinite period when the system starts from state i and the fixed policy $\boldsymbol{\sigma}$ is used.	79
$\bar{V}_i(n, \psi)$	The nth successive approximation to $\bar{V}_i(\psi)$.	82
var $[\cdot]$ or var $[\cdot \mid \psi]$	The variance operator.	—
$\boldsymbol{x}_n = (x_0, x_1, \ldots, x_n)$	A sample of n transitions in a Markov chain.	16

APPENDIX B

MAD PROGRAM VITERATION TO SOLVE EQUATIONS 3.3.1 AND 3.3.2

```
RPROGRAM NAME IS VITERATION.
RTHIS PROGRAM RECURSIVELY COMPUTES VALUES OF V(I, T1, M) FOR
RI=1,...N AND T1=S,...,T, FOLLOWING AN OPTIMAL POLICY.   THE
RREWARD MATRIX IS R AND THE TERMINAL REWARD VECTOR IS RHO.
RTHE MAXIMIZATION IS OVER THE MU(I) ALTERNATIVES IN STATE I.
RBETA IS THE DISCOUNT FACTOR.  A MATRIX BETA PRIOR IS
RASSUMED.

        PROGRAM COMMON R,RHO,RDIM,IND,MU,N,BETA,IND1,LIST,TOP,
       OINDIM,POL
        INTEGER IND,MU,N,IND1,TOP,S,T,I,J,K,MAXSP,N1,POL,V2
        DIMENSION R(500,RDIM),M(500,RDIM),RHO(10),IND(100,INDIM),
       OMU(10),IND1(10),LIST(21000),V1(10),V2(10)
        VECTOR VALUES RDIM=3,1,0,0
        VECTOR VALUES INDIM=2,1,0
  READ  READ FORMAT INPUT1, N,S,T,MAXSP,BETA
        PRINT FORMAT OUT1A, BETA
        RDIM(2)=N
        RDIM(3)=N
        INDIM(2)=N
        IND1(1)=0
        IND(1,1)=0
        THROUGH ALFA1, FOR K=1,1,K.E.N
 ALFA1  IND(1,K+1)=K*N
        N1=N*N
        THROUGH ALFA, FOR K=1,1,K.E.MAXSP
        IND1(K+1)=K*N
        IND(K+1,1)=K*N1
        THROUGH ALFA, FOR I=1,1,I.E.N
  ALFA  IND(K+1,I+1)=K*N1+I*N
        READ FORMAT INPUT2, MU(1) ... MU(N)
        PRINT FORMAT OUT1E, (I=1,1,I.G.N, MU(I))
        READ FORMAT INPUT3, R(1,1,1) ... R(MU(N),N,N), M(1,1,1)
       O... M(MU(N),N,N), RHO(1) ... RHO(N)
        PRINT FORMAT OUT1D, (I=1,1,I.G.N, RHO(I))
        PRINT FORMAT OUT1B, (I=1,1,I.G.N, (K=1,1,K.G.MU(I),
       O(J=1,1,J.G.N, M(IND(IND1(K)+I)+J))))
        PRINT FORMAT OUT1C, (I=1,1,I.G.N, (K=1,1,K.G.MU(I),
       O(J=1,1,J.G.N, R(IND(IND1(K)+I)+J))))
        SET LIST TO LIST
        LIST = 0
        THROUGH DELTA, FOR K=S,1,K.G.T
        THROUGH GAMMA, FOR I=1,1,I.G.N
        V1(I)=VMAX.(I,K,M)
 GAMMA  V2(I)=POL
        PRINT FORMAT OUT2, K, V1(1) ... V1(N)
 DELTA  PRINT FORMAT OUT3, V2(1) ... V2(N)
        TRANSFER TO READ

       RFORMAT SPECIFICATIONS
        VECTOR VALUES INPUT1=$4I10,F10.5*$
        VECTOR VALUES INPUT2=$10I7*$
        VECTOR VALUES INPUT3=$(7F10.5)*$
        VECTOR VALUES OUT1A=$7H1BETA =,G15.5*$
        VECTOR VALUES OUT1B=$6H0  M =,8G15.5/(8G15.5)*$
        VECTOR VALUES OUT1C=$6H0  R =,8G15.5/(8G15.5)*$
        VECTOR VALUES OUT1D=$6H0RHO =,8G15.5/8G15.5*$
        VECTOR VALUES OUT1E=$5H0MU =,10I5*$
        VECTOR VALUES OUT2=$8H0FOR T =,I2,14H  V(I, T, M) =,7G15.5/
       O8G15.5*$
        VECTOR VALUES OUT3=$7H POLICY,10I5*$
        END OF PROGRAM
```

```
      EXTERNAL FUNCTION (I1, N1, M)
      ENTRY TO VMAX.

     RTHIS FUNCTION RECURSIVELY COMPUTES MAX V(I1,N1,M)=Y, THE
     RMAXIMUM EXPECTED RETURN IN N1 STEPS IF THE SYSTEM STARTS IN
     RSTATE I1 WITH PARAMETER MATRIX M.  PRIOR DISTRIBUTION IS
     RMATRIX BETA.  MAXIMIZATION IS OVER THE MU(I1)
     RALTERNATIVES IN STATE I1.

      PROGRAM COMMON R,RHO,RDIM,IND,MU,N,BETA,IND1,LIST,TOP,
     OINDIM,POL
      INTEGER I1,N1,I,N2,K,IND,MU,N,RDIM,J,IND1,TOP,POL
      DIMENSION R(500,RDIM),RHO(10),RDIM(3),IND(100,INDIM),
     OLIST(21000),MU(10),IND1(10),INDIM(2),TM(500,RDIM)
      I=I1
      N2=N1
      Y=1.E-35
      WHENEVER N2.E.0, FUNCTION RETURN RHO(I)
      THROUGH ALFA, FOR K=1,1,K.G.MU(I)
      MSUM=0.
      THROUGH PHI, FOR J=1,1,J.G.N
  PHI MSUM=MSUM+M(IND(IND1(K)+I)+J)
      STOR=0.
      THROUGH GAMMA, FOR J=1,1,J.G.N
      SAVE RETURN
      SAVE DATA N2,POL,MSUM,STOR,Y,M(K,I,J) ... M(MU(I),I,N),I,J,K
      EXECUTE TR1.(I,J,K,M,TM)
      X=VMAX.(J,N2-1,TM)
      RESTORE DATA K,J,I,M(MU(I),I,N) ... M(K,I,J),Y,STOR,MSUM,
     OPOL,N2
      RESTORE RETURN
GAMMA STOR=STOR+(M(IND(IND1(K)+I)+J)/MSUM)*(R(IND(IND1(K)+I)+J)
     O+BETA*X)
      WHENEVER STOR .LE. Y, TRANSFER TO ALFA
      Y=STOR
      POL=K
 ALFA CONTINUE
      FUNCTION RETURN Y
      END OF FUNCTION
```

```
      EXTERNAL FUNCTION (I1,J1,K1,M,TM)
      ENTRY TO TR1.

     RTHIS FUNCTION EFFECTS THE TRANSFORMATION FROM THE PRIOR
     RPARAMETER MATRIX M TO THE POSTERIOR PARAMETER MATRIX
     RTR1.(I1,J1,K1,M)=TM, WHEN A TRANSITION IS OBSERVED FROM I1 TO
     RJ1 UNDER ALTERNATIVE K1.  PRIOR DISTRIBUTION IS MATRIX BETA.

      PROGRAM COMMON R,RHO,RDIM,IND,MU,N,BETA,IND1,LIST,TOP,
     0INDIM,POL
      INTEGER I1,J1,K1,I,J,K,IND,MU,N,IND1
      DIMENSION R(500,RDIM),RHO(10),RDIM(3),IND(100,INDIM),
     0LIST(21000),MU(10),IND1(10),INDIM(2)
      THROUGH ALFA, FOR I=1,1,I.G.N
      THROUGH ALFA, FOR J=1,1,J.G.N
      THROUGH ALFA, FOR K=1,1,K.G.MU(I)
ALFA  TM(IND(IND1(K)+I)+J)=M(IND(IND1(K)+I)+J)
      TM(IND(IND1(K1)+I1)+J1)=M(IND(IND1(K1)+I1)+J1)+1.0
      FUNCTION RETURN
      END OF FUNCTION
```

APPENDIX C

MAD PROGRAM PHI MATRIX TO COMPUTE EQUATION 4.1.2

```
     RPROGRAM NAME IS PHI MATRIX
     RTHIS PROGRAM RECURSIVELY COMPUTES VALUES OF PHI(I,J,T1,M)
     RFOR I,J=1,...,N AND T1=S,...,T.   A MATRIX BETA
     RPRIOR IS ASSUMED.

      PROGRAM COMMON IND,N,J,LIST,TOP,MDIM
      INTEGER N,IND,I,J,S,T,K,TOP
      DIMENSION M(100,MDIM),IND(10),LIST(21000),F(10)
      VECTOR VALUES MDIM=2,1,0
 READ READ FORMAT INPUT1, N,S,T
      MDIM(2)=N
      IND(1)=0
      THROUGH ALFA, FOR K=1,1,K.E.N
 ALFA IND(K+1)=K*N
      READ FORMAT INPUT2, M(1,1) ... M(N,N)
      PRINT FORMAT OUT1, N,S,T, (K=1,1,K.G.N,(L=1,1,L.G.N,
     0M(IND(K)+L)))
      SET LIST TO LIST
      LIST=0
      THROUGH GAMMA, FOR K=S,1,K.G.T
      THROUGH GAMMA, FOR I=1,1,I.G.N
      THROUGH DELTA, FOR J=1,1,J.E.N
DELTA F(J)=PHI.(I,K,M)
      F(N)=1.0
      THROUGH EPS, FOR J=1,1,J.E.N
  EPS F(N)=F(N)-F(J)
      WHENEVER I.E.1
      PRINT FORMAT OUT2, K, F(1) ... F(N)
      OTHERWISE
      PRINT FORMAT OUT3, F(1) ... F(N)
GAMMA END OF CONDITIONAL
      TRANSFER TO READ


     RFORMAT SPECIFICATIONS
      VECTOR VALUES INPUT1=$3I10*$
      VECTOR VALUES INPUT2=$(7F10.5)*$
      VECTOR VALUES OUT1=$3H1N=,I5,4H   S=,I5,4H   T=,I5/
     0(1H , 8G15.5)*$
      VECTOR VALUES OUT2=$7H0FOR T=, I2, 15H  PHI(I,J,T,M)=,
     06G15.5*$
      VECTOR VALUES OUT3=$S24, 6G15.5*$
      END OF PROGRAM
```

```
      EXTERNAL FUNCTION (I1, T1, M)
      ENTRY TO PHI.

     RTHIS FUNCTION RECURSIVELY COMPUTES PHI(I1,J,T1,M)=Y, THE
     RPROBABILITY THAT AT TIME T1 THE SYSTEM WILL BE IN STATE J,
     RGIVEN THAT AT TIME 0 IT WAS IN STATE I1 WITH PARAMETER
     RMATRIX M.  PRIOR IS MATRIX BETA.

      PROGRAM COMMON IND,N,J,LIST,TOP,MDIM
      INTEGER I1,J,T1,I,T,K,N,IND,TOP,MDIM
      DIMENSION IND(10),LIST(21000),MDIM(2),TM(100,MDIM)
      I=I1
      T=T1
      MSUM=0.
      THROUGH ALFA, FOR K=1,1,K.G.N
ALFA  MSUM=MSUM+M(IND(I)+K)
      WHENEVER T.E.1, FUNCTION RETURN M(IND(I)+J)/MSUM
      Y=0.
      THROUGH BETA, FOR K=1,1,K.G.N
      SAVE RETURN
      SAVE DATA Y,T,MSUM,M(1,1) ... M(N,N),I,K
      EXECUTE TR.(I,K,M,TM)
      X=PHI.(K,T-1,TM)
      RESTORE DATA K,I,M(N,N) ... M(1,1),MSUM,T,Y
      RESTORE RETURN
BETA  Y=Y+(M(IND(I)+K)/MSUM)*X
      FUNCTION RETURN Y
      END OF FUNCTION
```

```
      EXTERNAL FUNCTION (I,K,M,TM)
      ENTRY TO TR.

     RTHIS FUNCTION EFFECTS THE TRANSFORMATION FROM THE PRIOR
     RPARAMETER MATRIX M TO THE POSTERIOR PARAMETER MATRIX
     RT.(I,K,M)=TM, WHEN ONE TRANSITION FROM I TO K IS OBSERVED.
     RPRIOR IS MATRIX BETA.

      PROGRAM COMMON IND,N,J,LIST,TOP,MDIM
      INTEGER I,K,IND,J,L,N,J1,MDIM,TOP
      DIMENSION IND(10),MDIM(2),LIST(21000)
      THROUGH ALFA, FOR J1=1,1,J1.G.N
      THROUGH ALFA, FOR L=1,1,L.G.N
ALFA  TM(IND(J1)+L)=M(IND(J1)+L)
      TM(IND(I)+K)=TM(IND(I)+K)+1.0
      FUNCTION RETURN
      END OF FUNCTION
```

APPENDIX D

MAD PROGRAM PIAPROX TO COMPUTE EQUATIONS 4.2.42 AND 4.2.51

```
    RPROGRAM NAME IS PIAPROX.  THIS PROGRAM RECURSIVELY COMPUTES
    RVALUES OF THE SUCCESSIVE APPROXIMANT PI(I,T1,M) FOR
    RI=1,...,N AND T1=S,...,T.  A MATRIX BETA PRIOR IS USED.

     PROGRAM COMMON IND,N,LIST,MDIM,N1,ADIM,AIND
     INTEGER N,IND,I,K,S,T,N1,AIND
     DIMENSION M(100,MDIM),IND(10),LIST(21000),F(10),AIND(10)
     VECTOR VALUES MDIM=2,1,0
     VECTOR VALUES ADIM=2,1,0
READ READ FORMAT INPUT1, N,S,T
     MDIM(2)=N
     N1=N+1
     ADIM(2)=N1
     AIND(1)=0
     IND(1)=0
     THROUGH ALFA, FOR K=1,1,K.E.N
     AIND(K+1)=K*N1
ALFA IND(K+1)=K*N
     READ FORMAT INPUT2, M(1,1) ... M(N,N)
     PRINT FORMAT OUT1, N,S,T,(K=1,1,K.G.N, (I=1,1,I.G.N,
    OM(IND(K)+I)))
     SET LIST TO LIST
     LIST=0
     THROUGH GAMMA, FOR K=S,1,K.G.T
     THROUGH DELTA, FOR I=1,1,I.G.N
DELTA F(I)=PI.(I,K,M)
     PRINT FORMAT OUT2, K, F(1) ... F(N)
     SUM=0.
     THROUGH BETA, FOR I=1,1,I.G.N
BETA SUM=SUM+F(I)
     THROUGH EPS, FOR I=1,1,I.G.N
 EPS F(I)=F(I)/SUM
     PRINT FORMAT OUT3, F(1) ... F(N)
GAMMA PRINT FORMAT OUT4, SUM
     TRANSFER TO READ


    RFORMAT SPECIFICATIONS.
     VECTOR VALUES INPUT1=$3I10*$
     VECTOR VALUES INPUT2=$(7F10.5)*$
     VECTOR VALUES OUT1=$3H1N=,I5,4H  S=,I5,4H  T=,I5/
    O(1H ,8G15.5)*$
     VECTOR VALUES OUT2=$7H0FOR T=,I2,10H  PI(T,M)=,(6G15.5)*$
     VECTOR VALUES OUT3=$19H NORMALIZED VECTOR=,(6G15.5)*$
     VECTOR VALUES OUT4=$1H ,S11,7HC(T,M)=,G15.6*$
     END OF PROGRAM
```

```
      EXTERNAL FUNCTION(J1,T1,M)
      ENTRY TO PI.

     RTHIS FUNCTION RECURSIVELY COMPUTES PI(J1,T1,M), THE T1TH
     RSUCCESSIVE APPROXIMANT TO THE J1TH ELEMENT OF THE MEAN
     RSTEADY-STATE PROBABILITY VECTOR WHEN THE PRIOR IS MATRIX
     RBETA WITH PARAMETER M.

      PROGRAM COMMON IND,N,LIST,MDIM,N1,ADIM,AIND
      INTEGER J1,T1,I,J,K,N,T,IND,MDIM,N1,ADIM,AIND
      DIMENSION IND(10),LIST(21000),MDIM(2),TM(100,MDIM),PBAR(10),
     0ADIM(2),AIND(10)
      J=J1
      T=T1
      THROUGH ALFA, FOR K=1,1,K.G.N
      MSUM=0.
      THROUGH BETA, FOR I=1,1,I.G.N
 BETA MSUM=MSUM+M(IND(K)+I)
 ALFA PBAR(K)=M(IND(K)+J)/MSUM
      Y=0.
      THROUGH GAMMA, FOR K=1,1,K.G.N
      SAVE RETURN
      SAVE DATA Y,T,PBAR(K) ... PBAR(N),K,J, M(1,1) ... M(N,N)
      M(IND(K)+J)=M(IND(K)+J)+1.
      WHENEVER T.G.1, TRANSFER TO ZETA
      X=PIZRO.(K,M)
      TRANSFER TO ETA
 ZETA X=PI.(K,T-1,M)
  ETA RESTORE DATA M(N,N) ... M(1,1),J,K,PBAR(N) ... PBAR(K),T,Y
      RESTORE RETURN
GAMMA Y=Y+X*PBAR(K)
      FUNCTION RETURN Y
      END OF FUNCTION
```

```
       EXTERNAL FUNCTION(L1,M)
       ENTRY TO PIZRO.

      RTHIS FUNCTION COMPUTES THE TERMINAL FUNCTION PI(L1,0,M)
      RAS THE L1TH ELEMENT OF THE STEADY-STATE PROBABILITY VECTOR
      RCORRESPONDING TO THE MEAN OF THE PRIOR DISTRIBUTION.
      RPRIOR IS MATRIX BETA WITH PARAMETER M.

       PROGRAM COMMON IND,N,LIST,MDIM,N1,ADIM,AIND
       INTEGER L1,L,N,I,J,K,N1,IND,MDIM,ADIM,AIND
       DIMENSION IND(10),LIST(21000),MDIM(2),ADIM(2),A(110,ADIM),
      0AIND(10)
       L=L1
       THROUGH ALFA, FOR I=1,1,I.G.N
       MSUM=0.
       THROUGH BETA, FOR K=1,1,K.G.N
  BETA MSUM=MSUM+M(IND(I)+K)
       THROUGH GAMMA, FOR K=1,1,K.E.N
 GAMMA A(AIND(K)+I)=-M(IND(I)+K)/MSUM
       A(AIND(N)+I)=1.
  ALFA A(AIND(I)+N1)=0.
       A(AIND(N)+N1)=1.
       THROUGH DELTA, FOR K=1,1,K.E.N
       A(AIND(K)+K)=A(AIND(K)+K)+1.
       SCRAP=A(AIND(K)+L)
       A(AIND(K)+L)=A(AIND(K)+N)
 DELTA A(AIND(K)+N)=SCRAP
       DIAG=A(AIND(1)+1)
       THROUGH EPS, FOR J=2,1,J.G.N
   EPS A(AIND(1)+J)=A(AIND(1)+J)/DIAG
       THROUGH ZETA, FOR J=2,1,J.G.N
       THROUGH ETA, FOR I=J,1,I.G.N
       SUB=A(AIND(I)+J)
       THROUGH IOTA, FOR K=1,1,K.E.J
  IOTA SUB=SUB-A(AIND(I)+K)*A(AIND(K)+J)
   ETA A(AIND(I)+J)=SUB
       DIAG=A(AIND(J)+J)
       THROUGH ZETA, FOR I=J+1,1,I.G.N1
       SUB=A(AIND(J)+I)
       THROUGH LAMBDA, FOR K=1,1,K.E.J
LAMBDA SUB=SUB-A(AIND(J)+K)*A(AIND(K)+I)
  ZETA A(AIND(J)+I)=SUB/DIAG
       FUNCTION RETURN A(AIND(N)+N1)
       END OF FUNCTION
```

APPENDIX E

MAD PROGRAM VASYMP TO COMPUTE EQUATION 4.3.13

```
RPROGRAM NAME IS VASYMP.
RTHIS PROGRAM RECURSIVELY COMPUTES VALUES OF V(I,J,M) FOR
RI=1,...,N, J=S,...,T.  THE REWARD MATRIX IS R AND THE TERM-
RINAL REWARD VECTOR IS RHO.  A MATRIX BETA PRIOR IS ASSUMED.
RTHE DISCOUNT FACTOR IS BETA.

       PROGRAM COMMON R,RHO,RDIM,IND,N,BETA,LIST,TOP
       INTEGER N,IND,J,S,T,K,L,TOP
       DIMENSION R(100,RDIM),M(100,RDIM),RHO(10),IND(10),V1(10),
      0V2(10),LIST(21000)
       VECTOR VALUES RDIM=2,1,0
  READ READ FORMAT INPUT1, N,S,T,BETA
       RDIM(2)=N
       IND(1)=0
       THROUGH ALFA, FOR K=1,1,K.E.N
  ALFA IND(K+1)=K*N
  READ READ FORMAT INPUT2, R(1,1) ... R(N,N), M(1,1) ... M(N,N),
      0RHO(1) ... RHO(N)
       PRINT FORMAT OUT1A, BETA
       PRINT FORMAT OUT1B, (K=1,1,K.G.N,(L=1,1,L.G.N, M(IND(K)+L)))
       PRINT FORMAT OUT1C,(K=1,1,K.G.N,(L=1,1,L.G.N,R(IND(K)+L)))
       PRINT FORMAT OUT1D, (K=1,1,K.G.N, RHO(K))
       THROUGH PHI, FOR K=1,1,K.G.N
   PHI V2(K)=0.
       SET LIST TO LIST
       LIST=0
       THROUGH DELTA, FOR K=S,1,K.G.T
       THROUGH GAMMA, FOR L=1,1,L.G.N
       V1(L)=V.(L,K,M)
 GAMMA V2(L)=V1(L)-V2(L)
       PRINT FORMAT OUT2, K, V1(1) ... V1(N)
       PRINT FORMAT OUT3, V2(1) ... V2(N)
       THROUGH DELTA, FOR L=1,1, L.G.N
 DELTA V2(L)=V1(L)
       TRANSFER TO READ

      RFORMAT SPECIFICATIONS
       VECTOR VALUES INPUT1=$3I10, F10.5*$
       VECTOR VALUES INPUT2=$(7F10.5)*$
       VECTOR VALUES OUT1A=$8H1BETA  =,G15.5*$
       VECTOR VALUES OUT1B=$8H0   M  =,8G15.5/(1H ,8G15.5)*$
       VECTOR VALUES OUT1C=$8H0   R  =,8G15.5/(1H ,8G15.5)*$
       VECTOR VALUES OUT1D=$8H0 RHO  =,8G15.5/8G15.5*$
       VECTOR VALUES OUT2=$8H0FOR T =, I2, 14H V(I, T, M)  =,
      07G15.5/8G15.5*$
       VECTOR VALUES OUT3=$S3,21HDELTA V(I, T=1, M)  =,7G15.5/
      08G15.5*$
       END OF PROGRAM
```

```
          EXTERNAL FUNCTION (I1, J1, M)
          ENTRY TO V.

         RTHIS FUNCTION RECURSIVELY COMPUTES V.(I1,J1,M)=Y, THE TOTAL
         REXPECTED DISCOUNTED RETURN IN J1 STEPS IF THE SYSTEM STARTS
         RIN STATE I1 WITH PARAMETER MATRIX M.  PRIOR IS MATRIX BETA.

          PROGRAM COMMON R,RHO,RDIM,IND,N,BETA,LIST,TOP
          INTEGER I1,J1,I,J,K,IND,N,RDIM,TOP
          DIMENSION R(100,RDIM),RHO(10),RDIM(2),IND(10),LIST(21000),
         0TM(100,RDIM)
          I=I1
          J=J1
          WHENEVER J .E. 0, FUNCTION RETURN RHO(I)
          MSUM=0.
          THROUGH ALFA, FOR K=1,1,K.G.N
    ALFA  MSUM=MSUM+M(IND(I)+K)
          Y=0.
          THROUGH GAMMA, FOR K=1,1,K.G.N
          SAVE RETURN
          SAVE DATA J,Y,MSUM,M(I,K) ... M(I,N),I,K
          EXECUTE TR.(I,K,M,TM)
          X=V.(K,J-1,TM)
          RESTORE DATA K,I,M(I,N) ... M(I,K),MSUM,Y,J
          RESTORE RETURN
   GAMMA  Y=Y+(M(IND(I)+K)/MSUM)*(R(IND(I)+K)+BETA*X)
          FUNCTION RETURN Y
          END OF FUNCTION
```

```
          EXTERNAL FUNCTION (I, K, M, TM)
          ENTRY TO TR.

         RTHIS FUNCTION EFFECTS THE TRANSFORMATION FROM THE PRIOR
         RPARAMETER MATRIX M TO THE POSTERIOR PARAMETER MATRIX
         RT.(I,K,M)=TM, WHEN ONE TRANSITION FROM I TO K IS OBSERVED.
         RPRIOR IS MATRIX BETA.

          PROGRAM COMMON R,RHO,RDIM,IND,N,BETA,LIST,TOP
          DIMENSION R(100,RDIM),RHO(10),RDIM(2),IND(10),LIST(21000)
          INTEGER I,K,IND,J,L,N
          THROUGH ALFA, FOR J=1,1,J.G.N
          THROUGH ALFA, FOR L=1,1,L.G.N
    ALFA  TM(IND(J)+L)=M(IND(J)+L)
          TM(IND(I)+K)=TM(IND(I)+K)+1.0
          FUNCTION RETURN
          END OF FUNCTION
```

BIBLIOGRAPHY

[1] Anderson, T. W., and L. A. Goodman. "Statistical Inference About Markov Chains." *Ann. Math. Stat.*, **28** (1957), 89–109.

[2] Appell, P., and J. Kampé de Fériet. *Fonctions Hypergéométriques et Hypersphériques.* Gauthier-Villars, Paris (1926).

[3] Arden, B., B. Galler, and R. Graham. *The Michigan Algorithm Decoder.* [n.p.] (November 1963).

[4] Ayers, J. A. "Recursive Programming in FORTRAN II." *Comm. ACM*, **6** (1963), 667–668.

[5] Barnard, G. A. "Sampling Inspection and Statistical Decisions." *J. Roy. Stat. Soc.*, Ser. B, **16** (1954), 151–174.

[6] Bellman, R. *Adaptive Control Processes: A Guided Tour.* Princeton University Press, Princeton (1961).

[7] ———. "A Problem in the Sequential Design of Experiments." *Sankhya*, **16** (1956), 221–229.

[8] ———, and R. Kalaba. "On Adaptive Control Processes." *Trans. IRE*, **AC 4,** no. 2 (1959), 1–9.

[9] Bhat, B. R. "Bayes Solution of Sequential Decision Problem for Markov Dependent Observations." *Ann. Math. Stat.*, **35** (1964), 1656–1662.

[10] Billingsley, P. "Statistical Methods in Markov Chains." *Ann. Math. Stat.*, **32** (1961), 12–40; see also correction in *ibid.*, p. 1343.

[11] Blackwell, D. "Discrete Dynamic Programming." *Ann. Math. Stat.*, **33** (1962), 719–726.

[12] Chung, K. L. *Markov Chains with Stationary Transition Probabilities.* Springer Verlag, Berlin (1960).

[13] Cozzolino, J. M. *Optimal Sequential Decisions Under Uncertainty.* MS Thesis, Massachusetts Institute of Technology (May 1964).

[14] ———, R. Gonzales-Zubieta, and R. L. Miller. "Markovian Decision Processes with Uncertain Transition Probabilities." *Technical Report No. 11*, Research in the Control of Complex Systems. Operations Research Center, Massachusetts Institute of Technology (March 1965).

[15] Dawson, R., and I. J. Good. "Exact Markov Probabilities from Oriented Linear Graphs." *Ann. Math. Stat.*, **28** (1957), 946–956.

[16] Derman, C. "On Sequential Decisions and Markov Chains." *Mgmt. Sci.*, **9** (1963), 16–24.

[17] Erdélyi, A. et al. *Higher Transcendental Functions.* 3 vols. McGraw-Hill Book Company, New York (1953–1955).

[18] Freimer, M. "A Dynamic Programming Approach to Adaptive Control Processes." *Trans. IRE*, **AC 4,** no. 2 (1959), 10–15.

[19] ———. "Topics in Dynamic Programming—II. Truncated Policies." *Lincoln Laboratory Report 54G-0020.* Massachusetts Institute of Technology (April 18, 1960).

[20] Good, I. J. "The Frequency Count of a Markov Chain and the Transition to Continuous Time." *Ann. Math. Stat.*, **32** (1961), 41–48.

[21] Goodman, L. A. "Exact Probabilities and Asymptotic Relationships for Some Statistics from *m*th Order Markov Chain." *Ann. Math. Stat.*, **29** (1958), 476–490.

[22] Howard, R. A. *Dynamic Programming and Markov Processes.* John Wiley and Sons, New York (1960).

[23] ———. "Semi-Markovian Control Systems." *Technical Report No. 3*, Research in the Control of Complex Systems. Operations Research Center, Massachusetts Institute of Technology (December 1963).

[24] Jewell, W. S. "Markov-Renewal Programming. I: Formulation, Finite Return Models." *Opns. Res.*, **11** (1963), 938–948.

[25] ———. "Markov-Renewal Programming. II: Infinite Return Models, Example." *Opns. Res.*, **11** (1963), 949–971.

[26] Kemeny, J. G., and J. L. Snell. *Finite Markov Chains.* D. Van Nostrand, Princeton (1960).

[27] Knopp, K. *Theory and Application of Infinite Series.* Blackie, Glasgow (1928).

[28] Loève, M. *Probability Theory.* 3rd ed. D. Van Nostrand, Princeton (1963).

[29] McCarthy, J. "Recursive Functions of Symbolic Expressions." *Comm. ACM*, **3** (1960), 184–195.

[30] Mauldon, J. G. "A Generalization of the Beta-Distribution." *Ann. Math. Stat.*, **30** (1959), 509–520.

[31] Mosimann, J. E. "On the Compound Multinomial Distribution, the Multivariate β-Distribution, and Correlations Among Proportions." *Biometrika*, **49** (1962), 65–82.

[32] Naur, P. (ed.). "Report on the Algorithmic Language ALGOL 60." *Comm. ACM*, **3** (1960), 299–314.

[33] Raiffa, H., and R. Schlaifer. *Applied Statistical Decision Theory.* Graduate School of Business Administration, Harvard University, Boston (1961).

[34] Rosenblatt, D. "On Linear Models and the Graphs of Minkowski-Leontief Matrices." *Econometrica*, **25** (1957), 325–338.

[35] Rudin, W. *Principles of Mathematical Analysis.* 2nd ed. McGraw-Hill Book Company, New York (1964).

[36] Shapley, L. S. "Stochastic Games." *Proc. Nat. Acad. Sci.*, **39** (1953), 1095–1100.

[37] Shor, N. Z. "Pro optimal'ne regulyuvaniya Markovs'koi poslidovnosti z dvoma fazovimi stanami." (On the Optimal Control of a Markov Chain with Two Phase States; Ukranian, with Russian summary.) *Zbirnik Prats' z Obchislyuval'noi Matematiki i Tekhniki, Akademiya Nauk URSR, Kiiv*, **1** (1961), 119–124.

[38] Silver, E. A. "Markovian Decision Processes with Uncertain Transition Probabilities or Rewards." *Technical Report No. 1*, Research in the Control of Complex Systems. Operations Research Center, Massachusetts Institute of Technology (August 1963).

[39] Singer, A. "The Steady State Probabilities of a Markov Chain as a Function of the Transition Probabilities." *Opns. Res.*, **12** (1964), 498–499.

[40] Wetherill, G. B. "Bayesian Sequential Analysis." *Biometrika*, **48** (1961), 281–292.

[41] Whittle, P. "Some Distribution and Moment Formulae for the Markov Chain." *J. Roy. Stat. Soc.*, Ser. B. **17** (1955), 235–242.

[42] Zachrisson, L. E. "Markov Games." In *Advances in Game Theory*, Dresher, M., L. S. Shapley, and A. W. Tucker (eds). Princeton University Press, Princeton (1964), 211–253.

INDEX